THOMAS OF BRADWARDINE HIS TRACTATUS DE PROPORTIONIBUS

Thomas of Bradwardine·His
Tractatus de Proportionibus
Its Significance for the Development
of Mathematical Physics

Edited and Translated by

H. LAMAR CROSBY, JR.

The University of Wisconsin Press

MADISON ～ 1961

Published by the University of Wisconsin Press
430 Sterling Court, Madison 6, Wisconsin

Second printing, 1961

Printed in the United States of America
by Cushing-Malloy, Inc., Ann Arbor, Michigan

Library of Congress Catalog Card Number 54-6740

CARO PATRI

qui primus mihi orbis Latinae portas aperuit

FOREWORD

The rehabilitation of medieval mechanics first started by Pierre Duhem after the turn of the century and successfully carried on by the recent studies of Annaliese Maier now founders on one main obstacle, namely, poor or inadequate texts. Recently the University of Wisconsin Press published a corpus of medieval statical works edited by Ernest Moody and myself, The Medieval Science of Weights. It now undertakes to publish one of the most widely influential works in medieval dynamics and kinematics.

Bradwardine's work performed a crucial service to the development of mechanics, for in it we find the juncture of two important traditions of mechanics, the philosophical and the mathematical. It is generally recognized that Bradwardine stands in the Aristotelian scholastic tradition present at Oxford in the early fourteenth century in the giant figures of Duns Scotus and William Ockham. Less clearly recognized is the fact that Bradwardine draws from the revived Hellenistic mathematical tradition, represented in mechanics by the statical corpus of Jordanus and Gerard of Brussels' kinematic work entitled Liber de motu.

It was a re-examination on mathematical grounds of Aristotle's rules relating forces with distances and times that stimulated the writing of Bradwardine's Treatise on Proportions. As the result of that re-examination Bradwardine arrived at a new mathematical way of relating the variables involved in movement. As Dr. Crosby shows, Bradwardine related velocity exponentially to the ratio of force and resistance producing the movement. He did this primarily to save Aristotle's rules from what appeared to be mathematical inconsistencies. From the standpoint of empirical science Bradwardine's "law" was without even approximate verification. But his law had great consequences, for it appears to have been the first attempt to present a mechanical equation which represented instantaneous changes rather than completed changes as are involved in Aristotle's rules. It brought into prominence the idea of instantaneous velocity and led to rapid developments in kinematics by his colleagues and students at Merton College. It led particularly to a sound description of acceleration and a celebrated rule for representing uniform acceleration by its mean speed, so far as the traversal of distance in a given time is concerned. This rule, perhaps known by Bradwardine himself, was given manifold expression during the 1330's and 1340's by his junior contemporaries at Merton College: William Heytesbury, Richard Swineshead, and John Dumbleton. It was, of course, later used by Galileo and applied to the motion of falling bodies.

It is well known that Bradwardine's treatise was widely read at Paris, and, in fact, throughout Europe in the second half of the fourteenth and in the whole of the fifteenth century. In his stimulating introduction Dr. Crosby suggests that Dumbleton interpreted the Bradwardine dynamic formulation in a manner not unlike Newton. This I believe to be incorrect, but I urge the reader to examine the evidence for himself.

Considerable thanks are due to Dr. Crosby for this edition. The number of manuscripts of the text is large and presented a real problem in the establishment of a sound text. The inclusion of a translation makes the text accessible for those readers competent to evaluate the "scientific" content of the text, but unable to get behind the medieval Latin.

It is hoped that Dr. Crosby's efforts will encourage students of medieval mathematics and mechanics to undertake the publication of other monuments in the still little known area of medieval science.

Marshall Clagett
Professor of the History of Science
University of Wisconsin

ACKNOWLEDGEMENTS

I wish, first of all, to express my deep indebtedness to Professor Ernest A. Moody, of Columbia University, who not only conceived the plan of this study, originally, but whose selfless and untiring help in every department of its development alone made the fulfillment possible. Sincerest thanks are also due Professor Paul O. Kristeller, of Columbia University, to whom I owe whatever knowledge I have acquired of mediaeval paleography and whose meticulous criticism of the Latin text and variant readings was of particular assistance. My thanks too, to Professor Marshall Clagett, of the University of Wisconsin, for his many useful criticisms of both thought and expression, and to Mrs. Loretta Freiling for her expert and painstaking typewriter composition of this manuscript for photographic reproduction. Not least, I wish to thank my wife, Louise; her part has been so all-embracing that it would not be improper to say that this book is as much hers as mine.

CONTENTS

INTRODUCTION

THOMAS BRADWARDINI TRACTATUS PROPORTIONUM SEU DE PROPORTIONIBUS VELOCITATUM IN MOTIBUS

INTRODUCTION

INTRODUCTION

1. THOMAS OF BRADWARDINE

As is so frequently true of mediaeval authors, very little is known of the life of Thomas Bradwardine.[1] Yet he was a man whose contemporary prominence as a mathematician and philosopher was even exceeded by his fame as a theologian, churchman, and member of the King of England's retinue during the many years of Edward III's endless campaigns against the French.

Though his birthplace has been variously assigned as Bradwardine, Hertfield, and Cowden, he himself says he was born in Chichester.[2] There seems to be no good reason to doubt his statement, and it may have been at Chichester that Bradwardine first began what was to become a most fruitful acquaintance with Richard of Bury (later Bishop of Durham), who held a prebendal stall at Chichester Cathedral early in the fourteenth century.[3]

The date of his birth is yet more obscure; it is usually assigned by his biographers as c. 1290. In any event, one of the earliest genuine records establishes him as having attained the rank of Proctor at Merton College, Oxford, in the year 1325.[4]

This record tells of what now seems an amusing squabble between the mayor and the chancellor of Oxford, commencing in 1325 and lasting into 1326. The dispute was concerned with the moving of a certain pillory without the chancellor's consent, and (the record relates) in January, 1326, the mayor appeared before the chancellor's commissary and the proctors, begging pardon for moving the pillory and appealing the excommunication laid on him by the chancellor. Thereupon, all the litigants (presumably Bradwardine among them), together with a great crowd of townspeople, went to the pillory, and decision was taken to place it six feet nearer the North gate than the mayor had placed it. "At that time, the proctors of the University were William of Harrington and Thomas of Bradewardyn. And [the recording notary adds] the pillory was moved within fifteen days."[5] It seems perhaps ironic, and yet somehow not altogether deplorable, that this earliest attested fact in the life of a great man should touch upon a matter at once so trivial and at the same time so perennially human, in its careful recording of official foolishness.

Galhardus de Mora was archdeacon of Oxford at that time, and Bradwardine again took part, in behalf of the University, in a lengthy litigation with him concerning the question of where the spiritual authority over students at the University properly belonged. Edward III finally submitted the case to English judges and obtained autonomy for the University from episcopal interference.[6]

During his residence at Oxford, Bradwardine became a prominent figure through his work in mathematics, astronomy, geometry, moral philosophy, and theology, and this appears to have been the period of composition of all his works.[7] His magnum opus, the De causa Dei, though presented in its final form in 1344[8] (when Bradwardine was no longer at Oxford), presumably represents an elaboration upon the theological lectures he gave while at Merton College.[9]

It was for this last work (a volume of some nine hundred folio pages in Savile's edition) that Bradwardine was best known to his own and succeeding generations, and the De causa Dei long remained a touchstone of authority for Augustinian and Calvinist theologians.[10]

It is also recorded that during Bradwardine's years at Oxford, "at the time when John Bacondorpius returned from Paris, he [Bradwardine] held with him a famous disputation concerning foreknowledge and freedom of the will. But that, out of reverence for the old theology, and already many years versed in studies of that kind, he broke off the argument and condescended to agree with his [Bacondorpius'] point of view. Neither doctrine was contrary to faith, both being freely permitted by the Church." That Bradwardine not only attained considerable reputation as a theologian while still within the University, but later became known to the world at large is interestingly attested by a passage from Chaucer's Canterbury Tales. In his Nun's Priest's Tale, composed some time toward the close of the fourteenth century, Chaucer flatteringly couples Bradwardine's name with those of Boethius and St. Augustine.[12] In remarking the distinction between "simple" and "conditional" necessity and the difficulty of understanding it, the Nun's Priest speaks as follows:

> But I ne kan nat bulte it to the bren,
> As kan the hooly doctour Augustyn,
> Or Boece, or the Bisshop Bradwardyn . . . .

As might be expected, Bradwardine's contemporary reputation as a mathematician and natural philosopher is better shown by the widespread influence which his treatises exerted in succeeding generations (especially in the work of the English "Calculatores"[13]) than by the vague generalities of annals. It is interesting to note, however, that the significance of the De proportionibus was widely enough felt for it to have been made required reading for the B.A. degree at the University of Vienna and at Freiburg University by the close of the century.[14]

The date of Bradwardine's departure from the University is not known, but presumably it was not much before 1335, in which year he was called to London by Richard of Bury.[15] Bury made him his own chaplain, obtaining for him the chancellery of St. Paul's Cathedral, together with the prebend of Cadington Minor, these being in addition to the prebendal stall at Lincoln Cathedral which Bradwardine had accepted only two years previously.[16]

Bury, who continued to play a not inconsiderable part in Bradwardine's fortunes, seems to have been a powerful and picturesque figure. He had been made Bishop of Durham in 1333 and chancellor in 1334,[17] enjoyed having a large retinue of scholars about his person, and took Bradwardine into his household as a protege. William de Chambre, in a contemporary account, speaks of Richard of Bury as the "learned Bishop of Durham," a great bibliophile and patron of the arts, "and his house so full of books that a person had scarcely space to stand in or enter his room without kicking against them." [18] Richard, he tells us, died in 1345, after a full and gaudy career. "He was much pleased with a multitude of clerics and always had several in his menage. Among these were Thomas Bradwardyn (later Archbishop), Richard Fitz Raufe (later Bishop of Armagh), Walter Bury, John Maudyt, Robert Holcote and Richard Kilwington—all Doctors of Theology. . . . On any day there was ordinarily a reading at the table, unless perchance it was prevented by something important, and after dinner he used to hold disputation with selected clerics and others of his house, on appointed days."[19] Such chance scraps as the above are all that remain to us in record of Bradwardine's personal life, yet they do breathe some individuality into a figure now so remote.

It was again Bury who, together with the archbishop, Stratford, obtained for Bradwardine the post of chaplain-confessor to the king. He joined Edward III's court in Flanders, and, on August 16, 1338, was in the king's company in his progress up the Rhine to confer at Coblenz with his brother-in-law, Lewis of Bavaria. At Cologne, Bradwardine is said to have reminded Edward that Richard Coeur-de-Lion had there given thanks for his escape from the Duke of Austria and, the present cathedral being then in the process of construction, persuaded the king to contribute the sum of £1,500 (modern) to the project.[20]

Contemporary opinion was that Bradwardine's holy presence and virtuous influence greatly assisted the English army in its victories at Crecy, Calais, and Neville's Cross, after which he also served as peace emissary to King Philip of France.[21]

From this same period of Bradwardine's service with the armies dates the one extant letter of his, addressed to his friends in London; it lends an authentic touch to the history of these years when Bradwardine was rounding out the political and military phase of a varied and illustrious career. In July, 1346, he writes:

You must know that on the twelfth of July we made a good attack on a certain Norman port, called "le Hoghes," near Barflete. There my lord, the king, together with many armed men disembarked and bestowed military orders on his son (making him chief lord), on Lord Roger Mortimer, Lord William Montague, and a host of others. He also, as head of the army, bestowed afterwards the belt of Knighthood on many more. Our exceedingly small force won, thereafter, frequent victories from the enormous multitude of the enemy, killing and capturing many, seizing quite a large amount of booty, and winning the battle completely; so that in the circumadjacent countryside, for a distance of twenty miles and more, there was not a man left who stood against us. In this same place where we attacked we stayed till the following Monday, that is, St. Kenelm's Day. On that day decision was taken in the king's council to retreat the following day and turn against the major Norman states and thence, God leading us, to France at last. Written at Hoghes, St. Kenelm's Day. [22]

Presumably this letter went to his friend and patron, Bury, who, in turn, relayed this news from the fighting front, as he had before in a letter of his own, dated July 3, 1340. On that occasion, writing to the prior and convent of Durham, he tells of just receiving news from Bradwardine, telling of another great victory of the English armies. [23]

From this point onward the records connected with Thomas Bradwardine's life increase in number. In 1347 he was made archdeacon of Norwich and in 1348 was elected archbishop of Canterbury to fill the post left vacant by Stratford's death on August 23 of that year. Owing, apparently, to his anger that the clergy should have proceeded to elect an archbishop in his absence and without his approval, rather than to any dislike of Bradwardine, Edward III thereupon requested Pope Clement VII to appoint John Ufford, then a very old man, in his stead. This Clement did (lending, by the act, additional pungency to the incident at Bradwardine's subsequent consecration). But Ufford died of the black plague, which by then had reached its height in England, and Bradwardine was reappointed with royal sanction and consecrated at Avignon on July 19, 1349, Clement issuing a bull in confirmation of the election. [24]

William de Dene, in his Historia Roffensis, [25] gives a contemporary account of these most confusing events. After recording of John of Ufford that he was a man debilis et paraliticus who died elected but before his consecration, he writes as follows:

At that time the Canterbury chapter elected "Magister Thomas Bradewardyn"... for a second time, having previously elected him shortly after the death of John of Stratford, and even before the Pope heard of the election he gave the Archepiscopacy of Canterbury to Magister Thomas in the accustomed manner, not wishing to have less thanks than would the electors. The king . . . who formerly had opposed it, endorsed the election, but, sad to tell, the archbishopric was thus destroyed by so many dispensations, by an evil guardian, and by the actions taken by the Roman Curia. So that even today the harm is not thought to be reparable . . . .

The accounts contained in the Indiculus de Successione Archepiscoporum Cantuariensium and Birchington's Vitae Archiepiscoporum do not differ substantially from the above.[26]

Birchington's account of the insult offered to Bradwardine and to the English king, at the time of the former's consecration as archbishop, is, however, interesting, providing a documentary note on the tension and ill will existing between England and the Avignon papacy at that time. "In the same year (1349), during the Vigil of St. Margaret, Thomas being at Avignon, was there consecrated in the church of the Minorites. On the day of consecration, however, Hugo, cardinal of Tulle, and blood brother of the pope, while the archbishop [Thomas] was seated at table, brought great shame on him by someone riding in on a donkey, at which the rest of the cardinals were wickedly pleased."[27] Presumably this clumsy joke against Thomas was intended to indicate the opinion that Edward, military and political master of northern Europe, could send whom he would to the pope for consecration, even a donkey. At any rate, apologies were made to Bradwardine for the unhappy incident.[28]

Birchington's narrative concludes by telling how Bradwardine, returning to England to take up his new duties, was struck down by the plague, scarcely one month after his consecration. "Then, as is customary, having had a visit with the pope and cardinals, and embarking on his journey to England, he arrived on Wednesday the nineteenth of August at Dover and on that day was a guest at the castle, going forth from there by way of Chertham and, in the following days, coming through Dartford and, on Saturday of the Vigil of the Assumption of the Blessed Mary, coming to the king at Eltham, where he received the temporalities. The same day arriving at the manor of the bishop of Rochester at Lambeth, he was a guest there during Sunday, the Feast of the Assumption of the Blessed Mary, Monday, Tuesday and the ensuing Wednesday; on which Wednesday he died there, and on Saturday, the Feast of the Beheading of St. John the Baptist, was buried in the church at Canterbury. So it fell out that the church of Canterbury was three times vacated in one and the same year, excepting five days [i.e., by Stratford, Ufford and Bradwardine]."[29] The chronicles for the year 1349 are full of vivid and horrifying descriptions of the Black Death that was then devastating all of western Europe and in which the lives of so many of the great men of the time were simultaneously cut short.[30]

It should be of some comfort to scholars that, in spite of Bradwardine's prominence as a man of affairs, he was esteemed more especially by his own and succeeding generations for his intellectual achievements. Several honorifics have been bestowed on his name: "Sacrae paginae professor solempnis,"[31] "Egregius theologus,"[32] "Magnus logicus,"[33] and, most characteristically, "Doctor profundus."[34]

2. EDITIONS AND MANUSCRIPTS

With the exception of his De causa Dei (1618) and De praescientia et praedestinatione (1935), none of Bradwardine's works have appeared in any but the earliest editions. The Geometria speculativa, De quadratura circuli, Arithmetica speculativa, and De proportionibus (some of these in many editions) were printed over a period extending from 1495 to 1536 and in such various places as Paris, Venice, Vienna, Valencia, and Wittenberg. If the complete absence of Bradwardine's theological writings among this list of early editions is any criterion, it would seem that his work in natural philosophy was of considerably greater interest than his theological writings at the beginning of the sixteenth century.

Copies of these early printed editions of Bradwardine's scientific writings are relatively scarce, but an examination of some of the more important holdings of European libraries reveals large numbers in manuscript form. No systematic attempt was made to collect information regarding manuscripts other than those of the De proportionibus, yet considerable numbers of them were encountered in passing, and, in the case of the De proportionibus itself, the location of thirty widely scattered manuscripts was discovered with little difficulty. It would seem quite possible that at least double that number might still be in existence, and one is again impressed with the considerable esteem in which Bradwardine's mathematical and philosophical works were held in the years before the advent of printing.

Because of the relatively meager amount of modern scholarly study thus far devoted to the literature of the fourteenth century, bibliographical information concerning such a figure as Thomas Bradwardine is difficult to obtain and yet more difficult to substantiate. The following information is, therefore, presented, insofar as possible, in the order of its certainty.[35]

EDITIONS

De causa Dei contra Pelagium et de virtute causarum, ad suos Mertonenses. Ed. Sir Henry Savile, London, 1618.

This work, of more than nine hundred folio pages, contains in the editor's Preface the earliest modern biography of Bradwardine. The work itself, falling into three main divisions, develops deductively and in mathematical style the thesis that God is the immediate sustaining and moving cause of every being and every action.[36]

Variant titles: Summa theologica and, possibly, Summa scientiarum.[37]

Geometria speculativa. Ed. Petrus Sanchez Cirvelus, Paris, 1495: Guy Marchant, 22 fols., folio;[38] ed. Thomas Dura, Valencia, 1503: I. Iofre, 14 fols., folio.[39]

In four parts: (1) <u>Stellated polygons</u>: Formulae established in
extension of Campanus' work; (2) <u>Isoperimetric figures</u>: Demon-
strates, among other things, that the circle has the maximal area
of every isoperimetric figure. Bradwardine's source probably was
the anonymous <u>De isoperimetris</u>, based upon Zenodorus' original
work on the subject, which had become popular in the thirteenth
century; (3) <u>Theory of proportions</u>: A study of rational and irrational quantities (here called <u>communicantes</u>, <u>incommunicantes</u>,
<u>commensurabiles</u>, <u>irrationales</u> and <u>assimetri</u>); (4) <u>Solid geometry</u>:
The final propositions of this section are taken from the <u>Spherics</u>
of Theodosius of Bithynia (Ic.BC).[40]
   Variant titles: <u>Geometrica principia</u>,[41] <u>Geometria theoretica</u>.[42]
<u>De proportionibus</u>. Paris, "not before 1481": Geoffrey de Marnef,
      24 fols., folio;[43] Venice, 1505, folio.[44]
   For description of the contents of the <u>De proportionibus</u>, see
Part IV of this Introduction.
   Variant titles: <u>Proportiones</u>; <u>Tractatus proportionum</u>; <u>De veloci-
tate motuum</u>;[45] <u>Tractatus brevis</u> (or <u>epitomatus</u>) <u>de proportioni-
bus</u>.[46]
<u>Arithmetica speculativa</u>. Ed. Petrus Sanchez Cirvelus, Paris, 1495:
      Guy Marchant, 16 fols., 4to;[47] ed. Thomas Dura, Valencia, 1503:
      I. Iofre, 14 fols., folio;[48] Paris 1515 or 1502: M. Lesclencher,
      4to.[49]
   This work is described by Sarton as being of the "practical,
Boethian type" and, if equivalent to the edition at the Columbia
University Library,[50] is verified to be no more than an abridge-
ment of Boethius' <u>Arithmetica</u>: presumably designed for use as a
text book.
   Variant titles: <u>Arithmetica</u>;[51] <u>Arithmetica practica</u>.[52]
<u>Utrum Deus habeat praescientiam futurorum contingentium ad
utrumlibet</u>. Ed. Bartomeu Ma. Xiberta (O. Carm.). "<u>Fragments
d'una questio inedita de Tomas Bradwardine</u>," Martin Grabmann
<u>Festschrift</u>,(Munster i. W., 1935), pp. 1169-80.[53]
   This is the <u>Quaestio</u> already referred to in the biographical portion of the present chapter as having been disputed by Bradwardine
and Baconthorpe. It is, of course, one of the key problems of the
<u>De causa Dei</u>, also.
   Variant titles: <u>De praescientia et praedestinatione</u>,[54] <u>De futuris
contingentibus</u>.[55]

MANUSCRIPTS

<u>Tractatus de continuo</u>. MS. R4° 2, Stadtbibliothek, Torun (Thorn);
      MS. CA4 385, fols.17r-48r, Stadtbücherei, Erfurt.
   Of all the works of Bradwardine still existing in manuscript form
only, this is certainly the most interesting to historians of philo-

sophy and mathematics. Rediscovered only in modern times, it has thus far been examined by Curtze, Cantor, and Stamm, Stamm having promised an edition of it in his article, "Tractatus de continuo von Thomas Bradwardine." [56]

From references within the text, Stamm takes the attribution to Bradwardine to be sufficiently established, and the contents of the work, as described by him, would certainly seem consistent with the strongly Aristotelian position developed in the De proportionibus.

Progressing from "definitiones" to "suppositiones" to "conclusiones," the De continuo exhibits the same general form as the De proportionibus. The theme is mathematical and physical continuity ("de compositione continui quantum ad sua essentialia"), and, against the "atomism" of Grosseteste, Bradwardine maintains that a continuum can only be decomposed into continua similar to itself, and not into "atoms." Actual and potential infinities are distinguished ("categorimatice" and "syncategorimatice"),[57] and also "continuum permanens" (e.g., a line or surface) and "continuum successivum" (e.g., time or motion). [58]

Ars memorativa MS. 3744, Sloan Collection, British Museum.

This work is described as a plan for aiding the memory by the association of places and ideas.[59]

Variant title: De memoria artificiali. [60]

"Propositiones," MS. Vat. Lat. 3102.

This manuscript is of the Perspectiva communis of John Peckham (second half of the twelfth century), and is said to contain four propositions added by Bradwardine, which show him to have been familiar with "tangent" and "cotangent" and their reciprocal relation. [61]

Commentarii in quattuor libros sententiarum. MS. 505, Bibliothèque de Troyes. (Catalogue Générale des Manuscrits des Bibliothèques Publiques par Departements, Paris 1855, II, 222.)

Insolubilia. Erfurt, Stadtbücherei, Amplonian Collection: MS. F120 (frag.), MS. F135 (wrongly attributed to Roger Swineshead), MS. Q176 (frag.), MS. Q76. (Besch. Verzeichn. d. Amplon. Handschr. Samm. z. Erfurt.)

De fallaciis tractatus. Erfurt, Stadtbücherei, Amplonian Collection: MS. F 297. (Ibid. Such a work would seem appropriate to a "magnus logicus.")

Liber metricus rithmimachie, id est de pugna numerorum. Erfurt, Stadtbücherei, Amplonian Collection: MS. F313. (Attributed by Thorndike and Kibre, op. cit., Col. 284.)

Quaestiones physicae. Vatican, Palatine MS. 1049. (Attributed by Thorndike and Kibre, op. cit., Cols. 284, 758.)

Quaestiones de velocitate motuum et de proportionibus velocitatum. Erfurt, Stadtbücherei, Amplonian Collection: MS. F313. (Besch, Verzeichn. d. Amplon. Handschr. Samm. z. Erfurt.)

For the following works no manuscripts have been located and either their existence or attribution must therefore remain a matter of some doubt.

Tabulae astronomicae. (Mentioned by Savile, Fabricius, and Überweg.)

De sancta trinitate. (Mentioned by Pits, Hahn, and Überweg.)

Placita theologica. (Mentioned by Pits, Hahn, Überweg, and Fabricius.)

De praemio salvandorum. (Mentioned by Pits, Hahn, and Überweg.)

Sermones. (Mentioned by Pits, Hahn, Überweg, and Fabricius.)

Meditationes. (Mentioned by Hahn, Überweg, and Fabricius.)

De quidditate peccati. (Mentioned by Hahn and Überweg.)

3. THE GENERAL SIGNIFICANCE OF THE DE PROPORTIONIBUS

Before embarking upon the detailed and technical portion of the present study, it may first be well to consider more generally the significance and interest which Bradwardine's De proportionibus possesses for the contemporary student of the history of western thought.

Of the entire period of intellectual development in the West, those centuries which have thus far received the least attention are the fourteenth and fifteenth. From the standpoint of the theological interest which has, quite appropriately, motivated so much of the study of scholastic philosophy, this period has been traditionally considered as one of regrettable decay after the high tide of the great thirteenth century. More recently, a reawakened interest in the logic of William of Ockham, and in the more truly Aristotelian, or at least the more truly modern, spirit which he introduced into scholasticism, has carried historical studies forward into the early fourteenth century; but even this period (within which falls the work of Thomas Bradwardine) remains largely unexplored.

It was, however, during this first half of the fourteenth century that the studies then being carried out by Bradwardine and his successors were, for the first time since antiquity, making real progress in the wedding of mathematics to natural philosophy. On both sides of the channel the laying of foundations for what is now the characteristically modern treatment of the natural sciences moved ahead. The English (Bradwardine, Hentisberus, Dumbleton, Swineshead, and others) were concerning themselves with the more strictly mathematical treatment of problems in physics; at the University of Paris, John Buridan was making a more philosophical and Nicolas Oresme a more geometric approach to these problems.

Almost the only published work thus far to recognize the signal importance of Thomas Bradwardine's De proportionibus has been that of Anneliese Maier, whose brief but clear-sighted estimates cannot be too highly praised.[62]

Duhem, with what may be pardonable human pride in the brilliance of the University of Paris (to whose greater glory his Études sur Leonard de Vinci are quite explicitly composed) gives scant treatment to achievements on the other side of the channel. In general, he accuses the English of this period of being unregenerate Aristotelians in their studies of dynamics, possibly of some significance in the development of mathematics, but for the most part concerned with barren logic and theological quibbles. Bradwardine, he criticizes sharply (and, as we shall see, without much justification) for having taken the end rather than the midpoint of a moving radius as the measure of its velocity[63] and passes over, almost without mention, the central contributions of the De proportionibus: its employment of a complex mathematical function in the expression of a physical law and its clear distinction between velocity conceived as an instantaneous "quality" of a motion and velocity conceived as total distance traversed per total time elapsed. The clarification of this latter distinction and Bradwardine's association of his formula in dynamics with velocity conceived as an instantaneous rate pointed, as we shall see,[64] to the inevitable conclusion that constant forces produce constant accelerations rather than constant velocities. Bradwardine's successors at Merton College thereupon continued to the logical deduction of the correct kinematic law relating time elapsed to distance traversed in a uniformly accelerated motion.

Bradwardine's De proportionibus is, indeed, one of the key works in the history of the development of modern science, having been the first to announce a general law of physics whose expression calls for anything more than the most rudimentary mathematics. The ancient science of hydrostatics, for example, did not demand mathematics more complex than that of simple functions, or direct proportionality. The weight of any substance in water divided by its weight in air is constant for any constant volume of the same substance, and this constant, in turn, varies in direct proportion to the densities of different substances (i.e., weight in water ÷ weight in air = K). Independently of physical theory, mathematics had reached, even in ancient times, a high pitch of development, Archimedes, himself, having been familiar with the fundamental principle of what later came to be developed as the theory of logarithms. It was apparently in the De proportionibus of Thomas Bradwardine, however, that what may be called a logarithmic, exponential, or geometric function first came to be applied in the expression of a physical theory.

His theory of the relation of a force and the resistance impeding it to the resultant velocity may be expressed thus:

$$V = \log_n \left(\frac{F}{R}\right)$$

or, to avoid an anachronistic use of the term, "log"

$$n^V = \left(\frac{F}{R}\right)$$

That this formulation required alteration and a further clarification of the terms, "velocity," "force," and "resistance" before it could become a part of modern dynamics goes without saying. As we shall see in our further exploration of the Tractatus, this theory was primarily an ingenious solution to a specific problem which faced those who were attempting to uphold the Aristotelian laws, or axioms, concerning natural motion. As such, it has its own historic purpose and consequent limitations.

However faulty Bradwardine's application of the above formula to his own problem, it is nevertheless of considerable importance that he introduced this particular function to the consideration of those who were attempting to express physical relationships with the accuracy and generality of mathematics. Not only has the logarithmic function since become an indispensable tool for the expression of such phenomena as those in which growth is a function of size, but in Bradwardine's own day it provided a considerable stimulus to the development of mathematical analysis because of its capacity to overcome certain logical paradoxes to be encountered in the employment of simple functions for the expression of physical relations. The serious nature of these paradoxes and the obstacle they presented to fourteenth-century mathematical physics will be evident from our subsequent analysis of Chapter II, Theory III, of the present treatise.

Those following immediately in Bradwardine's footsteps at Oxford (often known as Calculatores and consisting for the most part of fellow Mertonians) were quick to realize the power of this general mathematical relation as a means for expressing an enormous variety of physical processes, and, in their hands, Bradwardine's exponential function came to be applied not only to "uniformly difform motion" (acceleration) but to qualitative and quantitative alteration and even to problems in psychology, ethics and theology. "Wherever one quantity is definable in terms of a relation between two others, and there is no express reason to the contrary, it is taken for granted [by the Calculatores] that Bradwardine's function expresses the relation." [65]

To appreciate the magnitude of the reorientation worked by the De proportionibus upon the character of theorizing within the field of natural philosophy, one need only cast a backward glance at the type of treatment accorded problems concerning motion during the preceding century. The existence of these problems and the necessity of dealing with them had been made quite evident to scholastic philosophers by the Arabian commentator on Aristotle's works, Averroes, who principally in his discussion of what was known to mediaeval scholars as "Text 71" of the Physics (IV, viii) had focussed attention on certain apparent paradoxes entailed by Aristotle's scanty remarks concerning dynamics.

What, in the first place, is to be considered the essential cause of the fact that some changes (i.e., those properly to be called "motions") occupy time? If, as is indicated in the Physics the successive character of motion is attributable to an opposition between moving and resisting powers, what of the motion of the heavens, where presumably no resistance is to be encountered? In spite of the fact that the scholastic students of Aristotle's natural philosophy were prepared to agree in the distinction between two kinds of natural motion (the one rectilinear and sublunar, the other circular and celestial), they were still inclined to believe that a single principle should explain the successive character of both.

Since, furthermore, Aristotle had claimed that velocity varies according to the proportion between the power of the mover and that of the thing moved, what was to be considered the correct interpretation of the term, ἀναλογία or "proportion"? The word, "proportion," has today a clarity of meaning which it has not always possessed; perhaps the more general meaning of the word, "function," better preserves the sense of the ancient and mediaeval usage. Ἀναλογία or proportio, might mean: "a function of the arithmetic difference," "a function of the ratio," or any one of a host of other functions. The problem of choosing between these alternatives is the second principal one posed by Averroes' commentary.

In his own efforts to find solutions for these two problems we find Averroes adhering as faithfully as possible to what seems most clearly to be Aristotle's general point of view. Regarding the question of what is to be viewed as the essential and generic cause of the successive character of motion, he argues that this is necessarily the presence of a force resistant to the moving power; therefore the temporal duration of celestial motions must indicate the presence of a real resistance offered by the spheres to the powers which move them. As to the other problem (that of establishing the true functional relationship between speed, force and resistance) it is clear that Averroes repudiates the thesis that this function is one of arithmetic difference. To mention only one of his arguments: If it were true that speed varies with the difference between force and resistance, then it would not follow that halving the resistance would double the speed (as Aristotle had claimed it would); more important still, if speed is to be understood as varying with the difference between opposing forces, not only does this commit us to the un-Aristotelian conclusion that motions in vacuo are possible but that all the so-called "natural" motions studied in physics are not really natural at all—the truly "natural" motions being the ideal speeds with which bodies would move in the absence of any resistance.

Although Averroes argues conclusively that, on Aristotelian grounds, speed cannot be a function of the arithmetic difference between force and resistance, it is not too clear just what he took the true function to be. If, according to the usual interpretation of Aristotle, he understood this function to be one of simple proportionality, then his position is open to the decisive mathematical objections which Bradwardine discusses in his refutation of Theory III in the second chapter of his treatise.

Whether or not the positive portion of Averroes' discussion of these problems was altogether satisfactory, his inclusion of an adverse criticism of the views of an earlier Arabian, Ibn Badja (Avempace), was of momentous influence for thirteenth-century scholasticism. Taking as his point of departure celestial rather than terrestrial phenomena, Ibn Badja had argued that, since the heavenly bodies move at determinate rates without encountering any apparent resistance, every resistance should, therefore, be understood as diminishing what would otherwise be a determinate, absolute speed. Fundamentally, this view resolves itself into a simple equation of force and speed, and the reason why finite forces do not produce instantaneous translations must, therefore, be that it is impossible for a force of any given magnitude to act, even without opposition, instantaneously. It is as though empty space itself must prevent the instantaneous translation of a body from one place to another. As a matter of fact, Ibn Badja is quoted as saying just this, and the scholastics who puzzled over the problem during the thirteenth century developed the idea at length.

Not only is the discussion of problems concerning motion that went on during this century of interest in the contrast exhibited between its dialectical method and the mathematical method which largely supplanted it during the post-Bradwardinian period, it is also of some interest as providing yet one more example of the easy freedom with which scholastic philosophers departed from Aristotelian teachings whenever that seemed to them the more reasonable course.[66] The bulk of the great figures of the thirteenth century quite emphatically preferred the absolutist, rather Platonic, solutions to these problems suggested by Ibn Badja to the relational and typically Aristotelian approach provided by Averroes; Thomas Aquinas, Roger Bacon, Pierre Jean Olivi, and Duns Scotus were all, in one way or another, adherents of Ibn Badja's views.[67]

Their complete neglect of mathematical considerations—not only a neglect which failed to deal with problems entailed by Ibn Badja's dynamics but one which failed even to make capital of the manifest difficulties inherent in the dynamic formula to which Averroes apparently subscribed—stands in striking contrast to the treatment

of these issues in Bradwardine's De proportionibus. Among the
first to re-establish the reputation of the Averroist-Aristotelian
position at the beginning of the fourteenth century, his course was
not to attack first the general problem of what is to be considered
the essential cause of successive motion but rather to deal directly
with the problem of developing an interpretation of the dynamic
function whose mathematical implications would be in harmony
with the general axioms concerning both motion and rest which had
been current since antiquity.

His handling of this question is, admittedly, pre-modern in its
failure to extend or refine the empirical observations upon which
the verification of any hypothesis necessarily depends; this latter
methodological innovation had to wait for Galileo. What he did accomplish was, in the first place, to make clear once and for all the
inescapable impossibilities entailed in Ibn Badja's view that speed is
a function of the difference whereby a moving power exceeds one
that is opposed to it. The general character of these difficulties
had already been indicated by Averroes' reply to that theory but
apparently had fallen on deaf ears so far as most of the earlier
scholastics were concerned. Rejecting also (because of the mathematical impossibilities to which it also leads) the theory that the
function in question is one of simple proportionality, Bradwardine's
second considerable achievement was the successful reinterpretation of this relationship in terms of a logarithmic function which
would satisfy consistently the accepted empirical generalizations
regarding motion and rest.

It is, indeed, no small honor to Aristotle that mediaeval natural
philosophers were able to proceed (on the assumption that the basic
theoretical structure and simple empirical content of Aristotle's
writings were correct) to the development of a scientific edifice
which in many directions far outreached its original. What may,
however, strike a contemporary as astonishing is that such an essentially deductive approach to the physical sciences should have
met with such success. Yet, Buridan's theory of "impetus" (which
foreshadowed Galileo's "impeto" and Descartes' "quantity of motion"), Nicolas of Oresme's discussions of the diurnal rotation of
the earth and his development of the elements of coordinate geometry, and the Mertonian proof of the correct law of uniform acceleration,[68] all were developed at this time and without benefit of
that experimentation which the modern is inclined to regard as indispensable to any advance in the sciences.

Bradwardine's De proportionibus represents, at any rate, a significant advance in two very important aspects of the scientific
enterprise: first, it moves forward with the task of developing
mathematical formulae for the expression of physcial laws whose
entailed consequences do not contradict other generally accepted
laws or observations—in other words the task of achieving self-

consistency in physics through mathematics; second, through the introduction of mathematical analysis, it sets the stage for the quantitative measurement of physical processes and, hence, that typically modern physics which was to appear with Galileo's wedding of mathematics and experimental observation. Bradwardine used mathematics for the systematic and general expression of theory; Galileo used it for the systematic generalization of experimental observation.

As has been already briefly noted, one of the interesting points of contrast between Bradwardine's approach to the problems of dynamics and the approach which was most prevalent during the preceding century is that between his own Aristotelianism and the quasi-Platonism of these predecessors. Quite the contrary to what one might expect, on the basis of that general contemporary opinion which would see in Platonism rather than in Aristotelianism the true paternity of modern science, we find that, in philosophic considerations, Bradwardine aligns himself consistently with Aristotle. Not only is his preference for a correlative rather than an absolute account of the nature and cause of velocities clearly Aristotelian, the careful concern with which the legitimacy of expressing physical correlations in mathematical terms is treated (in the distinctions drawn in Theory IV of Chapter IV, and elsewhere) arises explicitly on the basis of Aristotle's treatment of this problem in Physics VII, Chapter 4. Perhaps yet more strikingly, in his De continuo, Bradwardine bases his position (in which, according to Cantor, he foreshadows the theory of transfinite numbers) on a defense of the Aristotelian conception of a continuum against the atomism of Grosseteste.

Though Bradwardine has long been known as one of the realists, there is perhaps a greater degree of agreement between his philosophic views and those of William of Ockham than this contrast suggests. The central doctrine of the De causa Dei, that God is the immediate and omnipotent efficient cause of every effect, is substantially the same as that of Ockham and an obviously appropriate premise for the subsequent contention (by the "Ockhamites," Holkot and Mirecourt) that the will of God is the efficient cause of human sin. Though this return to an emphasis on the centrality of the doctrine of God's omnipotence, characteristic of the theological trend at the beginning of the fourteenth century, need hardly indicate that Bradwardine shared with Ockham a nominalistic theory of knowledge, both the De proportionibus and Ockham's Philosophia naturalis do show these men to be returning to a less Platonistic interpretation of Aristotle.

The foregoing should, then, indicate something of the considerable range of interest which Bradwardine's De proportionibus possesses, not only as a turning point in the development of the sciences, but as an example of scholastic natural philosophy in a period from which there survive very few readily available texts. It was, as is being increasingly better recognized, a richly creative period, and, in the intellectual scope and energy of its great innovators, truly comparable to the age of Galileo, Descartes and Newton.

4. DESCRIPTIVE AND CRITICAL ANALYSIS

The De proportionibus commences by taking as axiomatic Aristotle's statement that motions and their velocities exhibit a proportional relationship. There appears to have been little disagreement regarding the truth of this by any of the scholastics,[69] divergence of opinion centering, instead, on the question of (1) the nature of such a proportion, and (2) the factors properly to be understood as involved.

Bradwardine quite rightly points to the fact that in spite of the consequence that a study of proportions is thus necessarily involved in a study of velocities, no one had as yet carried out the task. He commences his treatise, therefore, with an exposition of the fundamental nature and properties of proportion, based primarily on Boethius' Arithmetica and Campanus de Novara's Commentarium super quintum librum Elementorum Euclidis. The fact that he considers such an exposition necessary seems indicative not only of the mathematician's desire for completeness in argumentation, but also of the almost complete neglect of mathematical considerations in the formulation of theories of motion which is so clearly manifested by those scholastic precursors of Bradwardine already mentioned. He begins the De proportionibus, therefore, with a lively awareness that he is embarking on a new course and yet one which had, from the beginning, been indicated as logically necessary from the very nature of the material involved (i.e., the axiom that velocities are, in some sense, proportional to forces).

The tone of Boethius' introduction to the Arithmetica is strongly neo-Platonic and neo-Pythagorean, being full of references to the Timaeus and Republic in which numbers are spoken of as "real" and as "generated" in a most literal sense. The idea is pervasively developed that the cosmos exhibits, in its form and behavior, numerical properties, and what strikes the modern reader as truly remarkable is that such a keen appreciation of the possibilities inherent to a mathematical physics, whereby the predominantly classificatory and qualitative physics of Aristotle might well be further explored, should have remained so long unused. The first steps toward the development of such a science had long been the property of the western mind as exemplified in the science of harmonics, yet nothing further had been done.

Many explanations may be made for this neglect of the possibilities of a mathematical physics, not the least of which is that Aristotle, the dominant figure on the scholastic scene, had himself done so little in this direction, having been primarily concerned with the erection of a science of classification and analysis rather than one of measurement and synthesis. Perhaps an equally powerful deterrent, however, was lack of mathematical symbolism for the easy manipulation of algebraic equations. The Arabic decimal system and notation were in common use some time before the composition of the De proportionibus, but although Leonardo of Pisa (c. 1225),[70] the greatest writer on algebra during the middle ages, had commenced the introduction of operational signs into western usage, their employment and improvement by other writers was long delayed. We find, for example, Bradwardine still using the "names" for different proportions, which had been handed down in a tradition of Boethian arithmetic in which these names were the result of an effort to develop a science of general fractions at a time when no good symbolism for that purpose existed. The difficulties presented in attempting to render algebraic equations without the aid of operational symbols is abundantly illustrated throughout the course of Bradwardine's treatise.

The first distinction drawn, at the beginning of Chapter I of the De proportionibus, is that between the general and the strictly accurate, the equivocal and the univocal, meaning of proportion. Between any two things which are comparable a proportion may be said to exist in respect to the factor compared. But, accurately speaking, a proportion can only be between quantities "of the same kind." The phrase, "eiusdem generis," is an important one.

Campanus (whose definition of proportion Bradwardine quotes)[71] when drawing the distinction between commensurable and incommensurable quantities, distinguishes the objects of arithmetic and geometric analysis from those not capable of the arithmetic but only of the geometric. It is, thus, clear that the term, "quantity," does not apply simply to number but also to geometric continua. The term, "quantity," is yet more explicitly broadened in Aristotle's usage. In the Categories, (Chapter 6) he distinguishes physical continuities (such as lines and surfaces) from the discontinuity or discreteness of number. These constitute, for Aristotle, different genera of quantity, and, as such, are held to be incommensurable. In Physics (VII, iv) he further points out that not only must quantities be of the same genus but also of the same species, if they are to be univocally commensurable.

According to this view, therefore, there could only be a proportion (proprie dicta) between numbers or between velocities, but not between a number and a velocity, since the one is discontinuous and the other continuous. Nor could there be such a univocal proportion even between continuous motions, if they be of different genera (e.g., locomotion and alteration) or different species (e.g., rectilinear and circular locomotion). In what sense, then, is a mathematical formulation of physical process justifiable? The answer to this question is given at the commencement of the second section of this chapter of the De proportionibus, wherein is discussed the general theory of proportionality; in the meantime, the strictly mathematical aspects of proportions remain to be described.

Proportions, Bradwardine continues, are of two orders or degrees, a "first order proportion" being called "rational" and defined as that which is immediately denominated by some number (e.g., "double proportion," denominated by the number 2, "triple proportion," denominated by the number 3, etc.). A "second order proportion," called "irrational," is one which is not immediately denominated by a number, but mediately (i.e., by mediation of a first order proportion). Bradwardine uses the example of "half a double proportion" (medietas duplae proportionis) which, he says, is the proportion of the diagonal of a square to its side. This is not expressible as a single, simple proportion of integers but may be expressed by two such immediately denominated integral proportions, the one being denominated by the other—i.e., $\left(\frac{2}{1}\right)^{\frac{1}{2}}$.

Here, for the first time in the De proportionibus, we encounter roots and powers, and this is only the first of several cases in which a terminology, which to the modern reader must seem vague and ambiguous, poses an important problem of interpretation. In this instance, it is obvious, from the nature of the example given, that we must understand a proportion of two integers to be "denominated" by another proportion, or number, in a geometric rather than arithmetic, exponential rather than factorial, sense. The proportion, $\frac{2}{1}$, cannot be multiplied by an integral arithmetical factor in order to yield that of the diagonal to the side of the square. It can be so multiplied, or denominated, by an exponential factor, however. Therefore, the "denomination" of one proportion by another is equivalent to raising it to a given power or extracting from it a given root. A power would be equivalent to denomination by a proportion of "greater inequality" (i.e., a proportion in which the denominator is 1 and the numerator is any integer greater than 1), and a root would be equivalent to denomination by a proportion of "lesser inequality" (i.e., a proportion in which the numerator is 1 and the denominator is any integer greater than 1).

It is of considerable importance to realize that this denomination of one proportion by another (or by a number, i.e., a proportion the denominator or numerator of which is 1) may be easily confused with simple arithmetic multiplication and division. Bradwardine, or at least the contemporary copyists of his treatise, fail to make a clear-cut terminological distinction between these two processes, the one exponential and the other factorial. Consider, for example, the term "double" (duplum). If A is said to be duplum B, it means "double" or "twice" in the sense that A = B + B, or 2B. If, on the other hand, $\frac{A}{B} = \frac{B}{C}$, then $\frac{A}{C}$ is duplum $\frac{A}{B}$ or $\frac{B}{C}$ in the sense that $\frac{A}{C} = \left(\frac{A}{B}\right)^2$, or $\left(\frac{B}{C}\right)^2$. This is tantamount to saying that $\frac{A}{C} = \frac{A}{B} \cdot \frac{A}{B}$, or $\frac{B}{C} \cdot \frac{B}{C}$ and therefore we may draw the general distinction that, in modern parlance, a factorial fraction or integer, as applied to integers, indicates arithmetic multiplication and, as applied to proportions, indicates the raising of that proportion to the given power, or the extraction from it of the given root.

Campanus[72] avoids this confusion by a circumlocution. Instead of saying that $\frac{A}{C}$ is dupla ad $\frac{A}{B}$, he says that proportio $\frac{A}{C}$ = proportio $\frac{A}{B}$ duplicata, thereby using our modern way of stating that $\frac{A}{C} = \frac{A}{B}$ "squared" (i.e., by using the past-participial form). Bradwardine, if he had used our terms, "square" and "squared", would have said that $\frac{A}{C}$ is the "square" of $\frac{A}{B}$, but since in his time the equivalent of both "square" and "twice" was duplum, the confusion which we have been describing was an ever-present danger.

Giovanni Marliani,[73] an important Italian theorist in the century succeeding that of Bradwardine, may have fallen into this very pitfall of misinterpretation in his attempt to refute the main thesis of Bradwardine's De proportionibus, and the modern reader need not be too surprised at the difficulty which this ambiguity presents today. That the question of which is the proper reading of such terms as duplum, triplum, etc., can be resolved with certainty in any particular case is not, however, to be doubted. The context of argument, together with the axioms and theorems cited in support of the statement in question, provide sure criteria of choice between the two possible readings, simply on the internal grounds of supposing the author's reasoning to be logically consistent.

Continuing his definition of the difference between rational and irrational proportions, Bradwardine goes on to point out that rational proportions are only found in commensurable quantities (those quantities for which there exists an exact common measure in the form of an aliquot part, or factor). Irrational proportions are found only in incommensurable quantities (i.e., those possessing no such aliquot factor, of which each would be an exact multiple). Rational proportions are found in numbers and also in all other kinds of quantities (commensurable ones); irrational proportions are not found in numbers (except "mediately", as explained above) but are found in all other kinds of quantities. Therefore, rational proportions belong both to arithmetic and to other branches of mathematics, whereas irrational proportions belong to all branches of mathematics other than arithmetic. This last observation would seem to indicate clearly that Bradwardine includes, as branches of mathematics, such "exact" physical sciences as that of music, which had been presented by Boethius in a wholly mathematical guise. Such a broad usage of the term, "mathematics," is at least as old as Plato, who, in the Republic (VII, 521c-531c; also Laws 817E), includes plane and solid geometry, astronomy and music in his classification of mathematical studies, as well as arithmetic.

The remaining portion of the first part of Chapter I is given over to an exhaustive description of various types of proportion which may be generated from the variation and permutation of no more than three interrelated terms. Since the text is both difficult to follow and also possesses a certain interest for the history of number-theory, a schematic presentation in modern notation is given, below.

Proportio aequalitatis: $\dfrac{n}{n}$

Proportio inaequalitatis:
 a) major: $\dfrac{n}{m}$
                                   [where n is greater than m]
 b) minor: $\dfrac{m}{n}$

Proportio maioris inaequalitatis:
 a) multiplex: $\dfrac{n}{1}$ [where n is any integer greater than 1] : $\dfrac{2}{1}$ (dupla); $\dfrac{3}{1}$ (tripla)...

 b) superparticular: $\dfrac{n+1}{n}$: $\dfrac{3}{2}$ (sesquialtera), $\dfrac{4}{3}$ (sesquitertia),... [where n is any integer greater than 1]

 c) superpartient: $\dfrac{n+m}{n}$ [where n and m are integers greater than one, and where n is greater than m]

   i. (m varied): $\dfrac{n+2}{n}$ (superbipartiens), $\dfrac{n+3}{n}$ (supertripartiens)...

   ii. (n varied): $\dfrac{3+m}{3}$ (superpartiens tertias) $\dfrac{4+m}{4}$ (superpartiens quartas),...

   iii. (m & n varied): $\dfrac{3+2}{3}$ (superbipartiens tertias, or superbitertia), $\dfrac{5+2}{5}$ (superbipartiens quintas, or superbiquintas),... $\dfrac{4+3}{4}$

(<u>superterpartiens quartas</u>, or <u>super-</u>
<u>terquartas</u>),...

d) <u>multiplex superparticularis</u>: $\dfrac{mn+1}{n}$ [where m and n are inte-

gers greater than 1]

   i. (m varied): $\dfrac{2n+1}{n}$ (<u>duplex superparticularis</u>),

                             $\dfrac{3n+1}{n}$ (<u>triplex superparticularis</u>),...

   ii. (n varied): $\dfrac{m2+1}{2}$ (<u>multiplex sesquialtera</u>), $\dfrac{m3+1}{3}$

                             (<u>multiplex sesquitertia</u>),...

   iii. (m & n varied): $\dfrac{2\cdot2+1}{2}$ (<u>dupla sesquialtera</u>), $\dfrac{2\cdot3+1}{3}$ (<u>du-</u>

                            <u>pla sesquitertia</u>),... $\dfrac{3\cdot2+1}{2}$ (<u>tripla ses-</u>

                             <u>quialtera</u>), $\dfrac{3\cdot3+1}{3}$ (<u>tripla sesquiter-</u>

                             <u>tia</u>),...

e) <u>multiplex superpartiens</u>: $\dfrac{kn+m}{n}$ [where k, m, and n are inte-

gers greater than one]

   i. (k varied): $\dfrac{2n+m}{n}$ (<u>duplex superpartiens</u>), $\dfrac{3n+m}{n}$

                           (<u>triplex superpartiens</u>),...

   ii. (m varied): $\dfrac{kn+2}{n}$ (<u>multiplex superbipartiens</u>),

                           $\dfrac{kn+3}{n}$ (<u>multiplex supertripartiens</u>),...

   iii. (n varied): $\dfrac{k3+m}{3}$ (<u>multiplex superpartiens ter-</u>

                         <u>tias</u>), $\dfrac{k4+m}{4}$ (<u>multiplex superpartiens</u>

                         <u>quartas</u>),...

   iv. (m & n varied): $\dfrac{k3+2}{3}$ (<u>multiplex superbipartiens ter-</u>

                         <u>tias or multiplex superbitertia</u>), $\dfrac{k4+3}{4}$

                         (<u>multiplex supertripartiens quartas</u>
                         or <u>multiplex supertriquarta</u>),...

   v. (k varied,
      m specified): $\dfrac{2n+2}{n}$ (<u>duplex superbipartiens</u>), $\dfrac{3n+2}{n}$

                         (<u>triplex superbipartiens</u>),...

      (m varied,
      k specified): $\dfrac{2n+2}{n}$ (<u>duplex superbipartiens</u>), $\dfrac{2n+3}{n}$

                         (<u>duplex supertripartiens</u>),...

vi. (k varied,
   n specified):

$\frac{2 \cdot 3 + m}{3}$ (duplex superpartiens tertias),

$\frac{3 \cdot 3 + m}{3}$ (triplex superpartiens tertias),...

(n varied,
  k specified):

$\frac{2 \cdot 3 + m}{3}$ (duplex superpartiens tertias),

$\frac{2 \cdot 4 + m}{4}$ (duplex superpartiens quartas),...

vii. (k varied, n &
   m specified):

$\frac{2 \cdot 3 + 2}{3}$ (duplex superbitertia), $\frac{3 \cdot 3 + 2}{3}$ (triplex superbitertia),...

(m varied, k &
  n specified):

$\frac{2 \cdot 3 + 2}{3}$ (duplex superbitertia), $\frac{2 \cdot 3 + 3}{3}$ (duplex supertritertia), $\frac{2 \cdot 3 + 4}{3}$ (duplex supertriquarta),...

Remarks

1. The above schema does not include an analysis of proportions of lesser inequality; this would be the inverse of the analysis of proportio maioris inaequalitatis.

2. It should also be noted that the break-down from genus to species is not carried out fully in all possible cases. Such a task would be infinite.

Within the genus, proportio, however, we are given the progressive analysis, through the sub-genera: inaequalitas, maior, and multiplex, to the species: dupla. Proportio maioris inaequalitatis dupla would be made up of the following individual proportions: 2/1, 4/2, 6/3, ... Another case in which the analysis from genus to species is completed is that of proportio maioris inaequalitatis tripla sesquitertia, the break-down being as follows: (genus): proportio; (sub-genera, differentiae): inaequalitas, multiplex and superparticular; (species): tripla sesquitertia. In this case the individuals would be: 10/3, 20/6, 30/9, ...

The plan is, at any rate, carried out in sufficient detail to show that each species may be individually named by quantifying the final sub-genus.

3. Aside from the more obvious meanings of such terms as: proportio, inaequalitas, etc., it is worth noting that multiplex means "multiplied by an integer," superparticular means "with an aliquot part added," and superpartient means "with more than one aliquot part added." With the above meanings in mind, it is not impossible to thread one's way through the maze of definitions.

Having established the definitional names of and the means of generating proportions in general, Bradwardine now turns to another aspect of the subject, that of "proportionality." Proportionality, as distinguished from what is simply called "proportions," is concerned with certain specific series of terms and the series of proportions which may be constructed from those terms, which possess, as series, formal properties of interrelationship from which various postulates and conclusions may be deduced. Proportionality may, therefore, be understood as referring to the formal aspects of a series and the deducible laws of interrelationship between terms of that series, as originally defined.

It will be seen that any given type of proportionality has two aspects: (1) the type of interrelationship possessed by the basic series of integral terms, and (2) the type of interrelationship possessed by proportions composed of those terms. Alluding to the types of proportional series described in the <u>Arithmetica</u>, Bradwardine says that, of the ten that Boethius discusses, three are of importance for the task in hand: arithmetic, geometric, and harmonic. The fundamental characteristic of the arithmetic series is that the arithmetical differences between the successive terms are equal (e.g., the series, 1, 2, 3, ..., in which the difference is 1, or the series, 1, 4, 7, 10, ..., in which the difference is 3). The fundamental characteristic of geometric series, on the other hand, is that proportions between successive terms are equal (e.g., the integral series, 1, 2, 4, 8, ..., is a geometric one, because the proportions between its successive terms are equal, i.e., $\frac{1}{2} = \frac{2}{4} = \frac{4}{8}$ ...). Harmonic series has, as its fundamental characteristic, the property of equality (among three terms, constituting the integral series) of the proportions of the extreme terms and of the differences between the first and second and second and third terms (e.g., the integral series, 6, 4, 3, is a harmonic one, because the proportion of the first term to the last is equal to the proportion of the difference between the first and second, to the difference between the second and third: $\frac{6}{3} = \frac{6-4}{4-3}$.

While arithmetic and geometric series may be produced indefinitely, harmonic proportions are limited to three terms. Further, the first two types of proportion may be either continuous or discontinuous, whereas the third can only be continuous. Continuity in arithmetic proportionality means that the equal differences possess common terms (as in the arithmetic proportions, 3−2 = 2−1, or, 8−6 = 6−4 = 4−2). Discontinuity means that the equal differences do not possess common terms (as in, 6−4 = 3−1). Continuity in geometric proportionality means that the equal proportions possess common terms (as in the geometric proportions, $\frac{4}{2} = \frac{2}{1}$). Discontinuity means that they do not possess common terms (as in $\frac{14}{7}$ = $\frac{6}{3}$ = $\frac{2}{1}$).

Bradwardine's differentiation of continuous from discontinuous proportions, involving, as it does, the Aristotelian distinction between continuous and discontinuous quantities and the incommensurability of quantities of different genera, introduces a crucial passage in the De proportionibus. How can numerical proportions, composed of discrete entities, express physical proportions, composed of continuous entities? How can a proportion of forces be accurately related to a proportion of velocities, whose terms must be of a different genus? To the first question Bradwardine gives no answer, presumably content with the Aristotelian doctrine that continua are numerable, though not numerated. To the second question, he replies by citing, as authority, the Epistola de proportione et proportionalitate of Ahmad Ibn Jusuf.[74]

In the Epistola it is claimed that, though continuous proportionality can only hold between terms of the same genus (because otherwise it would not contain common terms), discontinuous proportionality may hold between proportions of heterogeneous kinds. Why Aristotle had not, himself, made this reservation it is, perhaps, idle to speculate, but the legitimacy of such proportions was certainly known to him. Bradwardine's example of the divergence of genus permissible between terms in discontinuous proportion is drawn from the classic science of harmonics: as is the proportion between the lengths of two vibrating strings, so is the proportion between the tones which they, respectively, produce. In like manner, adds Bradwardine: as is the proportion between two motions, so is the proportion between their respective velocities. It does not greatly matter that we may find it difficult to understand the exact sense in which a motion differs in genus from its velocity; it is at least sufficiently clear that the velocity of a motion is a physically associated aspect of the motion qua motion in the same sense that the tone produced by a vibrating string is associated with the vibration of that string. In the case of Bradwardine's functional equation of forces to velocities, developed in Chapter III of the Tractatus, the justification lies in the fact that the two sides of the equation represent different aspects of the same motion, one side expressing its time-distance, or kinematic, aspect, the other expressing its force-resistance, or dynamic, aspect. In his arguments in favor of the justice of such equations, Ahmad ibn Jusuf expands this differentiation of genus to a considerable extent, admitting the equation of proportions of: lines to lines, to areas to areas, to volumes to volumes, to times to times, i.e., $\frac{L}{L'}$, may $= \frac{A}{A'}$, $= \frac{V}{V'}$, $= \frac{T}{T'}$.

Here again, therefore, we encounter the classic confidence in the mathematical character of physical processes to which attention has already been drawn. The heritage of a tradition which included both number and physical objects within the concept of quantity and included music and astronomy among the exact sciences became, inevitably, a powerful impulse to the development of a mathematical physics: a heritage to which today we stand in great debt, however much such an unhesitating confidence in the commensurability of the conceptual and the actual, the mathematical and the physical, may occasionally be deplored as a philosophic view. At any rate, it is of no small significance that, when Bradwardine speaks of proportion, he finds it legitimate to think of them as composed of existential terms, and that, consequently, his problem is to justify the equation of different genera of such terms, rather than to justify (as the contemporary theorist often feels he must) the commensurability of the mathematical ideal with the physical reality.

The second part of Chapter I closes with the definition of six properties of geometric proportions which will be of use later in the argument. Basically, they follow definitiones given in Campanus' "Euclid," Book V (given, the geometric series: 8, 4, 2, 1).

1. <u>Permutatim proportionalia</u>: since $\frac{8}{2} = \frac{4}{1}$, then "permutatively" (by interchanging the consequent of one proportion with the antecedent of the other) $\frac{8}{4} = \frac{2}{1}$. (<u>Cf</u>. Campanus, Definition 12.)

2. <u>Econtrario proportionalia</u>: since $\frac{4}{8} = \frac{1}{2}$, then "contrarily" (by interchanging antecedents and consequents in each proportion. separately) $\frac{8}{4} = \frac{2}{1}$. (<u>Cf</u>. Campanus, Definition 12.)

3. <u>Disiuncta (simplex) proportionalitas</u>: since $\frac{8+4}{4} = \frac{4+2}{2}$, then "disjunctively" (by eliminating the value of each consequent added to the antecedent) $\frac{8}{4} = \frac{4}{2}$.[75] (<u>Cf</u>. Campanus, Definition 14.)[76]

4. <u>Coniuncta proportionalitas</u>: since $\frac{8}{4} = \frac{4}{2}$, then "conjunctively" $\frac{8+4}{4} = \frac{4+2}{2}$. (<u>Cf</u>. Campanus, Definition 13.)

5. <u>Conversa proportionalitas</u>: since $\frac{8+4}{4} = \frac{4+2}{2}$ then, "conversely" (by substituting the antecedents, 8 and 4, for the consequents, 4 and 2) $\frac{8+4}{8} = \frac{4+2}{4}$. (<u>Cf</u>. Campanus, Definition 15, in which the term, <u>eversa</u>, is used to denote what is here called <u>conversa</u>.)

6. <u>Aequa proportionalitas</u>: given the series 3, 2, 1 and 6, 4, 2, these are in "equal proportionality" because proportions between corresponding terms in the two series are equal: $\frac{3}{2} = \frac{6}{4}, \frac{2}{1} = \frac{4}{2}, \frac{3}{1} = \frac{6}{2}$. (<u>Cf</u>. Campanus, Definition 16.)

The third and final portion of Chapter I contains the heart of the mathematical material on which Bradwardine's own theory, to be expounded in Chapter III, depends. It consists of the setting up of eight axioms or <u>suppositiones</u> (hypotheses, in the Greek sense) and in the deduction, from them, of eight conclusions.

Expressed in modern notation, the axioms are as follows:

1. All proportions are equal whose denominations are equal.

2. Given A and C, positing a mean, B, such that $\frac{A}{B} = \frac{B}{C}$, then $\frac{A}{C} = \frac{A}{B} \cdot \frac{B}{C}$.

3. Given A and N, positing means, B, C, M, ..., such that $\frac{A}{B} = \frac{B}{C} = \frac{C}{M} \cdots \frac{M}{N}$, then $\frac{A}{N} = \frac{A}{B} \cdot \frac{B}{C} \cdot \frac{C}{M} \cdots \cdot \frac{M}{N}$.

4. If A = B, then, given C, $\frac{C}{A} = \frac{C}{B}$ and $\frac{A}{C} = \frac{B}{C}$. (<u>Cf</u>. Campanus, Proposition 7.)

5. If A ≠ B, and given C, then, if A > B, $\frac{A}{C} > \frac{B}{C}$, and if A < B, $\frac{A}{C} < \frac{B}{C}$. (<u>Cf</u>. Campanus, Proposition 8.)

6. If $\frac{A}{C} = \frac{B}{C}$, then A = B, or if $\frac{C}{A} = \frac{C}{B}$, then A = B. (<u>Cf</u>. Campanus, Proposition 9.)

7. If $\frac{A}{B} = \frac{B}{C} = \frac{C}{D}$, then $\frac{A}{C} = \frac{B}{D}$. (<u>Cf</u>. Campanus, Proposition 25.)

8. If $\frac{A}{B} = \frac{B}{C} = \frac{C}{D}$, and A > B, then A+D > B+C. (<u>Cf</u>. Campanus, Proposition 25.)

Axioms 4 to 8, inclusive, follow closely the indicated Propositions in Campanus' <u>Euclid</u>, to which the text of the <u>De proportionibus</u>, itself, gives accurate reference. The first three, however, present something of a mystery. They are not contained in <u>Euclid</u>, in the form given by Bradwardine. He cites, as authority for them, a work called <u>De proportionibus</u>, which is unknown at present.[77]

Axiom 1, being very simple and more a matter of definition than of mathematical postulation, it is, perhaps, not surprising that no authority is cited for it. Axioms 2 and 3 correspond rather closely to Campanus' Definitions 10 and 11, but have a generality not possessed by Euclid's version. Campanus, himself, remarking on this lack of generality, in his comment on Definition 11,[78] explains Euclid's failure to generalize the axiom beyond four terms by the fact that three dimensional solids, which represent a natural limit to geometric abstraction, are denominated by no more than four terms. In his commentary, Campanus, indicates what the projection to "n" terms would yield,[79] but Bradwardine apparently was acquainted with some other work on the subject in which the general form of the axiom was directly expressed and which would, therefore, provide a more convenient reference.

The eight theorems developed from the preceding axioms are as follows.[80]

Theorem I.   Given $\frac{A}{B} = \frac{B}{C}$, then $\frac{A}{C} = \left(\frac{A}{B}\right)^2$

Proof. $\frac{A}{B} = \frac{B}{C}$ (Axiom 1)

$\frac{A}{C} = \frac{A}{B} \cdot \frac{B}{C}$ (Axiom 2)

$\therefore \frac{A}{C} = \frac{A}{B} \cdot \frac{A}{B} = \left(\frac{A}{B}\right)^2$

Theorem II.   Given $\frac{A}{B} = \frac{B}{C} = \frac{C}{D}$, then $\frac{A}{D} = \left(\frac{A}{B}\right)^3$; and, given $\frac{A}{B} = \frac{B}{C} = \frac{C}{D} = \frac{D}{L} \ldots = \frac{L}{M}$, then (if "n" = the number of terms in the series) $\frac{A}{M} = \left(\frac{A}{B}\right)^{n-1}$

Proof as for Theorem I, plus the definitions of tripla, quadrupla, etc.

Theorem III.   Given A > 2B and B = 2C, then $\frac{A}{C} < \left(\frac{A}{B}\right)^2$

Proof.   Posit D, such that $\frac{B}{D} = \frac{A}{B}$, then

$D \neq C$ (Axiom 4) and

$D \ngtr C$ (Axiom 5 and ex hypothesi)

$\therefore D < C$

$\frac{A}{D} > \frac{A}{C}$ (Axiom 5) and

$\frac{A}{D} = \left(\frac{A}{B}\right)^2$ (Theorem I)

$\therefore \frac{A}{C} < \left(\frac{A}{B}\right)^2$

Theorem IV.   Given A = 2B and B > 2C, then $\frac{A}{C} < \left(\frac{A}{B}\right)^2$

Proof as for Theorem III.

Theorem V.   Given A < 2B and B = 2C, then $\frac{A}{C} > \left(\frac{A}{B}\right)^2$

Proof as for Theorem III.

Theorem VI.   Given A = 2B and B < 2C, then $\frac{A}{C} > \left(\frac{B}{C}\right)^2$

Proof as for Theorem III.

Theorem VII. If $B > A$, then $\frac{B}{A} \ngtr \frac{A}{A}$ and $\frac{B}{A} \nless \frac{A}{A}$ and $\frac{B}{A} \neq \frac{A}{A}$; and if $B < A$, then $\frac{B}{A} \nless \frac{A}{A}$ and $\frac{B}{A} \ngtr \frac{A}{A}$ and $\frac{B}{A} \neq \frac{A}{A}$

Proof. Posit that $\frac{4}{1} = \left(\frac{1}{1}\right)^2$ and that $\left(\frac{x}{y}\right)^2 = \frac{4}{1}$, then $\frac{x}{y} = \frac{2}{1}$ and 4, 2, 1 are continuous proportionals

$\therefore \frac{4}{1} = \left(\frac{4}{2}\right)^2$ and $\frac{4}{2} = \sqrt{\frac{4}{1}}$ and $\frac{2}{1} = \sqrt{\frac{4}{1}}$ (Theorem I)

$\frac{1}{1} = \sqrt{\frac{4}{1}}$ (ex hypothesi)

$\therefore \frac{1}{1} = \frac{2}{1}$ and $1 = 2$ (impossible)[81]

Theorem VIII. If $A > B$, then $\frac{A}{B} \ngtr \frac{B}{A}$ and $\frac{A}{B} \neq \frac{B}{A}$

Proof as for Theorem VII.

The foregoing axioms and theorems present no particular difficulty, aside from Theorems VII and VIII. These are of crucial importance to Bradwardine's attempt to save the Peripatetic theses, that no motion results either from an equilibrium of forces or from a case in which resistive force is greater than motive force. The intricate argument which Bradwardine submits in their proof is reducible, in the final analysis, to a demonstration of the discontinuity of proportions of lesser inequality, equality, and greater inequality. He shows them to constitute discrete genera in a mathematical sense analogous to the physically discrete genera of force-resistance relations constituted by Aristotle's three dicta: (1) that no motion results from a proportion of forces in which resistance is greater than motive force, or (2) in which resistance equals motive force, and that (3) a proportion of forces in which motive force exceeds resistive force results in a motion proportional to the forces.

To put the principle on which these two theorems depend in the familiar language of Aristotle's argument concerning the void: just as there can be no motion in a void, because there is no proportion between the zero resistance of a void and a motive force having a positive value, however small, just so there can be no proportion by which any proportion exceeds a proportion of equality, because a proportion of equality possesses a zero amount of inequality, and any excess over a proportion of equality will be in an infinite proportion (viz., no proportion at all) to it. This is not to argue that 2 is not greater than 1, but that $\frac{2}{1}$ is not greater than $\frac{1}{1}$ by any given proportion (i.e., root or power); there can be no exponent which, when applied to $\frac{1}{1}$, will yield $\frac{2}{1}$.[82] So long as velocities are taken (as they are by Bradwardine) to vary according to the "proportion of proportions" and not simply according to a mathematical excess it would certainly follow that an equilibrium of forces would produce zero velocity, that no disequilibrium of forces would bear any proportion to an equilibrium, and that (insofar as the mathematical argument is concerned) there would be no proportion expressing the relation between equal and unequal proportions.

Having established the mathematical foundations of the particular theory of velocities which is to be put forward in Chapter III (by the simple expedient of formulating certain properties of the proportional interrelationship of terms belonging to a geometric series), Bradwardine commences Chapter II, more Aristotelis, with the destructive criticism of rival theories. These are four in number, each one based on a different interpretation of the meaning of Aristotle's statement, that velocities are proportional to the motive and resistive forces involved.

An examination of Bradwardine's mediaeval precursors in this field of theoretical physics makes it quite apparent that (with the exception of Avempace's[83]) none of the theories advanced are formulated in such a way as readily to suggest a strictly mathematical statement. To do these men justice, it must be realized that this was not their endeavor. Instead of attempting such a course, they were more interested to decide the nature of the constituent principles on which the successive character of motion is grounded. Any mathematical laws implied by their various conclusions remained unformulated, and it is, therefore, to some extent misleading for a later writer so to formulate and crystallize them.

With Bradwardine, the case is quite the opposite. Approaching the problem of establishing an adequate law of motion from the standpoint of a mathematician rather than that of a philosopher, it is the mathematical formulae which appear explicitly and the philosophical theory on which they are ultimately grounded, that remains implicit. It is indeed, quite conceivable that Bradwardine might have been almost wholly unconcerned with the philosophical issues involved, but simply interested in demonstrating the mathematical fallacies implied in previous theories and in showing how a proper understanding of the mathematics involved in the manipulation of exponential series could solve any objections against the classic notion that velocities are proportional to proportions of forces. In any event, this concern to eradicate mathematical fallacies and to demonstrate a law of motion mathematically consistent with the classic axioms is what most clearly appears to the reader of the De proportionibus.

As has already been pointed out, there had been, generally speaking, only two fundamentally divergent tendencies in the attempt to formulate an adequate theory of the relation of velocities and forces. First, there was the view which, largely on logico-mathematical grounds, sought to account for velocity in terms of an absolute. Second, there was the tendency to see velocity as a relative function. The former tended to view resistive force as something to be subtracted from motive force (the residuum being the cause of whatever velocity remained); the latter envisaged velocity as being simply the direct resultant of the interaction of opposed forces. Whether through the concept of "impetus," employed by Buridan, or through the concept of the logico-mathematical resistance of pure dimension, itself, the former theory was committed to the imagination of an absolute velocity.

Of the four "erroneous theories" which Bradwardine treats in his second chapter, the first is of the absolutist sort of which we have just now been speaking. The second represents a compromise between the absolutist and the relativist. The fourth theory represents the view of those who, on the ground that forces and resistances are "intensive" magnitudes, argued that a proportion of force and resistance is not to be taken as mathematically relatable to a velocity (distance and time), since velocity is an "extensive" magnitude.

The third theory, on the other hand, represents one form of the second main tendency in the development of a theory of velocity. This form of the theory (that commonly attributed to Aristotle) makes velocity the direct or simple function of a proportion of forces. It is in solving the paradoxes consequent upon this form of the theory, by changing the direct function to a geometric one, that Bradwardine achieves his reinterpretation, outlined in Chapter III of the De proportionibus.

Theory I.—After first citing texts from Aristotle and Averroes which might be taken as supporting the theory that "the proportion of velocities in motions follows the excess of the force of the mover over that of the thing moved," Bradwardine raises seven destructive arguments against it. In doing so, he follows, as elsewhere, the customary practice of giving, first, the arguments which make their appeal primarily to the need for a consistent rendering of the "authorities" and of then adding other arguments which appeal more independently to reason and experience. In the present case, refutations 1-3 are based directly on certain passages from Aristotle and Averroes, refutations 4-6 expose further impossible consequences, and refutation 7 appeals to common human experience.

For the sake of diagrammatic simplicity, we shall express the present theory by the formula, $kV = F-R$ where F = motive force, R = resistive force, or mobile, and k = a conversion constant.[84]

1. Given the above theory, it follows that if F moves R through S (space) in T (time), $\frac{F}{2}$ will not move $\frac{R}{2}$ through S in T, but only

through $\frac{S}{2}$. For, if $kV = F-R$ then $\frac{kV}{2} = \frac{F}{2} - \frac{R}{2}$. This contradicts Aristotle's statement that, if F moves R through S in T, then $\frac{F}{2}$ moves $\frac{R}{2}$ through S in T. Therefore, this is a false theory.

This refutation rests, of course, on the ground that a consistent interpretation of Aristotle is required by both parties. Though such hardy spirits as Olivi were quite capable of saying cruel things about the "Philosopher's" theories,[85] it does appear generally true that such observations as that "halving both the forces and the resistances does not change the velocity" were considered to be sufficiently obvious to serve as axioms for all.

2. On the basis of this theory, it also follows that, if F moves R through S in T, then two such forces together (F+F) will not move two such resistances (R+R), through S in T, but through 2S. For, if $kV = F-R$, then $2kV = 2F-2R$. This result is false, because it, too, contradicts Aristotle's statement that the combined forces and resistances will produce the same velocity.

3. On the basis of this interpretation of Aristotle, it also follows that, from geometric proportion (i.e., equality of $\frac{F}{R}$ proportions) there does not follow equality of velocity, for there is no equality of excesses. For example: $\frac{6}{3} = \frac{2}{1}$, but $6-3 \neq 2-1$. This result contradicts Aristotle's statement that equality of velocity depends on equality in the proportion of movers to <u>mobilia</u>, and is, therefore, also false.

Nor can it be argued that Aristotle here intends "arithmetic" rather than "geometric" proportion (i.e., equality of differences rather than equality of proportions). Such an interpretation was shown to be false in refutations 1 and 2.

In the course of the present refutation, as elsewhere, Bradwardine also cites Averroes' arguments; Averroes had, as we have seen, also recognized the inconsistencies consequent upon the supposition that Aristotle was speaking of "arithmetic" proportion (i.e., numerical differences).

4. It would also follow that a given "mixed body," possessing internal resistance, would move faster in a <u>plenum</u> than in a void. For let A = such a mixed body, falling in a medium, B, and let C = a body of pure earth, such that the motive force of C is less than the resultant motive force of A. Then let B be rarified until C moves in B with the same velocity as A moves in a void. Then let A be placed in the same medium as C. It will move faster, since it has a greater resultant motive force, and, since C now moves in B with the same velocity as that of A in a void, A will move faster in this <u>plenum</u> than in a void.

It will be easily seen, upon the most cursory examination, that it is impossible to specify a medium of sufficiently low resistance so that (given the formula, kV = F-R) A will move at the same velocity in it as C moves in the void, without making the resultant force of A equal to the force of the simple body, C. Bradwardine, himself, was doubtless aware of this mathematical dilemma, for he concludes this fourth refutation by pointing out that Aristotle posits an unlimited increase of velocity correspondent to an equivalent decrease of the resistance of the medium. Therefore, in the last analysis, this refutation, like the preceding ones, rests upon a demonstration of the theory's inconsistency with a given <u>dictum</u> of Aristotle, rather than on any impossibility to which it leads, in its own terms.

This type of argument typefies, in a most interesting way, the scholastic attitude toward Aristotle. The Philosopher was not taken to have worked out the details of all his theories nor to have been infallible, <u>a priori</u>, in all his statements. It was, on the other hand, felt that he was essentially correct in his natural philosophy, and that one could properly check the validity of a contemporary theory by seeing whether it was an interpretation consistent with Aristotle's observations, as far as those observations went.

5. It would also follow that, if $F-R < F'-R'$, then $V < V'$, which is visibly false. For (letting r = the internal resistance of a body, and m = the resistance of a given medium) let $F-r > F'-r'$, and let m be such that $(F-r)-m = (F'-r')-m'$. Then the velocities are equal, but the differences are unequal, which is contrary to the hypothesis.

6. It follows also that, if $F = 2R$ or $> 2R$, the velocity cannot be doubled in another medium, for, in that case, double the difference between F and R would be equal to F.

For example, if $F = 8$ and $R = 4$, produce a velocity, V, then to double the velocity (according to the present theory) one would have to double the "excess," or difference. The "excess" of F over R is 4; doubling it would make it 8 (the limiting velocity which F can produce, when $R = O$), and, therefore, the force in question cannot move any faster than this, even through a void. This was shown to be inconsistent with Aristotle's position, in refutation 4.

7. Since it follows that, if $F-R > F'-R'$, then $V > V'$, it also follows that the greater the difference between F and R, the faster will be the motion, and, since a strong man exceeds the power of what he moves by a greater excess than a fly exceeds anything that it moves, he should move it faster. This is easily seen to be false, by experiment.

Bradwardine, therefore, concludes that the proportion of velocities does not follow the "excess" of power of mover over <u>mobile</u> and adds that what Aristotle and Averroes meant, when they said that velocity "follows" such an excess, was simply that motion results from a proportion of greater inequality in which F, of necessity, exceeds R.

Theory II.—The second theory of velocity which Bradwardine criticizes may be expressed thus: $kV = \frac{F-R}{R}$.[86] In none of the pre-Bradwardine theorists whom we have examined does this combined variant of Theories I and III receive a full development; from the very cursory treatment accorded it, we might, indeed, be tempted to believe that no one had really considered it seriously. Theory II is, however, suggested by Averroes' Comment 36, Physics VII (which Bradwardine cites as its authority) and was, therefore, not to be overlooked by anyone writing a treatise on the theory of velocity. It is interesting to note that this theory was, at last, seriously taken up by Giovanni Marliani, in the fifteenth century.

1. The first of Bradwardine's two refutations of this view is most ingenious. He claims that, if F-R = R, then "no mover can move any mobile faster or slower than that motion." This follows, because (in Theorem VII, Chapter I) it has been demonstrated that no proportion can be greater or smaller than a proportion of equal- in log sense ity, and, if F-R = R, then $\frac{F-R}{R}$ is a proportion of equality. At the same time, the case in which F-R = R would not be one of equilibrium (since F exceeds R) and, hence, would represent a determinate velocity. In brief, if Theory II were true, everything that moved would move with the same velocity.

2. A moving force, moreover, moves the whole mobile with its whole force and not by an excess of force;[87] therefore, a motion and its velocity, primarily and essentially, follow the proportion of the whole mover to the whole mobile.

As noted above, Bradwardine does not develop a grand refutation of this theory. As a theory of arithmetic proportionality it had been sufficiently shaken in the criticism of Theory I; as a theory of geometric proportionality, it was too undeveloped to deserve special treatment.

Theory III.—Bradwardine's refutation of Theory III is highly significant for an understanding of the one which he, himself, adduces in Chapter III of the De proportionibus. This third theory is the one which seems most obviously implied by Aristotle's scanty treatment of the subject: the theory that velocity is a direct proportional function of forces (i.e., $kV = \frac{F}{R}$). Ostensibly, this is the theory held by the mediaeval Peripatetics.

That velocity should be a simple function of the proportion of opposed forces leads, however, to certain inconsistencies with other Aristotelian axioms concerning motion, on the basis of which Bradwardine is forced to reject the theory.

Of the two general criticisms raised against Theory III, the first is that it lacks generality, since it posits that either F or R must be considered as constant, if two velocities are to be compared.

Such a criticism might seem unwarranted, if Theory III is accurately expressed by our formula: $kV = \frac{F}{R}$, but, as will be easily understood from a reading of the text of the <u>De proportionibus</u>, translation into modern notation of verbally expressed mathematical theories may easily misrepresent, to some extent, the exact (and sometimes the inexact) meaning of the original. Keeping in mind that Theory III is more accurately expressed by the two formulae, $kV = \frac{F}{c}$ (where c = constant resistance) and $kV = \frac{c}{R}$ (where c = constant motive force) it is, perhaps, permissible to return to the less cumbersome $kV = \frac{F}{R}$, since all the criticisms, except that concerning lack of generality, apply equally well to the latter formulation.

The second general criticism (divided into three main arguments) is that Theory III leads to false consequents.

1. The first false consequent is that any force, however small, can move any resistance, however large. For if $kV = \frac{F}{R}$, then $\frac{kV}{2} = \frac{F}{2R}$ and $\frac{kV}{n} = \frac{F}{nR}$. Since, however large F may be, it will be possible to posit n such that nR will be larger than F, this theory is seen to be a violation of the universally accepted Aristotelian axiom, that F must exceed R, if there is to be any motion.

2. The second false consequent is similar. For if $kV = \frac{F}{R}$, then, because $\frac{kV}{n} = \frac{F}{nR}$, any <u>mobile</u> can be moved by any force.

3. Furthermore, sense experience teaches the opposite of this view, for we see, for example, that if one man can scarcely move a heavy rock, two men working together can move it much more than twice as rapidly. The same principle is illustrated in the case of clock weights; to double a weight may more than double the speed of its descent.

Therefore, Bradwardine concludes, $kV \neq \frac{F}{R}$.

The remainder of his discussion of Theory III is concerned with an attempt to show that Aristotle, Averroes and the author of the <u>Tractatus de ponderibus</u> could not have meant that $kV = \frac{F}{R} = \frac{D}{T}$ (D = distance, T = time), but that, instead, V varies as the proportion of $\frac{F}{R}$ or $\frac{D}{T}$ (i.e., $n^V = \frac{F}{R}$). This is, of course, a preview of Bradwardine's own theory, as it appears in Chapter III of the <u>De proportionibus</u>, but he goes on to point out that, although Aristotle, Averroes, and the conclusion concerning velocities contained in the <u>De ponderibus</u> had pointed toward the $n^V = \frac{F}{R}$ formula, no one had proved it by adducing mathematical principles (such as those which Bradwardine sets forth in Chapter I).

Theory IV.—The fourth erroneous theory takes, as has already been pointed out, a non-mathematical view of the relation of velocity to forces, claiming that velocities vary neither as a proportion of forces nor as an arithmetical excess of motive force over resistive force, but vary, instead, by a "natural relation of mover to moved."

This view is supported, in the first place, by the contention that force is not a body, that it therefore has no magnitude, and that consequently it cannot be made proportional to anything. Second, the objection is raised that motive and resistive forces are of different genera and thus cannot be compared. Thirdly, it is objected that to suppose a proportion of greater inequality to be involved would necessitate that this proportion be divided into "what is exceeded" and the "excess"; forces, being incorporeal, cannot be thus divided.

The groundwork necessary for a reply to these objections has already been laid by Bradwardine's remarks on "proportionality" in Chapter I, and in his present rebuttal, he argues that, if there were no proportion between forces because they are not quantities, by the same argument, there would be no proportion between musical pitches. The very existence of the science of harmonics is, therefore, taken as sufficient disproof of this objection. Moreover, Theory IV holds that a mover "dominates" its mobile, and such a dominance must be in accordance with some proportion: Aristotle and Averroes insist on this at many points. Therefore, some proportion of motive and resistive forces exists in every case.

The arguments in favor of Theory IV are refutable: first, because it was not claimed that opposed forces were proportionate univocally and proprie, but only equivocally and communiter; second, because anything exceeding another thing is not, in itself, divided into excess and what is exceeded, but only in comparison to that other thing. (It is interesting that Bradwardine, himself, invokes this principle, that forces are not to be considered as divided in their action, in his second refutation of Theory II.)

Bradwardine's argument against Theory IV is of interest, not only as involving the whole problem of justifying a mathematical physics in the face of that incommensurability between phenomena of different genera upon which Aristotle had insisted, but also as a step toward the establishment of force as a quantity and, therefore, as something measurable. This is not, of course, to maintain that force is a body. It is to support Ockham's position (the keynote of his Philosophia naturalis) that such things as natural motions and forces have no existence apart from bodies, but, on the contrary, are no more than the quantifiable behaviour of those bodies. From such a viewpoint it becomes foolish to argue that, since force is not a body, it cannot be measured; forces and velocities, by virtue of their relatively simple spatial behaviour, become, indeed, the measurable phenomena, par excellence. The older view, represented by Theory IV, that local motions are a forma fluens,[88] incorporeal, ceaselessly generated and destroyed, and unmeasurable, had to be overcome before real headway could be made in developing a mathematical physics.

The grand opening of Chapter III, "His ergo ignorantiae nebulis demonstrationum flatibus effugatis, superest ut lumine scientiae resplendeat veritas," introduces Bradwardine's own solution of the problem: "The proportion of the velocities of motions follows the proportion of the force of the mover to that of the moved."[89] Bradwardine commences his exegesis by quoting Aristotle and Averroes in general support of his view, after which he launches directly into his twelve theorems concerning velocity.

Theorem I. $V = \log_n \left(\frac{F}{R}\right)$ or $n^V = \frac{F}{R}$

This is the modernized statement of the general theory quoted above.[90] In a certain sense, it is an axiom rather than a theorem, since its physical components cannot, of course, be justified by a mathematical proof. It is, however, a theorem (or, in Bradwardine's words, a conclusio) in the sense that it is taken to have been proved by the refutation of the four preceding theories. The following eleven theorems are, however, mathematically demonstrable from the combination of Theorem I with the mathematical material set forth in Chapter I.

see Grant Theorem II.   If $F = 2R$, then $\frac{2F}{R} \rightarrow 2V$.
p 21 note

        Proof.   Let $F = 2R$ and $F' = 2F$, then

$\frac{F'}{F} = \frac{F}{R}$ +

$$\frac{F'}{R} = \left(\frac{F}{R}\right)^2 \text{ (Theorem I, Chapter I)}$$

        Then, if $\frac{F}{R} \rightarrow V$,

$$\therefore \frac{F'}{R} \text{ (or } \frac{2F}{R}) \rightarrow 2V$$

Theorem III.   If $F = 2R$, then $\frac{F}{\frac{1}{2}R} \rightarrow 2V$.

      Proof as for Theorem II.

It will be seen that Theorems I, II, and III are designed primarily to vindicate what Aristotle had said concerning the relation of velocity to a proportion of forces. Specifically, they support Aristotle's Physics (VII, v, 250a 2, and De caelo, I, vi, 274a 1-2) in the claim that velocity varies with a proportion of forces, that to double the force moving a given resistance will double the velocity, and that to halve the resistance will also double the velocity.

<u>Theorem IV.</u>   If $\frac{F}{R} > \frac{2}{1}$, then $\frac{2F}{R} < 2V.$

   Proof by Theorem IV, Chapter I, and Theorem I, Chapter III.

<u>Theorem V.</u>   If $\frac{F}{R} > \frac{2}{1}$, then $\frac{F}{\frac{1}{2}R} < 2V.$

   Proof by Theorem III, Chapter I, and Theorem I, Chapter III.

<u>Theorem VI.</u>   If $\frac{F}{R} < \frac{2}{1}$, then $\frac{2F}{R} > 2V.$

   Proof by Theorem VI, Chapter I, and Theorem I, Chapter III.

<u>Theorem VII.</u>   If $\frac{F}{R} < \frac{2}{1}$, then $\frac{F}{\frac{1}{2}R} > 2V.$

   Proof by Theorem V, Chapter I, and Theorem I, Chapter III.

Theorems IV, V, VI,[91] and VII show that Theorems II and III represent a special case; if the original force producing a motion is not exactly twice that of the resistance which it moves, then, whether that force is doubled or the resistance is halved, the velocities will in no case be doubled.

It also follows that, if the force is halved or the resistance doubled, the velocity will not be halved. For example:

$$\text{Given } n^V = \frac{F}{R}, \text{ let } \frac{F}{R} = \frac{2}{1},$$

$$\text{Then } \frac{V}{2} = \frac{\sqrt{2}}{1}; \text{ but } \frac{V}{2} \neq \frac{2}{2}.$$

Although Bradwardine does not give this Theorem, it follows from the basic formula and provides a satisfactory defense of Aristotle's <u>dictum</u> (<u>Physics</u>, VII, v, 250a 10-11) that to double the resistance is not to halve the velocity. It is, perhaps, idle to ask why Bradwardine does not draw this specific conclusion, but the awkwardness of indicating mathematical roots suggests itself as an obvious reason. Such a theorem would, at any rate, provide a neat solution to the dilemma posed by the twin Aristotelian <u>dicta</u>: that an equilibrium of forces produces no motion, and that velocity is the function of a proportion of forces.

<u>Theorem VIII.</u> If $\frac{F}{R} = \frac{1}{1}$ or $\frac{1}{1+}$, then $V = O.$

   Proof by Theorems VII and VIII, Chapter I, and Theorem I,
   Chapter III.

This theorem is designed to deal, in another way, with the axiom that no motion arises from an equilibrium of forces. This follows mathematically, on the ground that there is no proportion which expresses the relation of a proportion of equality to one of inequality, i.e., no exponential function of $\frac{1}{1}$ which will yield $\frac{1+}{1}$ or $\frac{1+}{1}$.[92]

Bradwardine sees the proof of Theorem VIII as resting on this essential discontinuity, this lack of proportional relation between proportions of greater inequality and those of equality. Since Theorem I and the general Aristotelian axiom state that motions are proportional to each other, therefore, since there is no proportion in this case, and since it is also axiomatic that motion is produced in all cases in which F exceeds R, no motion can arise from a proportion of equality.

Since, a fortiori, there is also an essential discontinuity between proportions of greater and lesser inequality, and, given the axioms that motions are relatable by a proportion and that motion does arise from a proportion of greater inequality, therefore, since any motion supposed to arise from a proportion of lesser inequality will not be proportionally relatable to one arising from a proportion of greater inequality, it is impossible for there to be such a motion.

Theorem IX. If $\frac{F}{R} = \frac{1+}{1}$, then V = +.

Proof by Theorems I and VIII, Chapter III.

This theorem follows, of course, from Theorem VIII by elimination and with the addition of the general axiom that, if F exceeds R, this is sufficient to produce motion.

Theorem X.   For any value of V, proportions of F to R can be found which will yield 2V and $\frac{1}{2}$V.

Proof by Theorems I and IX, Chapter III.

Theorem X shows an important consequence of the $n^V = \frac{F}{R}$ formula. Since velocities vary as the proportion between their proportions of force to resistance, any given velocity may be doubled by squaring or halved by extracting the square root of, the proportion associated with that velocity. Theorem X, therefore, presents the universal rule for the doubling and halving of velocities, on which the truth of Theorems II and III depends, and of which Theorems II and III are special cases. This theorem firmly establishes the power of the $n^V = \frac{F}{R}$ formula, not only to express any desired velocity by means of a proportion of forces, but to relate this velocity to any multiple or fraction of it, by means of another proportion (i.e., an exponential one).

Theorem XI.   For any constant value of R, $\frac{F}{R}$ may be: $> \frac{F'}{R}$, $= \frac{F'}{R}$, or $< \frac{F'}{R}$.

Proof.   Let F represent a mixed body $\left(\dfrac{f}{r}\right)$, and

let F' represent a pure body, and

let $\dfrac{F'}{R} = \dfrac{f}{r}$.

Then $\dfrac{f}{R+r} < \dfrac{F'}{R}$, and

∴ $\dfrac{F}{R} < \dfrac{F'}{R}$ and   V < V'   (Theorem V, Chapter III)

Let $\dfrac{F'}{R} < \dfrac{f}{R-r}$, and

∴   V > V'   (Theorem I, Chapter III)

Let $\dfrac{F'}{R} = \dfrac{f}{R-r}$, and

∴   V = V'   (Theorem I, Chapter III)

In the above theorem is illustrated a further special area for application of the $n^V = \dfrac{F}{R}$ formula, namely that of dealing with compound motions involving a body possessing intrinsic resistance arising from its mixed composition. An important idea embodied in Bradwardine's development of this theorem is that, in motions involving mixed bodies, the internal resistance is to be added to any external resistance which is present, i.e., if a mixed body may be represented by $\dfrac{f}{r}$, then the velocity of such a body through a medium possessing the resistance R, is to be represented as $V = \dfrac{f}{R+r}$, and not $V = \dfrac{\left(\dfrac{f}{r}\right)}{R}$. Therefore, though velocity remains the function of a proportion of forces, coacting forces are to be added to each other rather than made proportionate; the resultant motive force is proportionate to the resultant resistive force.

Theorem XII.   If R = O, then, if $\dfrac{f}{r} = \dfrac{f'}{r'}$, V = V', and if f > f', and $\dfrac{f}{r} = \dfrac{f'}{r'}$, then, if $\dfrac{f}{r}$ is balanced against $\dfrac{f'}{r'}$, $\dfrac{f}{r}$ will move $\dfrac{f'}{r'}$.

Proof.   Let f be > f' and $\dfrac{f}{r} = \dfrac{f'}{r'}$, then f+r' > r+f', (Theorem VIII, Chapter I), and since f+r' operates against r+f',

∴ $\dfrac{f}{r}$ will move $\dfrac{f'}{r'}$. [93]

This theorem should not, of course, be taken as an argument either in favor of or against the existence of a void. It serves, in fact, to point out the secondary importance of such a consideration. Here, again, Bradwardine treats Aristotle's argument against the existence of a void (on the ground that motion in it would be instantaneous and, therefore, not a motion at all) as a special case of the more general theory that an opposition of motive and resistive forces, of whatever sort, is what is essential to motion. If a void were to exist, then a mixed body, in which one of two elements tending in opposite directions possessed a preponderant force, would move at a determinate velocity dependent on the proportion of those opposed forces. Needless to say, mixed bodies possessing equivalent oppositions of force to internal resistance would move with equal velocity.

The second part of Theorem XII is particularly interesting in the connection it establishes between Bradwardine's general law of velocities and the mediaeval science of weights. Though mixed bodies whose motive forces are proportionately equivalent to their internal resistances would, in a void, move with equal velocity, the body possessing the greater motive force would, if the two bodies were balanced on a scale, descend. Thus a theorem concerning statics is deduced from a law of motion which is essentially dynamic; the consideration of weight is introduced, and "work" becomes related to velocity.

The second part of Theorem XII depends, moreover, on an even more generalized form of the combination or "addition" of forces already alluded to. In the present case it is primarily the motion of a balance bar that is involved rather than the motion of the two bodies themselves; consequently, we find that the motive force of one body is to be added to the resistive force of the other. This theorem makes it apparent, therefore, that, in an even more general sense, motions are the function of resultant oppositions of forces, whether the forces added are like or unlike. Seen in this light, the distinction of motive and resistive force becomes largely one which is relative to a given case. In the two gravia mixta to which Bradwardine refers, it remains, of course, true that the downward force of the heavy components possesses a natural distinction from the downward force of the light components, but it is heaviness added to lightness that produces the combined motion of the two bodies.

Bradwardine's development of these last two theorems clearly indicates the remarkable scope of his dynamic law. By its application to problems of statics and mechanics is foreshadowed once again the enormous synthesizing power of mathematics in the study of natural processes: its power to bring together separate fields of physical theory in terms increasingly more general.

One last point which is worth raising in connection with Theorems XI and XII is an objection to them based on the mediaeval conception of "mixed bodies." Such bodies were commonly conceived as being what in modern parlance are called chemical compounds. That is to say, they were not simply thought of as agglomerations of diverse elements, but as homogeneous bodies whose behavior, or "natural motion," was to be determinable in some way, as the resultant of their component elemental substances.

If these mixed bodies are to be conceived as natural compounds, then it becomes highly questionable whether they can properly be thought of as possessing "internal resistance." If they do not possess, in actu, such an opposition of forces, then, of course, Bradwardine's two final theorems fail on the ground of faulty premise. Without actual opposition of forces, all mixed bodies would move instantaneously in a void. This seems too obvious an objection to have been overlooked by any competent mediaeval theorist, and one can only conclude that Bradwardine either conceived corpora mixta as containing a distinction of component elements in actu, or else is here speaking not of natural compounds but of agglomerations of diverse elements.

The further objection then suggests itself that, supposing the compound to be composed of water and earth and to be falling through a vacuum contained within the realm of air, Bradwardine would see the two components as opposing each other and, thereby, giving rise to a determinate velocity. Though Bradwardine does not himself elucidate the matter, it seems reasonable that in such a case he would hold that since both elements tend in the same direction and since each, separately, would have an instantaneous velocity in the posited vacuum, the whole compound would move at an infinite velocity and without internal resistance. We must, therefore, conclude that, in both Theorems XI and XII, when a mixed body is said to possess a potentia resistiva, this is the case only when the natural motion of that component is in a direction opposite to that of the component designated as potentia motiva. This does not seem in any sense to distort the meaning which one associates with the relative terms, motiva and resistiva, and does seem to preserve the sense of the two theorems in question.

We have seen that a mixed body, each of whose components tend in the same direction, would move instantaneously in a vacuum. In Theorem XI, wherein motion of a compound through a plenum would be expressible by the formula, $n^V = \frac{F}{R+r}$, it is assumed that r represents a component whose natural motion is opposed to that of F. If the compound is so located and so composed that both of its elements tend in the same direction, then the formula should simply be altered to read

$$n^V = \frac{F+f}{R}.$$

The remaining portion of Chapter III is devoted to refutation of two further objections to Bradwardine's law of motion which had not previously been raised. The second seems of lesser interest; it raises the objection that a magnet (which should, according to Bradwardine, move a small piece of iron more rapidly than a large one) actually moves both at the same speed. Since the objection rests solely on the ground that a magnet in motion, with the pieces of iron in question adhering to it, would produce equal velocities in both pieces of metal, it does not seem to damage Bradwardine's theory particularly. The velocity in this case is not the function of a proportion of forces between magnet and metal but between magnet and whatever moves the magnet or obstructs its natural motion. It is conceivable, of course, that the motion of the magnet might involve a force component of the metal carried with it, but the theory of magnets is too complex a topic to enter upon in this brief discussion.

The first of the two objections raised is, however, of considerably greater significance. It is argued that if equal velocities are produced by equal proportions of forces, then, if a large quantity of earth bears the same proportion to a large quantity of air that a small quantity of earth bears to a small quantity of air, the velocities of the two bits of earth through their respective media should (by Bradwardine's account) be equal. But they cannot be, because the larger piece of earth, in traversing its medium in the same time that the smaller traverses its own medium must go farther (because the medium is bigger in extent, or quantity), and in such an event the velocities would not be equal.

This dilemma thus raises the problem of relating force to distance, dynamic to kinematic functions, and brings out the ambiguity inherent in Aristotle's remark that the "weight" of a body is a factor of its velocity in free fall.[94] Bradwardine offers, in solution of the above dilemma, a distinction between "qualitative" and "quantitative" proportionality as applied to motion. Qualitatively, the moving force bears the same proportion to any and all fractions of the impeding medium, and this qualitative proportion determines qualitative velocity. Quantitatively, however, the proportion is between the times of the two motions.

Velocity as an "instantaneous" quality of motion is thereby clearly distinguished from velocity as a simple function of time and distance. Needless to say, velocity of any sort must be thought of in terms of distance and time, but the distinction which Bradwardine here draws between quantitative and qualitative velocities is actually the distinction which may be rendered, in modern parlance, as that between $V = \dfrac{D}{T}$ and $V = \dfrac{dD}{dT}$. Thus, in Bradwardine's law, which is primarily dynamic, it must be understood that $V = \dfrac{dD}{dT}$ rather than simply $\dfrac{D}{T}$.

The treatment of this distinction between the "quality" and "quantity" of motion is extremely brief and does not attain a great generality of expression. For example, though this distinction is made with regard to resistances in order to overcome the objection that $\frac{V}{n} = \frac{F}{R}$ is incompatible with the fact that $V = \frac{D}{T}$, it is not made with regard to motive bodies or forces. It is however, the outline of an idea of "force per unit volume" essentially not unlike that contained in Archimedes' principle of specific gravity (which was familiar to mediaeval writers) and provides a theoretical basis for clarifying the above mentioned ambiguity of Aristotle some two and a half centuries before Galileo is said to have actually gone to the length of dropping things from the tower of Pisa in order to prove that different quantities of the same substance will fall at the same rate.

Chapter IV of the De proportionibus deals with circular motions and commences, in strict mathematical plan, with a series of definitions and axioms from which various conclusions are drawn. Squares, similar surfaces, and quadrilaterals are defined from the first, sixth, and first books of Euclid, respectively. The axioms are as follows:

1. All right angles are equal. (Euclid I)
2. Of any two similar polygons, the proportion of areas equals the proportions of any two corresponding sides, squared. (Euclid VI)
3. Of any two circles, the proportion of their areas equals the proportion of the squares of their diameters. (Euclid XII)
4. Of any two circles, the proportion of their circumferences equals the proportion of their diameters. (Archimedes De curvis superficiebus, Theorem V, actually Theorem III, see p. 194 below)
5. Of any two spheres, the proportion of their volumes equals the proportion of their diameters, cubed. (Euclid XII)
6. The surface of any sphere is equal to that of a rectangle whose opposite sides are equal to the diameter and greatest circumference of the sphere. (Archimedes De curvis superficiebus, Theorem VIII, actually Theorem VI, see p. 194 below)

From the above definitions and axioms, the following six conclusions are drawn:

1. Of any two circles, the proportion of their areas equals the proportion of their diameters, squared.
2. Of any two circles, the proportion of their areas equals the proportion of their circumferences, squared.
3. Of any two spheres, the proportion of their volumes equals the proportion of their greatest circumferences, cubed.
4. Of any two spheres, the proportion of their surfaces equals the proportion of their diameters, squared.
5. Of any two spheres, the proportion of their surfaces equals the proportion of their greatest circumferences, squared.
6. Of any two spheres, the proportion of their volumes equals the proportion of their surfaces, to the $1\frac{1}{2}$ power.[95]

In the second part of this fourth chapter, Bradwardine proceeds to a further solution of the problem of the relation of velocity considered as a function of a proportion of forces, to velocity considered as a function of distance and time, which had already been treated in terms of a distinction between qualitative and quantitative velocity at the conclusion of Chapter III.

The first suggestion concerning the relation of velocity to space, or distance, in local motion he rejects as false; namely, that the proportion of velocities equals the proportion of the volumes of space described by the respective moving bodies. That it is false follows from the fact that if it were true, then any body would move twice as fast as the half of it (since it would traverse double the volume of space). And, if the whole body moved one foot in an hour and half the body moved half a foot in an hour, this theory would have to suppose the velocities equal.

A second theory, that the proportion of velocities equals the proportion of the surfaces of the volumes of the contained spaces, is rejected on the same grounds as the first theory.

The third theory, that of Gerard of Brussels[96] as contained in his treatise De proportione motuum et magnitudinum, is that circular velocities are proportional to the arcs and areas traversed by a given radius. Bradwardine thinks that this earliest known account of "angular velocity" [97] is a considerable improvement upon the two theories already mentioned, but he objects to it, nevertheless, because it posits that any part of a rotating radius would move at the same speed as the radius' midpoint.

If Bradwardine's quotation of the theory in question is correct, one might well agree with his objection. After all, speed is a property belonging to bodies, and bodies are moved as rapidly or as slowly as any of their parts. It may be correct to speak of the average speed of a rotating radius as equal to that of its midpoint, but this does not support the thesis that this speed of the midpoint is that of any and all parts of the radius. Moreover, in the case of celestial motions, the midpoint of their radius to the earth would not even lie within the body whose motion it is supposed to express.

What we are faced with in this case is evidently a question of interpretation, and whether Bradwardine misinterpreted the theory in question it is impossible to say. Those, at any rate, who later upheld Bradwardine's definition of velocity as being the maximum attained by any part of an object, felt no hesitation in coupling this definition with the thesis that when velocity varies through time, the distance traversed by the motion as a whole is equivalent to that which would be traversed by a body moving uniformly at the mean degree of that velocity.

On the supposition, at any rate, that circular velocity may be properly measured by the motion of the circumferential locus, Bradwardine sets down three further physical axioms in addition to the preceding geometrical ones:

1. The velocity of any local motion is to be measured by the maximum distance traversed by any point of the moving object.
2. The proportion between the velocities of any two local motions equals the proportion between the maximum lines described by two points on the two <u>mobilia</u>.
3. Of the circular planes contained in a sphere, that which passes through the center of the sphere is the largest.

Proposing now to demonstrate the opposite of some of the conclusions to be found in the <u>De proportione motuum et magnitudinum</u>, Bradwardine launches into his exposition of the following six theorems drawn from the above geometric and physical axioms and basic theorems:

1. Of any two points describing the circumferences of circles uniformly and in equal times, the proportion of velocities equals the proportion of diameters.
2. Of any two diameters or radii describing circles uniformly and in equal times, the proportion of velocities equals the proportion of diameters or radii.
3. Any two circumferences of circles described uniformly and in equal times (whether described simply as circles, or on the surfaces of spheres, or the one as a circle and the other on the surface of a sphere) are proportional to their velocities.
4. Of any two circles revolving uniformly and in equal times (whether simply describing circles, or describing spheres, or one describing a circle and the other a sphere) the proportion of velocities equals the square of the proportion of areas.
5. Of any two spherical surfaces moving uniformly and in equal times on their axes, the proportion of velocities equals the square of the proportion of areas.
6. Of any two spheres revolving uniformly and in equal times on their axes, the proportion of velocities equals the cube of the proportion of volumes.

The final portion of the treatise is devoted to Bradwardine's theory of the size of elemental spheres and, not belonging to a study of velocities, is included simply because he feels that here is yet another case in which analysis by geometric series is justifiable. That the theory turned out to be false was unfortunate, for it came to be widely known and accepted. It does have an interest for the historian of science, however, in its exemplification of that perennial hope of the mathematician-physicist to find application for a general type of function in what might outwardly appear to be totally diverse phenomena.[98] The interesting thing is not so much that this particular application of the geometric function was off the mark but that Bradwardine's instinct in seeking such an application has turned out to be so dramatically justified in the history of modern mathematical physics.

Bradwardine commences with three assumptions; the first is supported by two comments of Averroes on Aristotle's De caelo, the second by the essential character of the theory of sublunar elements commonly held by all scholastics, and the third by the authority of Thabit ibn Qurra and Al-Farghani, two early Arabian astronomers.[99] They are as follows:

1. The four elements are joined in continuous proportionality.
2. The four elements occupy (or naturally should occupy) the whole corruptible sphere (i.e., the sublunar).
3. The radius of the whole corruptible sphere is equal to 33.3 times the radius of earth.

Algharganus, in Differentia 21 of his Elements, is not concerned, as is Bradwardine, to develop a theory of the distribution of the sublunar elements but, rather, to establish the relative distances between the several celestial spheres. Bradwardine simply makes use of Algharganus' estimate of the ratio between the radius of the sphere of the moon and the radius of the earth as the empiric content of his theory of the proportionality of the elements. Algharganus estimates that this ratio is 33.3 and, since the diameter of the earth is estimated as 6,500 miles, the diameter of the total sublunar sphere would be 216,450 miles. Bradwardine does not concern himself with working out his proportionate distribution of the sublunar elements in miles.

Employing the properties of the proportional series established in Chapter I, together with the theorems concerning spherical geometry given in Chapter IV, four theorems concerning the elements are developed.

1. The proportion of any larger element to the element immediately lesser is greater than the proportion of 32 to 1 and less than that of 33 to 1.
2. The proportion between the sphere of fire and that composed of the three remaining elements is greater than the proportion of 31 to 1.
3. The distance of the outer surface of the air from the center of the earth is more than 10 and less than 11 times the radius of the earth.
4. A point halfway between the inner surface of the heavens and the center of the earth will be much above the outer surface of the air.

Before taking final leave of the De proportionibus, it may be well to ask ourselves once again what importance this work had for the further development of physics. Aside from what significance it possesses as a major step forward in the mathematical treatment of problems in dynamics, the clear distinction which is drawn between the "qualitative" and the "quantitative" meanings of the term "velocitas", together with a concentration upon the former, provided a most fruitful point of departure for the work of the following generation at Merton College.

Owing, perhaps, to a failure to recognize that no undifferentiated formulation of a function between force, resistance, and velocity can adequately express both the motions involved in statics and those involved in the kinematics of inertial resistance, or "free mass", the particular form of Bradwardine's equation turned out to be erroneous. If such distinctions between the various kinds of "resistance" are not made, the difficulties which forced Bradwardine to reject a simply dynamic function in favor of a logarithmic one still persist. To see the truth of this, one has merely to compare, insofar as that is possible, the Bradwardinian to the Newtonian dynamics.

Having discovered, in our analysis of Chapter III, that Bradwardine intends his formula to apply to "qualitative" rather than to "quantitative" velocity, it is clear that, in the first place, the proportion of force to resistance is conceived to vary with what finds its modern counterpart in the concept of "instantaneous velocity." In modern dynamics it is, of course, recognized that such velocities, when associated with a constant proportion of force to mass, accumulate uniformly through time and are hence equivalent to rates of acceleration. If we then consider that Newtonian "mass" is to be measured in terms of its "weight", we have also a certain degree of equivalence between Bradwardine's "resistance" and Newton's "mass." Bradwardine's difficulty now becomes apparent, for $F = ma$ is subject to exactly the same criticisms which are raised against the formula, $\frac{F}{R} = V$—the theory which Bradwardine is at pains to refute in Chapter II. Unless the reservation is made that Newton's formula must be understood as applying only to "free mass" or "inertia", the impossibility follows that a force less than that exerted (in the form of weight) by a given mass can produce a positive acceleration upon that mass.

Fundamentally, therefore, the reasoning which underlay Bradwardine's objection to rendering positive motion of any sort in terms of a simple function of the proportion of force to resistance appears sound even today. What was required was a further clarification of the distinctions between various forms of resistance (e.g., those offered by the density of a medium, by inertia, and by weight).

Bradwardine's distinction of the "qualitative" meaning of velocity had, however, most important consequences. If the proportion of force to resistance was to be understood as producing a given "quality" of motion, how was this to be related to the "quantity" of a motion possessing that "quality"? how, in short, was the distance traversed during a time interval of qualitatively uniform motion

Part II, ch 16-23

to be calculated? In the work of John Dumbleton[100] and the other
Merton College Calculatores, of whom mention has already been
made, the basis for an answer to this problem was soon developed.

In dealing with the question of how physical magnitudes should
be understood to increase or diminish, Dumbleton argues with
great skill against two earlier theories which had enjoyed considerable prestige. The one claimed that a quality can, indeed, be said
to increase, but that the increase cannot be treated additively, as
a sum of qualitative parts, and the other that a quality cannot really
increase, but that instead, at each moment of an apparent increase,
the preceding quality is annihilated and one of a greater degree
substituted for it.[101] In combatting the former thesis, Dumbleton
is concerned to put the analysis of qualitative changes upon a quantitative basis amenable to mathematical manipulation and, in opposing the latter, to avoid the paradoxes attendant upon an atomic
treatment of continua.

Any "intensive magnitude" (such as a degree of heat), just as any
"extensive magnitude" (such as a distance), was to be conceived as
containing a certain "latitude," or quantitative span, extending from
a zero amount of the given quality to the maximum degree of that
quality which terminates its latitude. Moreover, just as a linear
distance, or "latitude" is equivalent to the sum of the parts into
which it may be divided, so also a qualitative latitude may be divided into parts of which it, too, is the sum.

Maier: this is Scotist idea of addition of part to part.

An analogy having thus been established between the quantifiable
aspect of both "extensive" (dimensional) and "intensive" (qualitative) magnitudes, Dumbleton goes on to point out that, just as an
"extensive magnitude" (e.g., a given distance) must be traversed
successively, so also an "intensive magnitude" must be acquired
part by part. The alternative would be that of instantaneous translation, or transmutation (in other words, not a true "change" at
all).

There is, however, a critical difference between the ways in which
"intensive" and "extensive" magnitudes are acquired. A distance
is traversed by a moving body only by its leaving behind the successive parts of that distance, whereas, in the acquisition of successive parts of an "intensive" magnitude, the intensive parts must,
of course, be accumulated by the body in question. Otherwise, whatever part of the intension could be produced by a given agent working through a given time would have to be recreated from zero after
each part, and (since these parts are infinitely divisible) thus no
change at all could take place.

The foregoing provides a brief summary of Dumbleton's position
regarding the quantification and the manner of generation of qualitative changes. In Part III (Chapters 2-7) of his Summa logicae et
philosophiae naturalis he then picks up the theme of Bradwardine's
treatise, and, after rehearsing much the same arguments as Brad-

wardine's against the theories of an arithmetic or a simple geometric proportionality between velocities and their correlative
proportions of force to resistance, proceeds to an elaboration of
Bradwardine's dynamics.

Since the meaning of "velocity" in Bradwardine's treatise has
been identified as that of a qualitative, or "intensive" magnitude,
Dumbleton points out that, if $\frac{F}{R} = n^V$, then we must understand this
to mean that the "latitudes" between different values of V are related to the equivalent "latitudes" between different values of $\frac{F}{R}$ in
the manner indicated. Since the quality in question is that of an instantaneous velocity, this portion of Dumbleton's thesis is actually
dealing with the correlation between changes in the proportion of
force to resistance and the corresponding changes in rates of qualitative or instantaneous velocity.

It now clearly follows that, if a given proportion of force to resistance produces a given intension, or "degree," of velocity in a
given time, then, if this proportion remains constant, in a second
such time the velocity will be doubled, after the third interval tre-
bled, etc. This is inevitable, on the assumption that "intensive latitudes" are accumulated and that constant causes produce constant
effects. Dumbleton does not, himself, give an explicit statement of
this consequence, being occupied with the more abstruse problems
to be encountered in cases where the value of the $\frac{F}{R}$ proportion
fluctuates within a given motion. This is quite appropriate to the
portion of his study in which he is remaining strictly within the
terms of the Bradwardinian function, but in the following chapter
(Chapter 8) he works out explicitly the relation of time elapsed to
distance traversed in a uniformly accelerated motion.

Dumbleton's demonstration concerning this relationship centers
on the thesis that the distance traversed in any motion in which
there is a uniform "intension" of velocity (commencing from zero
and ending at any given degree) must be equal to the distance which
would be traversed by a body moving uniformly at one half the terminal degree of that accelerated motion. In other words, $S = \frac{1}{2}V \cdot t$
(where V is the terminal velocity). This is, of course, strictly
equivalent to the more familiar, $S = \frac{1}{2}at^2$, and of considerable interest as having been among the very first successful attempts to
relate time elapsed to distance traversed in a uniformly accelerated motion. Dumbleton's proof is a purely formal one, by no means
dependent upon experimentation or involving the thesis that any
natural motions are, in fact, uniformly accelerated. We have already seen that such a thesis is, in fact, entailed in the supposition
of constant proportions of force to resistance accumulating equal

latitudes of velocity in equal times, but it was apparently not until sometime later that this conclusion was made explicit.

The concept of "impetus," by which John Buridan sought to explain the accumulating velocity of bodies in free fall, seems clearly to have been either inspired or anticipated by this earlier theory of the manner in which intensive qualities are acquired, which we have just been examining. In the passage in which he suggests the "impetus" theory of accelerated fall,[102] Buridan nevertheless makes no use of the mathematical analysis relating time and distance which Dumbleton had worked out, and it is, of course, conceivable that Buridan was actually unfamiliar with this work or with the theory of intension which underlay its correlation of velocity, distance and time. Whatever the answer to this question, it is nonetheless of considerable interest to note that not only was the successful kinematic analysis of uniform acceleration worked out by the mathematician-physicists of Merton College quite independently of the hypothesis of any entity such as the force of "impetus" posited by Buridan, but that the kinematics of John Dumbleton grew naturally from the earlier analyses in dynamics which were summed up and given a clear, mathematical definition by Bradwardine. Bradwardine's conclusion, that a proportion of force to resistance must be understood as correlate with an instantaneous rate, rather than with the traversal of an extended distance in an extended time, was, of course, to be coupled with the standard assumption that constant causes produce constant effects. Dumbleton's theory of the manner in which an "intensive" magnitude may be said to increase then leads inevitably, not only to his conclusions regarding the relation of distance to time in a uniformly accelerated motion, but to the realization that a constant proportion of force to resistance must produce just such a motion.

It is, of course, true that neither Bradwardine nor Dumbleton are here discussing the problems of projectile motion; they are dealing solely with cases in which an acting force is required for the production of a motion, and the question of whether a motion can continue in the absence of an acting force is never raised. One may, perhaps, doubt that they envisaged the possibility of the continuance of a motion in the absence of a propelling force, but one may be certain that Buridan did not. His concept of "impetus" as "a certain energy (_vis_) capable of moving the projectile in the direction in which the mover set it in motion" is certainly more clearly an explanation in terms of continuing force than in that of "inertia" or "natural motion." It is, if anything, the Mertonian kinematics, treating "velocity" simply as a quality induced in a body by an acting power and not entailing the notion of some additional "force," which seems closer to the modern point of view.

Pierre Duhem overlooks entirely the possibility that Buridan's "impetus" theory may well have originated in the recognition, by

Bradwardine and Dumbleton, that it is instantaneous velocity which should be understood as proportionate to a proportion of force to resistance and that such a quality, accumulating through time, will produce an accelerated motion. It is, in fact, to Albert of Saxony that he attributes the recognition of the important distinction between the dynamic and the kinematic aspects of motion,[103]—this in spite of the fact that the Tractatus proportionum of Albert is so clearly dependent upon Bradwardine's treatise in both its organization and content. Dumbleton's further development of Bradwardine's dynamics Duhem takes to be no more than an exploration of the way in which velocity would vary (according to Bradwardine's function) if the moving force were to increase.[104] A careful examination of Bradwardine's Tractatus and Dumbleton's Summa shows that what is actually being compared is not an increase of force associated with an increase of velocity through time, but rather an increase of force associated with an increase of instantaneous rate.

Fortunately, the errors of Duhem's work and his unreasonable hostility to the natural philosophers of Merton have, to a large extent, been corrected by the further researches of Anneliese Maier. Some few oversights nevertheless remain. Miss Maier has, for example, perpetuated Duhem's attribution of the distinction between dynamics and kinematics to Albert of Saxony.[105] This we have found already quite clearly developed in Bradwardine's reply to possible objections against his theory; the dynamic relation of force to resistance is there explicitly related to an instantaneous rate, and this meaning of velocity is sharply distinguished from the kinematic relation of time elapsed per distance traversed.

Miss Maier makes also the further claim that it was axiomatic for scholastic physics that a constant proportion of force to resistance produces a constant velocity and that the "impetus" theory of John Buridan is the clearest expression of this kind of mechanics.[106] Such a theory is, as she says, the inevitable outcome of an attempt to account for accelerated motion in terms of the two suppositions that (1) force is required for the continuance of motion and that (2) a given force working on a given resistance produces a determinate velocity.[107] Buridan's "impetus" theory is, therefore, seen to be a development of Aristotle's theory of "contactual" causation into one entailing the notion of a cause-effect relationship internal to the body in motion, such a mechanics being unknown, either to ancient or to modern physics.

The above views seem essentially sound, especially as an interpretation of Buridan's thought, but they, unfortunately, leave out of account the important line of development in physical theory whose history we have just now been attempting to trace. It may well be that the majority of the scholastics thought of a given proportion of force to resistance as associated with a "constant velocity," but it does not necessarily follow that "constant velocity" had the same unambiguous meaning which it possesses today.

In the mathematical portion of Bradwardine's treatise we have already seen the ambiguity (from a contemporary viewpoint) of the term, "<u>proportio</u>." A careful examination of the meaning of this term shows it to be much more closely akin to that of the modern term, "function," than to that of the term, "proportion," for it included (in its scholastic sense) not only the relationship of an equality of arithmetic ratios but also that of an equality of arithmetic differences. In the case of the term, "<u>velocitas</u>," another ambiguity was at least latent. "<u>Velocitas</u>" might refer simply to a given distance traversed in a given time, or it might refer to the speed of the moving body at a given moment during its traversal of that distance.

Once Bradwardine had formulated clearly this distinction and had pointed out that it is to instantaneous and "qualitative" rather than to total and "quantitative" velocity that proportions of force to resistance are to be related, it followed that the "constant velocity" to be associated with such a proportion would be what would now be called an "instantaneous rate." Dumbleton then shows that such a rate (interpreted as a "quality" intensively acquired) gives rise to an accelerated "quantitative," or total, velocity.

The upshot of this development is that force becomes understood primarily as related to an instantaneous quality of motion which, considered quantitatively, gives rise to an accelerated motion rather than one of uniform velocity. The logical conclusion of such a realization is <u>not</u> that in the absence of force there is no motion, but that in the absence of force there is no acceleration. It would, admittedly, be going too far to claim that this revision in the understanding of how force is related to motion was worked out completely by the Merton physicists, but it should at least be clear that it is their point of view, rather than that of the advocates of Buridan's "impetus" theory, which appears closer to the spirit of modern physics.

On the basis of Dumbleton's work in kinematics, one must, at all events, disagree with Miss Maier's statement that the notion of velocity as a qualitative magnitude shut out the possibility of any progress in the quantitative analysis of motion.[108] It is, in fact, this very viewpoint which has been shown to lead directly to a correct understanding of the relationship between dynamics and kinematics.

THOMAE BRADWARDINI TRACTATUS PROPORTIONUM SEU DE PROPORTIO-NIBUS VELOCITATUM IN MOTIBUS

PROLEGOMENA

THE TEXT

The following text of Thomas of Bradwardine's Tractatus de proportionibus, based upon a collation of four fourteenth-century manuscripts, was developed for the purpose of making available to the modern reader an important work at present extant only in manuscript form and in the relatively scarce copies of the late fifteenth- and early sixteenth-century editions already mentioned in the bibliographical section of the present study.

The Venice edition of 1505 has not been examined by the present editor, but on the basis of a comparison of the earlier Paris edition[1] with seven yet earlier manuscripts it was felt that the most satisfactory procedure for the preparation of a text (which, for many reasons, could not be carried out with critical completeness) would be to disregard the early editions altogether and to concentrate, instead, on the collation of what appeared to be the best available early manuscripts. The Paris edition (Chapter I of which was carefully compared to the manuscripts mentioned) was found to suffer not only from a number of minor omissions approximately equal to that found in single manuscripts but also from frequent instances in which its highly abbreviated manuscript sources were quite clearly misread, or from passages (apparently corrupt in the sources employed by the early editor) which were badly reconstructed.

During the course of an examination of some of the more important printed library catalogues and other bibliographical sources the location of some thirty manuscripts of the De proportionibus was discovered, and it would appear quite possible that at least as many more are still in existence. From among these, twenty-three were eliminated on the grounds of their probable dating, provenance, completeness, and similar considerations, and (in the case of the very promising Erfurt manuscripts) because of their inaccessibility. Enlargements were then made of microfilm of the seven remaining manuscripts, and, on the basis of the above-mentioned collation of Chapter I, three of the less reliable manuscripts were set aside for use only in those passages in which some doubt concerning the correct reading of the text might not be resolved by the other four.

Of the four basic manuscripts employed, the Vatican 176 and Bruges 500 are the only two which manifest any clear interdependence not attributable to their common dependence upon the original source. Their frequent concurrence in the matter of omissions and additions is the strongest indication that they form a manuscript group. A large number of these concurrences against the readings of the other two manuscripts are to be found in cases where the text is repetitive in its structure and the eye of the copyist might easily lose its place, and the Bruges manuscript (which, of the four, appears to be the most clearly a product of a professional copyist) manifests several errors of this kind in addition to those contained in the Vatican copy.

In the variants which they contain, the other two manuscripts (the Bibliotheque Nationale 14576 and Bodleian 228) appear to be independent both of each other and of the Vatican-Bruges group. The B.N. 14576 is of some interest as including the date of publication of the De proportionibus at the close.[2] The Bodleian 228, on the other hand, is notable as frequently giving readings which are grammatically correct against grammatical errors in which the other three manuscripts agree. Aside from the few qualifications noted above, however, all four manuscripts show remarkably little disagreement among each other, and, in general, each has been given equal weight in establishing the present text. The occasions upon which it became necessary to draw upon the three auxiliary manuscripts were very few in number, and there seems little reason to expect that a full critical edition of the work would introduce any substantial changes.

Glancing through the rather large apparatus of variant readings which accompanies the present text, the reader may perhaps wonder whether the above remarks concerning the high degree of agreement between the manuscripts are justified. The large number of variants is, however, not inconsistent with this claim. In the first place, perhaps all but one of the manuscripts employed were not the work of professionals, and, since they were copies presumably intended primarily for the private use of the copyist, there was little need to observe a careful accuracy in the recording of the correct inflectional endings. In the second place, the policy of the present editor has been to record as accurately as possible the readings of the manuscripts in exactly the form in which they appear to be set down. This undoubtedly does violence to the intentions of the original copyists, who were obviously not striving for a meticulous accuracy either in grammar or in the use made of abbreviations and who relied upon the reader's grasp of the context to carry him safely over letters and words incorrectly or illegibly spelled. The considerable dangers to be encountered in an attempt to distinguish between cases in which one might legitimately transcribe what the copyist "must have intended" and those in which he has set down a true variant dictated, however, a policy of unmodified transcription.

In the primary apparatus to the present text have been recorded all variant readings with the exceptions of simple transpositions

and those peculiarities of spelling which are grammatically and
semantically irrelevant. Variations in the spelling of proper names
have, however, been included. Though the employment of classical
orthography in the present edition may, perhaps, be open to certain criticisms, it was felt that in the interests of legibility for the
modern reader and of shortening the textual apparatus (which would
otherwise have become unmanageably large) this policy was sufficiently well justified. The orthography of the manuscripts is,
moreover, by no means consistent enough to indicate clearly what
would be a legitimate policy in attempting to employ mediaeval
spellings. It should also be mentioned that the expansion of certain
abbreviations has been unavoidably arbitrary (iste and ille, ergo
and igitur, for example, being often indistinguishable in their abbreviated forms).

The secondary apparatus comprises the verification of references to other works, wherever such verification has been possible.

The arrangement, punctuation, and the division of the text into
sentences and paragraphs is, of necessity, almost wholly the work
of the present editor. The manuscripts show no particular consistency or care in these matters, and the reader should be warned
that it is occasionally possible to construe certain passages in ways
slightly different from those indicated. Punctuation has been employed in a somewhat modern fashion. There having been introduced into the body of the text no interpolations of any kind, paren-
theses have been employed solely for the purposes of setting apart
material which might well be treated in the same way nowadays
and for marking off clauses within larger clauses so as to make
an intricate sentence structure more readable. The titles of works
referred to have been underscored, and underscoring has likewise
been employed to set off terms which are being defined, definitions,
and certain of the more important conclusions.

The four basic manuscripts for the text are as follows:

1. Paris. Bibliothèque Nationale, MS. lat. 14576, fols. 255v-262r.
     See Bibliothèque de l'école des chartes (Paris, 1839-1944),
     XXX, 26.
2. Rome. Biblioteca Vaticana, MS. Ottob. lat. 176 fols. 92r-98r.
     See Rev. Philotheus Boehner, O.F.M., The Tractatus de Prae-
     destinatione et de Praescientia Dei et de Futuris Contingenti-
     bus of William Ockham (Franciscan Institute Publications No.2,
     St. Bonaventure, New York, 1945), p. ix.
3. Bruges. Bibliothèque Publique de la Ville de Bruges, MS. 500,
     fols. 158r-172v.
     See Catalogue général des manuscrits des bibliothèques de
     Belgique, II: Catalogue des manuscrits de la Bibliothèque de
     la Ville de Bruges (Gembloux, 1934), pp. 581-584.
4. Oxford. Bodleian Library, MS. Digby 228, fols. 56r-61r.

Elenchis interested in fol 261 col a, b, c

See Catalogus Codicum Manuscriptorum Bibliothecae Bodleianae (Oxford, 1883), Part IX: Digby MSS., pp. 239-41.

The three auxiliary manuscripts are as follows:

5. Oxford. Bodleian Library, MS. Digby 76, fols. 110r-120r.
   See ibid., pp. 82-83.
6. ——. MS. Canonici 177, fols. 164r-171v.
   See ibid., Part III: Greek and Latin, Canonicianos, col. 164.
7. Rome. Biblioteca Vaticana, MS. lat. 1108, fols. 69r-81r.
   See Cod. Vat. Lat. (Vatican Library, 1931), Vol. II, Part I, pp. 719-25.

The following manuscripts, not employed in the establishment of the present text, constitute the remainder of those discovered.

8. Vienna. Biblioteca Palatina, MS. 4951 (Univ. 320), fols. 260r-271v.
   See Tabulae codicum manuscriptorum in Biblioteca Palatina Vindobonensi (Vienna, 1810), IV, 444.
9. Bruges. Bibliothèque de la Ville de Bruges, MS. 497, fols. 59v-64r.
   See Catalogue général des manuscrits des bibliothèques de Belgique, II: Catalogue des manuscrits de la Bibliothèque de la Ville de Bruges (Gembloux, 1934), pp. 578-80.
10. Cambridge. Corpus Christi College Library, MS. 244(245). fols. 78r-83r.
    See A Descriptive Catalogue of the Manuscripts in the Library of Corpus Christi College, Cambridge (Cambridge, 1912), I, p. 543.
11. Oxford. New College Library, MS. Chaunder 289, fols. 63v-68r.
    See Catalogus codicum manuscriptorum qui in Collegiis Aulisque Oxoniensibus hodie adservantur (Oxford, 1852), Part I, pp. 103-5.
12. Oxford. University College Library, MS. 26, fols. 146v-150r.
    See ibid., pp. 7-8.
13. Oxford. Corpus Christi College Library, MS. 228, fols. 4r-8r.
    See ibid., Part II. pp. 92-93.
14. Paris. Bibliothèque Nationale, MS. lat. 625, fols. 59v-62r.
    See Bibliothèque Nationale nouvelles acquisitions du Département des Manuscrits (Paris, 1890), pp. 9-10.
15. ——. MS. lat. 16621, fols. 110v-212v.
    See Bibliothèque de l'école des chartes (Paris, 1870), XXXI, 155.
16. Erfurt. Stadtbücherei, MS. Amplon. F135, fols. 20v-25r.
    See Beschreibendes verzeichniss der Amplonianischen handschriften-Sammlung zu Erfurt (Berlin, 1887), pp. 88-89.
17. ——. MS. Amplon. F313, fols. 166r-190r.
    See ibid., pp. 216-17.

18. ——. MS. Amplon. F380, fols. 49r-58r.
   See ibid., pp. 266-68.
19. ——. MS. Amplon. Q325, fols. 150r-167r.
   See ibid., pp. 559-61.
20. ——. MS. Amplon. Q348, fols. 13r-22r.
   See ibid., pp. 581-83.
21. ——. MS. Amplon. Q349, fols. 48r-55v.
   See ibid., pp. 583-87.
22. ——. MS. Amplon. Q385, fols. 1r-16v.
   See ibid., pp. 641-44.
23. ——. MS. Amplon Q387, fols. 1v-8r.
   See ibid., pp. 648-49.
24. Venice. Biblioteca Marciana, MS. VI.62, fols. 99-111.
   See Biblioteca Nazionale Marciana, Bibliothecae Manuscriptorum ad. S. Marci venetiarum Codices manuscriptorum latini
   (Venice, 1868-1873), IV, 233-34.
25. ——. MS. VI.155, fols. 92-105.
   See ibid., pp. 229-31.
26. ——. MS. VIII.38 (Valentinelli XI.14), fols. 1-8.
   See ibid., pp. 225-26.
27. ——. MS. VIII.77, fols. 1-14.
   See ibid., pp. 257-58.
28. New York. Columbia University Library, MS. Plimpton 181,
   fols. 101-15.
   See Census of Mediaeval and Renaissance Manuscripts in the
   United States and Canada (New York, 1935-40), II, 1786.
29. London. British Museum Library, MS. Old Royal 8AXVIII,
   item 6.
   See British Museum Catalogue of Western Manuscripts in
   the Old Royal and Kings Collections (Oxford, 1921), I, 215.
30. ——. MS. Harleian 267, fols. 228-30.
   See British Museum Department of Manuscripts, Catalogue
   of the Harleian Manuscripts (London, 1808), I, 101.

THE TRANSLATION

In making the following translation of Bradwardine's Tractatus
de proportionibus the primary intention has been to provide for the
English-speaking reader as clear and fluent a version of this work
as possible. Not only have both the punctuation and arrangement
been chosen with this end in view, but, since a Latin text is available for purposes of comparison, it has also seemed permissible
to make occasional departures from a style that is frequently over-
cumbrous to the modern taste.

The translation of technical terms has, of course, presented its
special difficulties, and the only general policy adopted has, again,
been simply that of attempting to gain as high a degree of intelli-

gibility as possible. In the absence of English equivalents for Latin mathematical terms, the translation of Chapter I has had to resort to new and, it is feared, rather barbarous coinages. The reader should, however, experience no particular difficulty with these, since this first chapter is largely concerned with their definition, anyway. Even the use of the term, "proportion," for example, is no longer misleading, if one pays close attention to the manner in which it is defined.

Other terms, however, have presented more of a problem. "Mobile" has, perhaps, sufficient currency to stand untranslated or to be understood when rendered as "the moved" or "the moved body." "Velocitas" has been rendered as "speed," rather than "velocity," in order to avoid the erroneous inference that a vector quantity is to be understood as involved. "Potentia" has been translated as "power," rather than "force," for the reason that "potentia" is conceived most fundamentally as a capacity to do work. It is, of course, true that important ambiguities remain, the distinction developed between "total" and "instantaneous" velocity being, for example, one of the important contributions of the De proportionibus. Nevertheless, the terms, "speed," and, "power," seemed the best available, and the careful reader should experience no greater difficulty in understanding these or other usages than he would in understanding the Latin terms, themselves.

For a verification of other works alluded to in the De proportionibus, the reader is referred to the secondary apparatus to the Latin text.

TEXT AND TRANSLATION

THOMAE BRADWARDINI TRACTATUS PROPORTIONUM SEU DE PROPORTIONIBUS VELOCITATUM IN MOTIBUS

PROEMIUM

Omnem motum successivum alteri in velocitate proportionari 1
contingit; quapropter philosophia naturalis, quae de motu con-
siderat, proportionem motuum et velocitatum in motibus ignorare
non debet. Et quia cognitio illius est necessaria et multum difficilis,
nec in aliqua parte philosophiae tradita est ad plenum, ideo de pro- 5
portione velocitatum in motibus fecimus istud opus. Et quia, tes-
tante Boethio, primo <u>Arithmeticae</u> suae: Quisquis scientias mathe-
maticales praetermiserit, constat eum omnem philosophiae perdidisse doctrinam,—ideo mathematicalia quibus ad propositum
indigemus praemisimus, ut sit doctrina facilior et promptior 10
inquirenti. Et propter maiorem promptitudinem et facilitatem
doctrinae, istud negotium in quattuor differentias seu capitula
separatur.

Quorum primum mathematicalia, quibus ad propositum indigemus, proponit; quod in tres partes dividitur. Quarum prima pro- 15
portionis definitiones, divisiones et ceteras proprietates ostendit.
Secunda, simili modo, de proportionalitate determinat. Tertia vero
quasdam suppositiones adiungit, ex quibus quasdam mathematicas
conclusiones demonstrat.

Capitulum autem secundum disputat quattuor opiniones, seu sec- 20
tas exortas de proportione velocitatum in motibus; quod etiam,
secundum numerum opinionum illarum, in partes quattuor est
divisum.

Tertium capitulum veram sententiam de proportione velocitatum
in motibus, in comparatione ad moventium et motorum potentias, 25
manifestat; quod etiam in duas partes est divisum. Quarum prima
quasdam conclusiones de proportione velocitatum in motibus docet
et determinat. Secunda vero contra easdem obicit et solvit.

Capitulum autem quartum de proportione velocitatum in motibus,
in comparatione ad moti et spatii pertransiti quantitates, pertractat, 30
et specialiter ad motum circularem descendit; quod in partes tres
similiter est partitum. Quarum prima quaedam mathematicalia,
ad illud necessaria, primo docet. Secunda vero quaedam opiniones
de proportione velocitatum in motibus, in comparatione ad magnitudines motorum et spatiorum pertransitorum, redarguit, et veri- 35
tatem ostendit. Tertia autem circa proportiones elementorum
quasdam latentias manifestat.

Igitur ad propositum transeamus.

THOMAS OF BRADWARDINE'S TREATISE ON PROPORTIONS, OR ON THE PROPORTIONS OF THE SPEEDS OF MOTIONS

INTRODUCTION

Since each successive motion is proportionable to another with respect to speed, natural philosophy, which studies motion, ought not to ignore the proportion of motions and their speeds, and, because an understanding of this is both necessary and extremely difficult, nor has as yet been treated fully in any branch of philosophy, we have accordingly composed the following work on the subject. Since, moreover (as Boethius points out in Book I of his <u>Arithmetic</u>), it is agreed that whoever omits mathematical studies has destroyed the whole of philosophic knowledge, we have commenced by setting forth the mathematics needed for the task in hand, in order to make the subject easier and more accessible to the student. For the sake of this same ease and accessibility, the work is also divided into four sections, or chapters.

The first of these, setting forth the necessary mathematics, is subdivided into three parts, of which the first takes up the definitions, types and other properties of proportion. The second deals with proportionality in a similar fashion. The third adds certain axioms, from which several mathematical conclusions are drawn.

Chapter two, on the other hand, argues against four opinions, or schools of thought, which have arisen concerning the proportion between the speeds of motions and, following the number of those opinions, is divided into four parts.

Chapter three makes clear the correct understanding of the proportion between the speeds of motions, with respect to both moving and resisting powers, and this also is divided into two parts. The first of these develops several theorems concerning the proportion between the speeds of motions, and the second raises and settles objections to them.

Chapter four treats of the proportion between the speeds of motions with respect to the quantities of the moved body and the interval traversed, and includes a special discussion of circular motion. It is divided into three parts, the first of which commences by establishing the requisite mathematical material. Part two undertakes the refutation of several opinions concerning the proportion between the speeds of motions, with respect to the magnitudes both of moved bodies and of intervals traversed, and sets forth the correct account. The third, finally, discloses certain hidden truths concerning the proportions between the elements.

Let us then pass on to the task in hand.

CAPITULUM PRIMUM

Omnis proportio vel est dicta communiter, vel proprie est 1
accepta. Communiter in omnibus quae aequale, vel maius vel
minus, seu etiam simile, vel etiam magis minusve, suscipiunt
reperitur. Ideo, in quibuscumque potest aliqua comparatio fieri,
est inventa. Quae sic potest definiri: Proportio est duorum com- 5
paratorum, in aliquo in quo comparantur, unius ad alterum habitudo.

Proportio autem quae proprie est accepta, in solis quantitatibus
reperitur. Quae definitur hoc modo: Proportio est duarum quantitatum eiusdem generis unius ad alteram habitudo. Et haec est dup- 10
lex; nam rationalis, et in primo gradu proportionalitatis, est illa
quae immediate denominatur ab aliquo numero: sicut proportio
dupla, et tripla, et sic de aliis. Secundum vero gradum illa tenet
quae irrationalis vocatur, quae non immediate denominatur ab aliquo numero, sed mediate tantum (quia immediate denominatur ab 15
aliqua proportione, quae immediate denominatur a numero: sicut
medietas duplae proportionis, quae est proportio diametri ad
costam, et medietas sesquioctavae proportionis, quae toni medietatem constituit).

Proportio autem rationalis differt a proportione irrationali, quia 20
haec tantum in quantitatibus commensurabilibus seu rationalibili-
bus reperitur; illa in solis quantitatibus incommensurabilibus seu
irrationalibilibus invenitur. Quantitates communicantes seu com-
mensurabiles seu rationales sunt quibus est una mensura communis, illarum quamlibet praecise mensurans: sicut linea 25
bipedalis et linea tripedalis, quarum utramque linea pedalis
praecise mensurat. Quantitates autem non-communicantes seu
incommensurabiles sive irrationales sunt quibus non est aliqua
mensura communis, quamlibet illarum praecise mensurans: cuiusmodi sunt diameter et costa quadrati. 30

Proportio autem rationalis reperitur in numeris et aliis quantitatibus quibuscumque; proportio vero irrationalis non in numeris,
sed in omnibus aliis quantitatibus, potest esse. Haec autem arithmeticae et aliis mathematicis pertinet; illa vero non arithmeticis,
sed omnibus aliis mathematicis, dignoscitur pertinere. 35

Proportio autem magis proprie dicta, quae arithmetico pertinet,
ab arithmeticis dividitur isto modo: Proportio quaedam est aequalitatis, quaedam inaequalitatis.

Proportio aequalitatis est duarum quantitatum aequalium adinvicem habitudo. Proportio autem inaequalitatis est duarum 40
quantitatum inaequalium adinvicem habitudo. Et haec est duplex:
quaedam enim est maioris inaequalitatis, et quaedam minoris.
Quarum prima est habitudo quantitatis maioris ad minorem;
secunda vero est habitudo minoris quantitatis ad maiorem.

Harum autem prima species habet quinque. Quarum tres sunt 45
simplices: scilicet multiplex, superparticularis, et superpartiens.
Duae vero residuae sunt compositae ex prima et duabus aliis

CHAPTER ONE

Every proportion is to be taken either in the general or in the strict sense. In the general sense it is found to exist between all things capable of being termed equal, greater, and lesser or similar, greater, and lesser. It is, in fact, found to exist between whatever things are open to some comparison and may be defined as follows: "A proportion is the relation of one thing to another, with respect to that in which they are compared."

In the strict sense, however, proportion is found only between quantities and is defined as follows: "A proportion is the relation between two quantities of the same kind." There are two types of such proportions, for one that is "rational" and in the first order of proportionality is immediately denominated by a given number (as is the case with the proportions of two to one, three to one, and so forth). The second order comprizes those proportions which are called "irrational." These are not immediately but only mediately denominated by a given number, for they are immediately denominated by a given proportion, which is, in turn, immediately denominated by a number. Of this sort is the square root of the proportion of two to one, which is the proportion of the diagonal of a square to its side, and the square root of the proportion of nine to eight, which constitutes a musical half-tone.

Rational differs from irrational proportion, moreover, in that the former exists only between commensurable or rational quantities, whereas the latter is found to exist only between incommensurable or irrational quantities. "Communicative," "commensurable," or "rational" quantities are those for which there exists a common measure which measures each of them exactly (as is the case with a two foot line and a three foot line, both of which a one foot line measures exactly). "Non-communicative," "incommensurable," or "irrational" quantities are those for which there does not exist such a common measure (of which sort are the diagonal and side of a square).

Further, a rational proportion may exist both between numbers and between quantities of any other kind, whereas an irrational proportion cannot exist between numbers but can between all other kinds of quantity. The former belongs both to arithmetic and to the other mathematical studies; the latter does not belong to arithmetic but does to all other branches of mathematics.

Proportion in its stricter sense (as pertaining to arithmetic) is subdivided by arithmeticians as follows:

A proportion may be either one of "equality" or one of "inequality." A proportion of equality is the mutual relation of two equal quantities. A proportion of inequality, on the other hand, is the mutual relation of two unequal quantities and may be of two types: either one of "greater inequality" or one of "lesser inequality." The first of these is the relation of a larger quantity to a smaller one, and the second is that of a smaller quantity to a larger.

Of these two types the first has five further sorts. Three of these are simple, namely: "multiple," "superparticular" and "superpartient." The

simplicibus: scilicet multiplex superparticularis et multiplex superpartiens.

Multiplex vero proportio est habitudo quantitatis maioris ad   50
minorem, illam multotiens continentis. Et haec ulterius in species
infinitas partitur. Si enim maior bis minorem contineat, duplex
sive dupla proportio nominatur; si autem ter, triplex sive tripla;
et sic in infinitum proceditur.

Superparticularis autem proportio est habitudo quantitatis   55
maioris ad minorem, illam semel et eius partem aliquotam continentis. Pars autem aliquota est illa quae, aliquotiens sumpta,
reddit aequaliter suum totum. Pars vero non-aliquota est illa quae
nullatenus, aliquotiens sumpta, reddit aequaliter suum totum: ut
binarius respectu quinarii. Haec autem proportio infinitam recipit   60
sectionem, quia, si maior quantitas semel minorem et eius medietatem contineat, sesquialtera et hemiolia proportio nuncupatur: ut
est proportio trium ad duo. Si autem maior quantitas semel minorem et eius tertiam partem contineat, sesquitertia dicitur: sicut
quattuor ad tria se habent. Et sic, in infinitum, species producun- 65
tur.

Superpartiens vero proportio est habitudo quantitatis maioris
ad minorem, illam semel et aliquot eius partes aliquotas (ex quibus
non sit una pars aliquota) continentis. Et haec, sicut aliae, in species
infinitas secatur. Et hoc tripliciter: Uno modo ex parte numeri   70
partium praedictarum; secundo modo ex parte denominationis
partium eorumdem; et tertio modo mixtim ex ambobus. Et ideo,
si maior quantitas semel minorem et eius duas tales partes (ut
quinque, tria) contineat, dicitur ista proportio superbipartiens; si
tres, supertripartiens; et sic non est status. Si autem maior quan-   75
titas semel minorem et aliquot tales partes eius contineat, quae sunt
tertiae totius, superpartiens tertias vel supertertia proportio nuncupatur; si istae partes sint quartae, superpartiens quartas; et sic
semper procedit.

Ex mixtione harum specierum aliae infinitae generantur. Si   80
enim maior quantitas semel minorem et eius duas tales partes
contineat, quae sunt tertiae totius, superbipartiens tertias vel
superbitertia proportio dici debet: cuiusmodi est proportio quinque ad tria. Et si istae partes sint quintae totius, superbipartiens
quintas vel superbiquinta dicetur: qualis est proportio septem ad   85
quinque. Et processus huius nullatenus terminatur. Si autem maior
quantitas semel minorem contineat et tres tales partes eius, quae
sunt quartae totius, superterpartiens quartas vel superterquarta
proportio appellatur: qualis est septem ad quattuor. Et sic, utroque
modo, sine termino sit processus.   90

Proportio autem multiplex superparticularis est habitudo quantitatis maioris ad minorem illam multotiens et eius partem aliquotam continentis; quae in species infinitas tripliciter est partita.
Primo, ex parte multiplicitatis: ut duplex superparticularis, triplex superparticularis, et sic semper proceditur. Secundo, ex   95
parte superparticularitatis: ut multiplex sesquialtera, multiplex

two remaining are formed by compounding the first of the simple species with the other two, namely, "multiple superparticular" and "multiple superpartient."

Now, a "multiple proportion" is the relation of a larger quantity to
a smaller one in which the larger contains the smaller a number of
times, and this type is open to division into an infinite number of further subclasses; if the larger quantity contains the smaller twice, it
is called a "double," or "duplex," proportion, if three times "treble,"
or "triplex," and so on, indefinitely.

A "superparticular proportion," on the other hand, is the relation of
a larger quantity to a smaller one in which the larger contains the
smaller one once, plus an aliquot part of it. An "aliquot part" of a
quantity is that which, taken a given number of times, will reconstitute
the whole quantity. A "non-aliquot part," however, is one which, no
matter what number of times it be taken, will not reconstitute the original quantity exactly, as is the case with two in relation to five.

The above type of proportion is again open to infinite subdivision.
If the larger quantity contains the smaller one once, plus a half of it,
it is called a "sesquialternate" or "hemiolian" proportion (as is the
proportion of three to two). If the larger contains the smaller one once,
plus a third of it, it is called "sesquitertian" (as four is related to
three). Thus, additional subtypes may be produced, ad infinitum.

As for "superpartient proportion," it is the relation of a larger quantity to a smaller one, in which the larger contains the smaller one
once, plus more than one of its aliquot parts. This, like the others, is
divisible into infinite subtypes, and that in three ways. In one way,
according to the number of the abovementioned parts; in a second way,
according to the denomination of those parts; and in the third way, by
a combination of the two. If, for example, the larger quantity contains
the smaller one once, plus two such parts of it (as five contains three),
the proportion is called "superbipartient"; if three parts, "supertripartient"; and so forth, endlessly. If, on the other hand, the larger quantity contains the smaller one once, plus a given number of such parts
as are thirds of it, it is called a "superpartient tertian" or, "superter-
tian" proportion; if these parts are fourths, then "superpartient quartan"; and so on, indefinitely.

From a combination of the preceding types,an infinite number of
others are generated. If, for example, the larger quantity contains the
smaller one once, plus two such parts as are thirds of the whole, it is
to be called a "superbipartient tertian," or "superbitertian," proportion
(of which sort is the proportion of five to three). If these parts are fifths
of the whole, it is called "superbipartient quintan," or "superbiquintan"
(of which sort is the proportion of seven to five). This series has no end.
If, on the other hand, the larger quantity contains the smaller one once,
plus three such parts as are fourths of the whole, it is called a "supertripartient quartan" or "supertriquartan" proportion (of which the proportion of seven to four is an example. Thus, in both ways, the series
is without end.

"Multiple superparticular proportion" is the relation of a larger

sesquitertia, et sic sine fine. Tertio, mixtim ex utrisque: ut dupla
sesquialtera, dupla sesquitertia, tripla sesquialtera, tripla sesquitertia, et sic proceditur sine fine, quorum definitiones et exempla
ex praedictis apparent.   100

Proportio autem multiplex superpartiens est habitudo quantitatis maioris ad minorem, illam multotiens et aliquot eius partes
aliquotas (ex quibus non fit una pars eius aliquota) continentis.
Haec autem septem modis dividitur in infinitum. Primo, ex parte
multiplicitatis, sic dividendo: duplex superpartiens, triplex super- 105
partiens, et sic sine fine. Secundo, ex parte superpartientis, dividitur tribus modis; primo sic: multiplex superbipartiens, multiplex
supertripartiens; secundo sic: multiplex superpartiens tertias,
multiplex superpartiens quartas; tertio sic: multiplex superbipartiens tertias vel multiplex superbitertias, multiplex supertri- 110
partiens quartas vel multiplex supertriquartas; et sic sine aliquo
numero. Iterum, ex mixtione primae divisionis cum tribus mem-
bris divisionis sequentis, tribus modis proceditur absque fine.
Primo sic: duplex superbipartiens, triplex supertripartiens, et
conversim, superbipartiens duplex, superbipartiens triplex.   115
Secundo sic: duplex superpartiens tertias, triplex superpartiens
tertias, et conversim, duplex superpartiens quartas. Tertio sic:
duplex superbitertia, triplex superbitertia, et econtra, duplex
superbitertia, duplex superbiquarta. Et sic istorum numerorum
interminabilis est processus, quorum omnium definitiones et   120
exempla ex praecedentibus satis liquent.

Proportio minoris inaequalitatis est habitudo minoris quantitatis ad maiorem; cuius tot sunt species quot proportiones inaequalitatis maioris et eisdem nominibus appellantur (hac preposi-
tione, "sub", addita; ut submultiplex, subsuperpartiens, et ita de 125
eius omnibus aliis speciebus). Et horum omnium definitiones cum
exemplis satis ex prioribus innotescunt.

Ex istis notandum quod omnis proportio tantum inter duos terminos reperitur. Scias etiam quod quanta est proportio unius
quantitatis ad aliam, tanta est illa ad reliquam: ut si dupla, dupla: 130
et si subdupla, subdupla. Et quanta est una quantitas ad aliam,
tanta est proportio eius ad illam. Est etiam advertendum quod
haec praedicta primo et proprie in sola proportione proprie accepta existant, communiter autem et secundum translationem in
proportione dicta communiter sunt reperta. Igitur de divisione   135
et definitione proportionis et specierum suarum sic patet.

quantity to a smaller, in which the larger contains the smaller more than once, plus an aliquot part of it. This type is infinitely divisible in three ways. First, with respect to multiplicity (e.g., "double superparticular," "treble superparticular," etc.). Second, with respect to superparticularity (e.g., "multiple sesquialtern," "multiple sesquitertian," etc.). Third, by a combination of the two others (e.g., "double sesquialtern," "double sesquitertian," "treble sesquialtern" "treble sesquitertian," etc.). Further definitions and examples will be evident from the foregoing.

"Multiple superpartient proportion" is the relation of a larger quantity to a smaller, in which the larger contains the smaller more than once, plus more than one of its aliquot parts. This type is indefinitely divisible in seven ways. First, with respect to multiplicity, it is to be divided thus: "double superpartient," "treble superpartient," etc. Second, with respect to being superpartient, it is divided in three ways: (1) "multiple superbipartient," "multiple supertripartient," etc., (2) "multiple superpartient by thirds," "multiple superpartient by fourths," etc., (3) "multiple superbipartient by thirds" (or "multiple superbitertian"), "multiple supertripartient by fourths" (or "multiple supertriquartan"), etc. Again, by combining the first method of division with the three branches of the second method, three more infinite series are generated: (1) "double superbipartient," "treble supertripartient," etc.—and conversely—"superbipartient duplex," "superbipartient triplex," etc., (2) "double superpartient by thirds," "treble superpartient by thirds," etc.—and conversely—"double superpartient by fourths," etc., (3) "double superbitertian," "treble superbitertian," etc.—and the opposite—"double superbitertian," "double superbiquartan," etc. Thus, the series of these numbers is without end, all the definitions and examples of which may be easily worked out from the foregoing.

A proportion of lesser inequality is the relation of a smaller to a larger quantity and this type possesses as many subdivisions as that of greater inequality. They are also identified by the same names, by adding the prefix, "sub" (e.g., "submultiple," "subsuperpartient," etc.). The definition and exemplification of all these is sufficiently well understood from the above.

From what has been said it is to be noted that each proportion consists of only two terms. It will also be recognized that, whatever the magnitude of the proportion which one quantity bears to another, that is the magnitude of the one quantity as related to the other; if the proportion is double, the first quantity is twice the second—if the proportion is subdouble, the first quantity is half the second. However great one quantity is in comparison to another, just so great is the proportion between them.

It is also to be kept in mind that the foregoing statements apply primarily and strictly only to proportion taken in the strict sense; they apply generally and by transference, however, to proportion taken in the general sense.

Thus the situation is clear regarding the division and definition of proportion and its subtypes.

SECUNDA PARS CAPITULI PRIMI

Modo sequitur secunda pars huius capituli, quae de proportionalitate determinat. Scias ergo quod differentia sive excessus unius
quantitatis ad aliam est illud quo minor quantitas exceditur a
maiori. Proportionalitas, quae secundo Arithmeticae Boethii et   140
secundo Musicae eiusdem medietas nominatur, propter sui multi-
plicitatem in sua communitate definitionem unam non habet, sed
in decem membra dividitur, ut secundo Arithmeticae Boethii satis
patet; quorum tantum tria sunt famosa et ad veterum locutiones
intelligenda utilia. Ideo septem residuis praetermissis, tria prima 145
membra remanent declaranda.

Quorum primum proportionalitas seu medietas arithmetica
appellatur; secundum proportionalitas seu medietas geometrica
appellatur; tertium proportionalitas sive medietas harmonica nominatur. Prima est aequalitas differentiarum: scilicet, quando   150
quarumlibet duarum quantitatum comparatarum adinvicem differentiae sunt aequales: ut tria, duo, unum. Et hoc arithmeticis
pertinet.

Secunda autem quae geometricas speculationes concernit, quinto
Elementorum Euclidis isto modo definitur: "Proportionalitas est   155
similitudo proportionum"; quando scilicet quarumlibet duarum
quantitatum comparatarum adinvicem proportiones sunt similes
vel aequales: ut quattuor, duo, unum.

Tertia est, in tribus terminis, aequalitas seu similitudo proportionum extremorum et differentiarum; quando, scilicet, in tribus   160
terminis proportio primi ad ultimum est similis vel aequalis proportioni differentiae primi et medii ad differentiam medii et ex-
tremi: ut sex, quattuor, tria. Senarii enim ad ternarium est dupla
proportio; et binarii, quae est differentia sex et quattuor, ad unitatem, quae est differentia quattuor et tria, etiam dupla proportio 165
reperitur.

Et differunt istae medietates abinvicem, quia duae primae in
tribus terminis reperiuntur ad minus, sed nullus est maximus
numerus terminorum in quo existunt. Tertia autem tantum in tribus terminis reperitur. In alio etiam differunt, quia primae duae   170
possunt esse continuae et discontinuae, tertia autem semper continua reperitur.

Est autem tam medietas arithmetica quam geometrica duplex:
quaedam continua, quaedam discontinua. Medietas autem arithmetica continua est aequalitas differentiarum per communem ter-   175
minum medium, vel per communes terminos medios, copulata;
per unum terminum, ut sic dicendo: sicut tria ad duo, ita duo ad
unum; per plures sic: sicut quattuor ad tria, ita tria ad duo, et
duo ad unum. Discontinua est aequalitas differentiarum per nullum
terminum communem, nec communes terminos copulata: ut dicen-   180
do sicut sex ad quattuor, ita tria ad unum.

Geometrica vero medietas continua est similitudo proportionum
per communem terminum medium, vel per communes terminos

CHAPTER ONE, PART TWO

There now follows the second part of this chapter, which is concerned with "proportionality." It is to be recognized, in the first place, that the difference, or excess, of one quantity over another is that by which the smaller quantity is exceeded by the larger. Proportionality (called "mediety" in Book II of Boethius' Arithmetic and also in Book II of his Music) has no general definition, owing to its multiplicity, but is divided into ten classes (as is clear enough in Book II of Boethius' Arithmetic). Since only three of these are well known and useful for an understanding of the ancients, omitting the seven others, we will take up the three primary classes.

The first of these is called "arithmetic" proportionality (or mediety); the second is called "geometric" proportionality (or mediety); the third is called "harmonic" proportionality (or mediety).

The first consists in an equality of differences, namely, when the differences between any two pairs of quantities are equal to each other (as is true of the series: three, two, one). This class belongs to arithmetic.

The second, which concerns geometric speculations, is defined, in Book V of Euclid's Elements, as follows: "Proportionality consists in a similarity of proportions," whenever, namely, the proportions between any two pairs of quantities are similar, or equal, to each other (as is true of the series: four, two, one).

The third consists in an equality, or similarity, among three terms, between the proportion of the extremes and the proportion of the differences—when, namely, the proportion of the first to the last of three terms is similar, or equal, to the proportion of the difference between the first and middle terms to the difference between the middle and last terms (as is the case with the series: six, four, three). Here the proportion of six to three is a double one, and that of two (the difference between six and four) to one (the difference between four and three) is likewise found to be double.

These classes of mediety also differ from each other in that, though the first two involve at least three terms, there is no upper limit to the number of terms which may be so related, while the third is constituted by three terms only. They differ in yet another respect in that, while the first two may be either continuous or discontinuous, the third must always be continuous.

The fact is that both arithmetic and geometric mediety may be of these two kinds: continuous and discontinuous. "Continuous" arithmetic mediety consists in an equality of differences united by a common, mean term, or terms (by a single term in the example: as three is to two, so two is to one—and by more than one as in the example: as four is to three, so three is to two, and two is to one). "Discontinuous" arithmetic mediety consists in an equality of differences not united by a common term, or terms (as in the example: as six is to four, so three is to one).

"Continuous" geometric mediety, on the other hand, consists in a

medios, copulata: per unum, ut sicut quattuor ad duo, ita duo ad
unum: per plures, ut sicut octo ad quattuor, ita quattuor ad duo,   185
et duo ad unum. Discontinua autem est similitudo proportionum
per nullum terminum communem nec aliquos terminos communes
copulata: ut sicut sex ad tria, ita duo ad unum.

Ista autem dicuntur de istis medietatibus non primo nec proprie,
sed secundum transsumptionem a quantitate continua (cuius partes 190
ad communem terminum copulantur) et discreta (cuius partes ad
nullum communem terminum coniunguntur), ut in praedictis apparet. Et haec etiam differunt, quia medietas continua in tribus
terminis et quotlibet pluribus reperitur, discontinua vero in
quattuor terminis ad minus et in quotlibet pluribus reperitur.   195

Aliter autem et notabiliter differunt secundum Ametum filium
Iosephi in epistula sua, De proportione et proportionalitate, in hoc
quod in proportionalitate continua oportet omnes terminos in genere convenire, sed in discontinua sive disiuncta possunt aliqui termini in genere diversari. Verbi gratia, sicut chorda ad chordam   200
ita sonus ad sonum; et sicut movens ad movens, ita velocitas unius
motus ad velocitatem alterius motus. Et quia proportionalia a proportionalitate dicuntur, possunt, per relationem ad proportionalitatem in sua communitate, per unam definitionem analogam, non autem
univocam, definiri hoc modo: Proportionalia sunt quae in aliqua   205
proportione conveniunt. Et quia proportionalitas dividitur decem
modis, et proportionalia similiter dividuntur, quorum tantum tres
primi modi ad praesens sunt tractandi, igitur proportionalia proportionalitate arithmetica sunt illa quorum differentiae sunt aequales.
Proportionalia autem proportionalitate geometrica sunt illa quor-   210
um proportiones sunt aequales vel similes, vel quorum est una
proportio, ut placet Euclidi. Proportionalia autem proportionalitate
harmonica sunt illa quorum extremorum et differentiarum proportiones sunt similes seu aequales. Haec omnia, cum suis exemplis,
patent per praedicta. Ex istis patet quod ternarius est paucissi-   215
mus numerus terminorum in quibus proportionalitas reperitur, et
quod nullus est maximus numerus terminorum in quibus existit.

Permutatim proportionalia proportionalitate geometrica sunt
illa quorum proportionalium proportionalitate geometrica, sicut
antecedens unius proportionis ad antecedens alterius propor-   220
tionis, sic consequens illius ad consequens alterius. Verbi gratia,
octo, quattuor, duo, unum sunt proportionalia proportionalitate
geometrica; est enim eadem proportio octo ad quattuor sicut duo
ad unum, et etiam sicut octo ad duo, ita quattuor ad unum; et ideo
illi quattuor termini permutatim proportionales existunt.   225

Econtrario proportionalia proportionalitate geometrica sunt
illa quorum proportionalium proportionalitate geometrica, sicut
consequens unius proportionis ad antecedens illius, ita reliquum
consequens ad proprium antecedens. Verbi gratia, sicut octo ad
quattuor, ita duo ad unum, et econtrario sicut quattuor ad octo, ita 230
unum ad duo.

similarity of proportions united by a common, mean term, or terms (by a single term in the example: as four is to two, so two is to one—and by more than one in the example: as eight is to four, so four is to two, and two is to one). A similarity of proportions not united by a common term, or terms, is "discontinuous" (as in the example: as six is to three, so two is to one).

The foregoing is not predicated of these classes of mediety in the primary or strict sense, but only by transference from continuous quantity (whose parts are joined by a common term) and discrete quantity (whose parts are not so joined), as is clear from what was said earlier. Continuous also differs from discontinuous mediety in that the former may be exhibited in three terms or more, whereas the latter requires at least four terms.

According to Ahmad ibn Jusuf (in his letter, On proportion and proportionality) they differ in yet another and most important way in that, in the case of continuous proportionality, all the terms must be of the same kind, whereas in discontinuous, or disjunct, proportionality, some of the terms may be of different kinds. For example: as the length of one musical string is to that of another, so is the pitch of the one to the pitch of the other—and as one moving power is to another, so is the speed of the one motion to the speed of the other. Inasmuch as proportionals are classified according to proportionality, they can be defined by their relation to proportionality in general in a single, analogous (though not univocal) definition: Those quantities are proportionals which agree in a given proportion. Since proportionality is divided into ten classes and proportionals are similarly divided (the three primary forms being our only concern at the moment), therefore those quantities whose differences are equal are proportionals by arithmetic proportionality. Those quantities whose proportions are equal, or similar, or which have a single proportion (as Euclid has it) are proportionals by geometric proportionality. Those quantities the proportions between whose extremes and differences are similar, or equal, are, in turn, proportionals by harmonic proportionality. All this, together with examples, is evident from the foregoing, from which is also evident that the smallest number of terms between which proportionality may be found is three, and that there is no upper limit to the number of such terms.

Those terms are "permutatively" proportionals by geometric proportionality for which the antecedent of the one proportion is to the antecedent of the other, as the consequent of the one is to the consequent of the other. For example, the terms: eight, four, two, one, form a series of proportionals by geometric proportionality, for the proportion of eight to four is the same as that of two to one, and eight is also to two as four is to one. Thus these four terms are proportionals permutatively.

Those terms are "contrarily" proportionals by geometric proportionality for which the consequent of the one proportion is to its antecedent as the consequent of the other is to its respective anteced-

Disiuncta sive simplex proportionalitas geometrica est quorumlibet antecedentium separatim ad sua consequentia proportionum
aequalitas; ut sicut octo ad quattuor, ita duo ad unum.

Coniuncta proportionalitas geometrica est quorumlibet antece-   235
dentium cum suis consequentibus, in disiuncta sive simplici proportionalitate, unius antecedentis illorum cum suo consequente ad
idem consequens, et cuiuslibet alterius antecedentis illorum cum
suo consequente ad proprium consequens, similitudo proportionum;
ut sicut octo et quattuor, ad quattuor, ita duo et unum ad unum.   240

Eversa proportionalitas geometrica est quorumlibet antecedentium cum suis consequentibus, in disiuncta sive simplici proportionalitate, unius antecedentis cum suo consequente ad idem
antecedens, et cuiuslibet alterius antecedentis illorum cum suo
consequente ad ipsum antecedens, proportionum similitudo; ut   245
sicut octo et quattuor ad octo, ita duo et unum ad duo.

Aequa proportionalitas geometrica est duabus multitudinibus
quantitatum propositis, quarum quaecumque duae proximae unius
ad duas sibi correspondentes alterius geometrice proportionales
existant, primorum ad sua ultima proportionum similis habitudo;   250
ut, istis multitudinibus propositis: tria, duo, unum: sex, quattuor,
duo—sicut tria ad duo ita sex ad quattuor, et duo ad unum, sicut
quattuor ad duo; et sicut unum primum ad suum ultimum, ita reliquum ad suum: sicut enim tria ad unum, ita sex ad duo se habent.

Hae sex definitiones ex quinto Elementorum Euclidis, licet   255
obscure, poterunt apparere. Consimiles etiam definitiones proportionalitati arithmeticae ex proportionibus ista proportionalitate attendendo aequalitatem differentiarum poterunt adaptari, ut,
istis intellectis, facile est videre.

TERTIA PARS CAPITULI PRIMI

Iam superest tertia pars huius capituli, quasdam suppositiones   260
praemittens.

Quarum haec est prima: Omnes proportiones sunt aequales
quarum denominationes sunt eaedem vel aequales.

Secunda est ista: Quibuscumque duobus extremis, interposito
medio, cuius ad utrumque est aliqua proportio, erit proportio   265
primi ad tertium composita ex proportione primi ad secundum et
proportione secundi ad tertium.

Tertia est ista: Duobus vel quotcumque mediis interpositis duobus extremis, proportio primi ad extremum producitur ex proportione primi ad secundum et secundi ad tertium et tertii ad   270
quartum et sic deinceps usque ad extremum.

(Harum autem duarum prima est secunda De proportionibus,
secunda vero tertia est eiusdem.)

Quarta est ista: Si duae quantitates aequales ad tertiam quamlibet comparentur, earum ad istam erit una proportio, iterum   275
illius ad ambas eadem est proportio.

ent. For example, as eight is to four, so two is to one, and, contrarily, as four is to eight, so one is to two.

"Disjunct" or "simple" geometric proportionality is equality of the proportions between each antecedent, separately, and its consequent. For example, as eight is to four, so two is to one.

"Conjunct" geometric proportionality (given proportions in disjunct, or simple, proportionality) is equality between the proportions of one of the antecedents, plus its consequent, to that consequent and another antecedent, plus its consequent, to its respective consequent. For example, as eight plus four are to four, so two plus one are to one.

"Everse" geometric proportionality (given proportions in disjunct, or simple, proportionality) is equality between the proportions of one of the antecedents, plus its consequent, to that antecedent and another antecedent, plus its consequent, to its respective antecedent. For example, as eight plus four are to eight, so two plus one are to two.

Given two series of quantities, for which the proportions between successive pairs of terms in the one are geometric proportionals of corresponding pairs in the other, "equal" geometric proportionality is the similar relation of the proportions between the first and the last terms. For example, positing the two series: three, two, one, and six, four, two—as three is to two, so six is to four, and two is to one as four is to two—and as the first term of the one series is to the last term of that series, so is the first term of the other to its respective last term, for as three is to one, so six is to two.

Although obscurely expressed, these six definitions will be found in Book V of Euclid's _Elements_. Similar definitions may also be developed for arithmetic proportionality on the basis of proportions of the present type, simply by taking into account an equality of differences (as may be easily seen, once the foregoing has been grasped).

CHAPTER ONE, PART THREE

There now remains part three of the present chapter, commencing with certain axioms.

The first is that all proportions are equal whose denominations are the same, or equal.

The second is that, given two extreme terms, and interposing an intermediate term possessing a given proportion to each, the proportion of the first to the third will be the product of the proportions of the first to the second and the second to the third.

The third is that, given two or more intermediate terms placed between two extremes, the proportion of the first to the last will be the product of the proportions of the first to the second, the second to the third, the third to the fourth, and so on, to the last term.

(Of the latter two axioms, the first is Axiom 2 of the _De proportionibus_ and the second is Axiom 3 of the same work.)

The fourth is that, if two equal quantities are compared to a third, they will bear the same proportion to it and it to them.

Quinta est ista: Si duae quantitates inaequales ad unam quantitatem proportionentur, maior quidem maiorem, minor vero minorem obtinebit proportionem; illius vero ad ambas, ad minorem
quidem proportio maior, ad maiorem vero minor erit.   280

Sexta est ista: Si fuerit aliquarum quantitatum ad unam quantitatem proportio una, ipsas esse aequales, si vero unius ad eas una
est proportio, aequales esse necesse est.

Septima est ista: Si fuerint quattuor quantitates proportionales,
permutatim proportionales erunt.   285

Octava est ista: Si fuerint quattuor quantitates proportionales
et fuerit prima illarum maxima et ultima minima, primam et
ultimam pariter acceptas ceteris duabus maiores esse necesse
comprobantur.

Istarum quinque ultimarum suppositionum, prima est septima   290
quinti Euclidis, secunda autem octava, tertia vero nona, quarta
quidem sexta decima, quinta vero ultima est eiusdem.

Prima conclusio: Si fuerit proportio maioris inaequalitatis
primi ad secundum ut secundi ad tertium, erit proportio primi
ad tertium praecise dupla ad proportionem primi ad secundum   295
et secundi ad tertium.

Hanc probes ostensive hoc modo: Eaedem vel similes sunt denominationes proportionum primi ad secundum et secundi ad tertium;
igitur, per primam suppositionem, istae sunt aequales et, per
secundum suppositionem, proportio primi ad tertium componitur   300
praecise ex illis. Igitur, per definitionem dupli, ista est praecise
dupla ad utramque illarum. Et hoc est quod ostendere volebamus.

Secunda est ista: Si fuerint quattuor termini continue proportionales, proportio primi ad ultimum, cuiuslibet proportionis
alicuius illorum terminorum ad proximum sequentem est tripla.   305
Si quinque, quadrupla, et sic in infinitum semper uno minus, ita
quod semper denominatio proportionis sit unitate minor numero
terminorum. Sic istam per suppositionem primam et tertiam,
adiuncta definitione "tripli" et "quadrupli" et sic de aliis, ut proximam demonstrabis.   310

Tertia conclusio est ista: Si fuerit primum maius quam duplum
secundi et fuerit secundum aequaliter duplum tertii, erit proportio primi ad tertium minor quam dupla proportionis primi ad
secundum.

Hanc similiter ostensive demonstrabis: Sit enim A primum   315
maius quam duplum secundi, quod sit B, et sit B aequaliter duplum tertii, quod sit C, et sit B ad D sicut A ad B. Tunc D non est
aequale C, propter quartam suppositionem, nec est maius propter
quintam suppositionem cum hypothesi; igitur D est minus C.
Igitur per quintam suppositionem, proportio A ad D est maior   320
proportione A ad C, et per primam conclusionem, proportio A ad
D est dupla ad proportionem A ad B; ergo proportio A ad C est
minor quam dupla ad proportionem A ad B.

Haec eadem potest aliter demonstrari per nunc probata: C est
maius D et inter ista est proportio maioris inaequalitatis; igitur,   325

The fifth is that, if two unequal quantities are made proportionate to a third, the larger will bear a larger proportion to it and the smaller a smaller proportion; the proportion of that third quantity will be greater to a smaller quantity and lesser to a larger one.

The sixth is that, if there is a single proportion of a number of quantities to some other quantity, or of it to them, it follows necessarily that these quantities are equal.

The seventh is that, if four quantities are proportionals, they will be permutatively proportionals.

The eighth is that, if four quantities are proportionals and the first the largest and the last the smallest, the sum of the first and last will be necessarily found greater than the sum of the other two.

(Of these five latter axioms, the first is Axiom 7 of Book V of Euclid, the second is Axiom 8, the third is Axiom 9, the fourth is Axiom 16, and the fifth is the last axiom of the book.)

Theorem I: If a proportion of greater inequality between a first and a second term is the same as that between the second and a third, the proportion of the first to the third will be exactly the square of the proportions between the first and the second, and the second and the third.

This you may prove conclusively as follows: The denominations of the proportions between the first and second and the second and third are the same, or similar. Therefore (by Axiom 1) these are equal, and (by Axiom 2) the proportion of the first to the third is their exact product. Therefore (by the definition of "square") this proportion is exactly the square of each of the others, and this is what we wished to show.

Theorem II: If four terms are continuously proportional, the proportion of the first to the last will be the cube of the proportion between any of them to the one succeeding it. If there are five terms, it will be to the fourth power, and so forth, ad infinitum, in such a way that the denomination of the proportion is always one less than the number of terms. This, like the preceding theorem, may be demonstrated by Axioms 1 and 3, and with the additional definitions of "cubed," "to the fourth power," etc.

Theorem III: If the first term is more than twice the second and the second is exactly twice the third, the proportion of the first to the third will be less than the square of the proportion of the first to the second.

This may also be conclusively demonstrated: For let A be a first term more than twice a second term, B, and let B be exactly twice a third term, C, and let B be to D as A is to B. Then D is not equal to C (by Axiom 4) nor is it greater (by Axiom 5 and by hypothesis); therefore, D is less than C. Then (by Axiom 5) the proportion of A to D is greater than the proportion of A to C, and (by Theorem I) the proportion of A to D is the square of the proportion of A to B, and, therefore, the proportion of A to C is less than the square of the proportion of A to B.

This same theorem can be demonstrated otherwise by means of

A et D duobus extremis, interponatur C medium. Tunc, per secundam suppositionem, proportio A ad D componitur ex proportionibus A ad C et C ad D. Igitur proportio A ad C est minor proportione
A ad D, et ista est aequaliter dupla proportioni A ad B, ut prius
est probatum. Igitur proportio A ad C est minor quam dupla ad   330
proportionem A ad B. Et hoc est quod quaesivisti.

Quarta conclusio est haec: Si fuerit primum duplum secundi
fueritque secundum maius quam duplum tertii, erit proportio
primi ad tertium minor quam dupla proportionis secundi ad tertium.   335

Haec cum proxima similem omnino demonstrationem sortitur.

Quinta: Si fuerit primum minus quam duplum secundi fueritque
secundum aequaliter duplum tertii, erit proportio primi ad tertium
maior quam dupla ad proportionem primi ad secundum.

Haec, ut tertia, dupliciter demonstratur. Primo capiatur D, ad   340
quod se habet B sicut A ad B, et probetur quod D sit maius C, et
ex hoc ut in probatione tertiae conclusionis propositum concluditur.
Secundo, sumatur D praecise duplum B et ostendatur D esse maius
A, et ex illo demonstratur propositum sicut in secunda ostensione
conclusionis tertiae erat factum.   345

Sexta conclusio: Si fuerit primum duplum secundi fueritque
secundum minus quam duplum tertii, erit proportio primi ad tertium maior quam dupla proportionis secundi ad tertium. Haec cum
proxima similem demonstrationem habebit.

Septima conclusio: Proportione aequalitatis nulla proportio est   350
maior vel minor.

Nam nulla proportione aequalitatis aliqua proportio aequalitatis
est maior vel minor propter primam suppositionem. Nec aliqua
proportio maioris inaequalitatis est maior vel minor proportione
aequalitatis, quia tunc proportio aequalitatis secundum aliquam   355
proportionem maioris inaequalitatis ab alia proportione maioris
inaequalitatis excederetur; et cum secundum aequalem proportionem aliqua proportio maioris inaequalitatis excedatur ab illa
proportione maioris inaequalitatis, sequitur, per sextam suppositionem, proportionem aequalitatis et proportionem maioris inae-   360
qualitatis esse aequales; et tunc, per eandem suppositionem,
sequitur maius et minus invicem adequari.

Verbi gratia, ponatur proportionem quadruplam esse in duplo
maiorem proportione aequalitatis, et capiatur proportio maioris
inaequalitatis in duplo minor proportione quadrupla, quod fieri   36⁵
potest si, duobus extremis quorum maius est quadruplum minoris,
interponatur medium quod se habeat ad minus extremum sicut
maius ad ipsum: quaternario enim et unitati interponatur binarius.
Tunc isti sunt tres termini continue proportionales; igitur per
primam conclusionem, proportio primi ad ultimum est dupla pro-   37⁰
portionis primi ad secundum. Igitur proportio primi ad secundum
est subdupla proportionis primi ad ultimum; igitur proportio dupla
est subdupla proportionis quadruplae. Et, secundum falsigraphum,
proportio aequalitatis est subdupla proportionis quadruplae, igitur,

what has now been proved. C is greater than D and between them
there exists a proportion of greater inequality. Therefore, taking A
and D as two extremes and interposing an intermediate term, C,
then (by Axiom 2) the proportion of A to D is the product of the proportions of A to C and C to D. Therefore, the proportion of A to C
is less than the proportion of A to D, and the latter is also the square
of the proportion A to B (as was proved above). Therefore, the proportion of A to C is less than the square of the proportion A to B,
and this is what we were after.

Theorem IV: If the first term is twice the second and the second
is more than twice the third, the proportion of the first to the third
will be less than the square of the proportion of the second to the
third.

This may be demonstrated by a proof altogether similar to that
of the preceding theorem.

Theorem V: If the first term is less than twice the second and the
second is also twice the third, the proportion of the first to the third
will be greater than the square of the proportion of the first to the
second.

This, like Theorem III, may be demonstrated in two ways. First,
let a D be posited such that B is related to it as A is to B, and let it
be proved that D is greater than C; from this, as in the proof of
Theorem III, the conclusion is arrived at. Secondly, let a D be posited that is exactly twice B, and let it be shown that D is greater
than A, and from this the theorem is demonstrated as in the second
proof of Theorem III.

Theorem VI: If the first term is twice the second and the second
is less than twice the third, the proportion of the first to the third
will be greater than the square of the proportion of the second to the
third.

This theorem will have a proof similar to that of the preceding
one.

Theorem VII: No proportion is either greater or less than a proportion of equality.

In the first place, by Axiom 1, no proportion of equality is either
greater or less than any other proportion of equality.

Nor is any proportion of greater inequality either greater or less
than a proportion of equality, for, if it were, then the proportion of
equality would be exceeded by a proportion of greater inequality to
the extent of some proportion of greater inequality, and, since some
proportion of greater inequality would be exceeded by that proportion of greater inequality in that same proportion, it follows (by
Axiom 6) that the proportion of equality would be equal to that of inequality. Then (by the same axiom) it follows that a greater and a
lesser quantity would be equal to each other.

For example, posit that the proportion of four to one is the square
of a proportion of equality, and let a proportion of greater inequality
be chosen which is the square root of the proportion of four to one.
This is possible, if, given two extreme terms of which the greater is

per sextam suppositionem, ipsa est aequalis proportioni duplae;   375
igitur duorum ad unum et unius ad unum proportiones sunt aequales.
Igitur, per sextam suppositionem, binarius et unitas sunt aequales.
Et de qualibet alia proportione maioris inaequalitatis potest fieri
simile argumentum. Nulla ergo proportio maioris inaequalitatis
proportione aequalitatis est maior.   380

Nec minor, quia tunc proportio aequalitatis aliqua proportione
maioris inaequalitatis secundum aliquam proportionem maioris
inaequalitatis esset maior. Detur igitur quod proportio aequalitatis sit dupla proportionis duplae, et capiatur proportio maioris
inaequalitatis dupla ad proportionem duplam; quod fieri potest   385
si ad maiorem duorum terminorum, quorum unus est duplus ad
alium, accipiatur terminus duplus: sicut si ad binarium, qui est
duplus unitati, capiatur terminus duplus, scilicet quarternarius.
Tunc, per primam conclusionem, proportio quarternarii ad unitatem est dupla proportionis binarii ad unitatem. Igitur proportio 390
quadrupla est dupla proportionis duplae et, per hypothesim, proportio aequalitatis similiter. Ergo, per sextam suppositionem,
proportio aequalitatis et proportio quadrupla sunt aequales. Et
tunc, per eandem, quadruplum alicuius et aequale eidem essent
aequalia.   395

Vel sic: si proportio maioris inaequalitatis esset minor proportione aequalitatis, tunc aliquotiens sumpta illam praecise
redderet vel maiorem. Quod est falsum, quia quotienscumque
proportio maioris inaequalitatis sumatur, semper maiorem proportionem inaequalitatis maioris constituit, ut per primam et   400
secundam conclusiones poterit apparere.

Similiter potest ostendi quod proportio aequalitatis non sit
minor proportione inaequalitatis maioris, quia tunc aliquotiens
sumpta illam redderet vel maiorem, consequens falsum, quia
quotienscumque aequalia apponantur proportio primi ad ultimum   405
non est maior proportione primi ad secundum, sed omnia in aequali
proportione aequalitatis integre perseverant.

Nec aliqua proportio minoris inaequalitatis, aliqua proportione
aequalitatis est maior vel minor, quod sicut de proportione inaequalitatis maioris poterit demonstrari.   410

Sed contra istam conclusionem potest sic obici:

Sit A aequale B, C autem maius, D vero minus. Tunc, per quintam suppositionem, C habet maiorem proportionem ad B quam
habet A ad B, et D minorem. Et proportio A ad B est aequalitatis,
igitur et cetera.   415

Ad idem: Sint A et C aequalia et sit utrumque illorum duplum
ad B; tunc, A et C duobus extremis, interponatur B medium, cuius
ad utrumque sit aliqua proportio. Igitur, per secundam suppositionem, proportio A ad C componitur ex proportionibus A ad B et
B ad C, et proportio A ad C est proportio aequalitatis. Igitur tam 420
proportio dupla quam subdupla proportione aequalitatis est minor.

Ad idem: Sint A et B et C tria aequalia. Tunc, per secundam

four times the smaller, an intermediate term is interposed whose proportion to the smaller extreme is equal to the proportion of the greater extreme to it. Now, let two be interposed between four and one. These three terms are continuously proportional, and, therefore (by Theorem I) the proportion of the first to the last is the square of the proportion of the first to the second. Then the proportion of the first to the second is the square root of the proportion between the first and the last, and the proportion of two to one is the square root of the proportion of four to one. Now, according to our false hypothesis, the proportion of equality is the square root of the proportion of four to one, and, consequently (by Axiom 6) it is equal to the proportion of two to one, and the proportions of two to one and one to one are equal. Therefore (by Axiom 6) two equals one. Now, since a similar argument can be constructed with respect to any other proportion of greater inequality, therefore no proportion of greater inequality is greater than a proportion of equality.

Nor can any such proportion be less than one of equality, for in that event a proportion of equality would be greater than some proportion of greater inequality by some proportion of greater inequality. It would, therefore, be necessary that the proportion of equality be the square of the proportion of two to one. Now, take a proportion of greater inequality which is the square of the proportion of two to one; this can be done, if a term be chosen which is double the larger of two terms of which one is twice the other (as, for example, if we take four, which is twice two, with respect to two, which is twice one). Then (by Theorem I) the proportion of four to one is the square of the proportion of two to one. Therefore, both the proportion of four to one and (by hypothesis) the proportion of equality are the square of the proportion of two to one. Then (by Axiom 6) the proportion of equality is equal to the proportion of four to one, and (by the same axiom) a quantity four times as great as another is equal to one that is equal to that other.

Or we can proceed as follows: If a proportion of greater inequality were to be less than a proportion of equality, then some multiple of it would either be exactly equal to or greater than that proportion of equality. This is false for the reason that, whatever multiple be chosen, it will always be a proportion of greater inequality (as is clear from Theorems I and II).

It can likewise be shown that a proportion of equality is not less than a proportion of greater inequality for the reason that, if it were, then some multiple of it would either be equal to or greater than that proportion of greater inequality. This consequence is false, for, however many times equals are added to equals, the proportion of the first pair to the last is no greater than the proportion of the first to the second. Instead, they all remain unchanged as equal proportions of equality.

That no proportion of lesser inequality can be either greater or less than a proportion of equality may be demonstrated in a manner

suppositionem, proportio A ad C componitur ex proportionibus A
ad B et B ad C, et istae proportiones sunt aequales. Igitur ista est
dupla utrisque istarum.   425

Idem potest argui per quintam <u>Elementorum</u> Euclidis dicentis,
"Cum fuerint tres quantitates continue proportionales, dicetur
proportio primae ad tertiam proportio primae ad secundam duplicata." Sed A, B, C sunt tres quantitates continue proportionales.
Igitur proportio A ad C est proportio A ad B duplicata; igitur una   430
aequalitatis proportio alia proportione aequalitatis est dupla.

Pro primo istorum dicendum quod Euclides intelligit quintam
suppositionem de quantitatibus inaequalibus comparatis ad tertiam eodem genere proportionis, ita quod utraque comparetur illi
in proportione inaequalitatis maioris, vel utraque in proportione   435
inaequalitatis minoris.

Pro secundo dicendum quod secunda suppositio intelligitur de
talibus extremis et medio, quorum primum est inaequale tertio,
medium quoque utroque.   440

Per idem patet ad tertium.

Ad quartum dicendum quod Euclides intelligit tantum de quantitatibus proportionalibus proportionalitate inaequalitatis maioris.

Et sic cessat omnis obiectio.

Octava: Nulla proportio maioris inaequalitatis aliqua proportione
minoris inaequalitatis est maior vel minor.   445

Istam, sicut proximam, per impossibile demonstrabis, et deduces adversarium ad hoc impossibile: quod aliqua proportio inaequalitatis maioris et aliqua proportio inaequalitatis minoris sunt
aequales, et per consequens quod maius aliquo et minus illo invicem
adaequantur.   450

Igitur de mathematicis praemittendis haec dicta sufficiant.

similar to that employed with respect to proportions of greater inequality.

But, on the other hand, objections may be raised against this theorem, as follows:

Let A be equal to, C be greater than, and D be less than B. Then (by Axiom 5) C bears a greater proportion to B than A does to B, and D bears a lesser such proportion. Now, the proportion of A to B is one of equality, and it becomes apparent that the theorem in question is invalid.

To the same effect: Let A and C be equals and each of them be twice B. Then, taking A and C as extremes, interpose a term, B, bearing a certain proportion to each of them. Therefore (by Axiom 2) the proportion of A to C is the product of the proportions of A to B and B to C. Since the proportion of A to C is one of equality, therefore, both the proportions of two to one and one to two are less than a proportion of equality.

And again: Let A, B and C be three equal terms. Then (by Axiom 2) the proportion of A to C is the product of the proportions of A to B and B to C. Since these proportions are equal, therefore the proportion of A to C is the square of each of them.

The same objection can be raised by appealing to Book V of Euclid's _Elements_, where it is stated that: "When three quantities are continuously proportional, the proportion of the first to the third is the square of the proportion between the first and the second." Now, A, B and C are three continuously proportional quantities, and therefore the proportion of A to C is the square of the proportion of A to B. Thus, one proportion of equality is twice another.

As for the first of these objections, it should be stated that Euclid understood Axiom 5 to apply to unequal quantities compared to a third quantity in the same kind of proportion, in such a way that each is compared to that third quantity either in a proportion of greater inequality or in one of lesser inequality.

To the second objection, it should be pointed out that Axiom 2 is understood as applying only to such extreme and intermediate terms as are not equal to each other.

The same remark clears up the third objection.

To the fourth objection, the reply is that Euclid was only talking about quantities proportional in the proportionality of greater inequality.

This disposes of all the objections.

Theorem VIII: No proportion of greater inequality is either greater or less than one of lesser inequality.

This theorem, like the preceding one, you may demonstrate _per impossibile_, one's opponent being led to the following impossibility: that a proportion of greater inequality is equal to one of lesser inequality, and that, consequently, terms greater and less than some third term are equal to each other.

By way of mathematical preliminaries, the foregoing will be sufficient.

CAPITULUM SECUNDUM

Istis introductoriis praelibatis, ad illud quod propositum est ab   1
initio accedamus. Et primo, more Aristotelis, reprobemus opiniones erroneas ut magis veritas patefiat.

Opiniones erroneae proposito pertinentes sunt quattuor, quarum
prima ponit proportionem velocitatum in motibus sequi excessum   5
potentiae motoris ad potentiam rei motae. Et hoc capit evidentiam
primo De caelo et mundo, capitulo de infinito, ex textu dicente:
"Proportionaliter oportet secundum excellentiam motoris," et ex
dictis Averrois super quartum Physicorum, commento 71, dicentis
quod, "Omnis motus est secundum excessum potentiae motoris   10
super rem motam." Et septimo Physicorum, commento 35, sic
dicit: "Velocitas propria unicuique motui sequitur excessum potentiae motoris super potentiam moti," et commento 39, scilicet ultimo,
dicit sic: "Secundum excessum potentiae alterantis super potentiam alterati erit velocitas alterationis et quantitas temporis." Et   15
multa similia asserit multis locis.

Haec autem opinio destrui poterit multis modis. Primo sic:
Secundum istum modum sequitur quod, aliquo motore movente aliquod mobile per aliquod spatium in aliquo tempore, medietas
motoris medietatem moti per medietatem excessus; sicut quarter-   20
narius excedit binarium per binarium, et medietas eius (scilicet
binarius) excedit medietatem eius (scilicet unitatem) per unitatem
tantum, quae est medietas prioris excessus. Et falsitas consequentis patet per Aristotelem, septimo Physicorum, in fine, ubi
probat istam conclusionem: "Si aliqua potentia moveat aliquod   25
mobile per aliquod spatium in aliquo tempore, medietas movebit
medietatem per aequale spatium in aequali tempore." Et haec ratio
Aristotelis satis probat, nam "similiter se habet et secundum
eandem proportionem medietas ad medietatem sicut totum ad
totum. Igitur motus sunt aequeveloces."   30

Secundo sic: Tunc sequitur quod, duobus motoribus moventibus
duo mobilia per aequale spatium in aequali tempore, illi duo
motores coniunctim non moverent illa duo mobilia coniuncta praecise per aequale spatium in aequali tempore, sed semper per duplum. Consequentia patet, quia excessus istorum duorum motorum   35
coniunctorum ad ista duo mobilia coniuncta est duplus ad excessum
unius istorum motorum super suum mobile; sicut quilibet binarius

CHAPTER TWO

Having looked into these introductory matters, let us now proceed
with the undertaking which was proposed at the outset. And first,
after the manner of Aristotle, let us criticize erroneous theories,
so that the truth may be the more apparent.

There are four false theories to be proposed as relevant to our
investigation, the first of which holds that: <u>the proportion between
the speeds with which motions take place varies as the difference</u> $F - R$
<u>whereby the power of the mover exceeds the resistance offered by</u>
<u>the thing moved</u>.

This theory claims in its favor that passage from Book I of the
<u>De Caelo et Mundo</u> (in the chapter on the "infinite") in the text
which reads: "It is necessary that proportionally as the mover is
in excess, etc.," together with Averroes' Comment 71 on Book IV of
the <u>Physics</u>, in which he says: "Every motion takes place in accordance with the excess of the power of the mover over that of the
thing moved." In Comment 35, on Book VII of the <u>Physics</u>, he further states that: "The speed proper to any given motion varies
with the excess of the power of the mover over that of the thing
moved," and in the final Comment, Comment 39, he says that: "The
speed of alteration and the quantity of time will vary in accordance
with the amount whereby the power of that which is causing the alteration exceeds the resistance offered by what undergoes the alteration." Many other passages afford similar remarks.

The present theory may, however, be torn down in several ways:

First, according to this theory, it would follow that, if a given
mover moved a given <u>mobile</u> through a given distance in a given
time, half of that mover would not move half of the <u>mobile</u> through
the same distance in an equal time, but only through half the distance. The consequence is clear, because, if the whole mover exceeds the whole <u>mobile</u> by the whole excess, then half the mover
exceeds half the <u>mobile</u> by only half the former amount; for, just as
4 exceeds 2 by 2, half of 4 (namely, 2) exceeds half of itself (that is, 1)
by 1, which is only half of the former excess.

That such a consequence is false is apparent from the fact that Aristotle proves, at the close of Book VII of the <u>Physics</u>, that: "If a given
power moves a given <u>mobile</u> through a given distance in a given time,
half that power will move half the <u>mobile</u> through an equal distance in
an equal time." Aristotle's reasoning is quite sound, for, since the half
is related to the half by the same proportion as the whole is to the
whole, the two motions will, therefore, be of equal speed.

Secondly, it follows from this theory that, given two movers moving
two <u>mobilia</u> through equal distances in equal times, the two movers,
conjoined, would not move the two <u>mobilia</u>, conjoined, through an exactly equal distance in an equal time, but, instead, through double that
distance. This consequence follows necessarily because the excess of
the two movers, taken together, over the two <u>mobilia</u>, taken together,
is twice the excess of each of them over its own <u>mobile</u>; for, just as

excedit unitatem per unitatem, duo autem binarii (qui quarternarium faciunt) excedunt duas unitates (quae dualitatem constituunt) per dualitatem, quae est dupla ad excessum binarii super   40
unitatem. Et ita est in omnibus aliis ubi duo excessa a duobus
excedentibus aequaliter exceduntur. Falsitas consequentis patet
per Aristotelem, septimo Physicorum, ut prius, ubi probat istam
conclusionem: "Si duae potentiae divisim moveant duo mobilia per
aequalia spatia in aequali tempore, illae duae potentiae coniunctae   45
movebunt illa duo mobilia coniuncta per aequale spatium in aequali tempore cum priori." Et haec ratio Aristotelis satis probat
hoc, scilicet: Proportionaliter se habet motor compositus ad motum
compositum et motor simplex ad motum simplex.

Tertio sic: Tunc ex proportione geometrica, scilicet similitu-   50
dine proportionem motorum ad sua mota, non sequitur aequalis
velocitas motuum, quia nec excessuum; quoniam eadem est proportio duorum ad unum et sex ad tres, excessus tamen unius est unitas, alius autem ternarius. Consequens autem ad quod deducitur
est falsum, et contra Aristotelem septimo Physicorum, in fine et   55
multis locis, ubi semper, ex aequalitate proportionum motorum
ad sua mota, arguit aequalitatem velocitatum in motibus. Idem vult
Averroes super loca praedicta, et similiter quarto Physicorum,
commento 71, et super primum De caelo et mundo, commento 63,
et aliis multis locis.   60

Nec potest dici quod Aristoteles et Averroes intelligunt, in locis
praedictis, per proportionem seu analogiam, proportionalitatem
who arithmeticam seu aequalitatem excessuum, ut dicunt quidam; quia,
septimo Physicorum, probat Aristoteles istam conclusionem: "Si
aliqua potentia moveat aliquod mobile per aliquod spatium in ali-   65
quo tempore, medietas motoris movebit medietatem moti per
aequale spatium in aequali tempore, quoniam similiter secundum
analogiam sicut se habet medietas motoris ad medietatem moti
et totus motor ad totum motum," quod tamen de proportionalitate
arithmetica, quae significat aequalitatem excessuum, dignoscitur   70
esse falsum (ut in primo argumento contra hanc opinionem sufficienter est ostensum). Et Averroes ibidem dicit quod sic erit
eadem proportio, "sicut universaliter demonstrant geometri." Et
potest hoc demonstrari geometrice per hunc modum: Sicut totus
motor ad medietatem motoris, ita totum motum ad medietatem   75
moti. Igitur permutatim, per septimam suppositionem primi capituli, sicut totus motor ad totum motum, ita medietas motoris ad
medietatem moti; et hoc erat probandum.

Glosa etiam praedicta stare non potest, quia Aristoteles, septimo
Physicorum, probat hanc conclusionem: "Si duo motores divisim   80
moveant duo mobilia per aequalia spatia in aequali tempore, illi
duo motores coniunctim movebunt illa duo mobilia coniuncta per

anything having a value of 2 exceeds unity by 1, so two such "2's"
(which make 4) exceed two "1's" (which make 2) by 2, which is twice the
excess of 2 over 1. The foregoing holds in all cases in which two sub-
trahends are equally exceeded by two minuends.

That the above consequence is false is evident from the foregoing
argument of Aristotle, in Book VII of his Physics, where he demon-
strates the following conclusion: "If two powers move two mobilia, separately, through equal distances in equal times, those powers conjoined,
will move the two mobilia conjoined, through an equal distance in a
time equal to the former one." This argument of Aristotle is sufficient
proof that the relation between a single mover and its mobile, and a
compound mover and its mobile, is a proportional one.

In the third place, it would follow that a geometric proportion (that
is, a similarity of proportions) of movers to their mobilia would not
produce equal speeds, since it does not represent an equality of excesses; for, although the proportions of 2 to 1 and 6 to 3 are the same,
the excess of the one term over the other is 1 in the first case and 3 in
the second case.

The consequence to which we are thus led is, however, false and
opposed to Aristotle's opinion, as expressed at the close of Book VII of
the Physics and in many other places, where, from an equality of proportions of movers to their mobilia, he always argues equal speeds.
Averroes supports the same view in his remarks on the passages just
mentioned and also in his Comment 71 on Physics IV, Comment 63 on
De Caelo et Mundo I, and in many other places.

Nor can it be legitimately maintained that, in the passages cited,
Aristotle and Averroes understand, by the words "proportion" and "analogy," arithmetic proportionality (that is, equality of differences), as
some have claimed. Indeed, in Book VII of the Physics, Aristotle
proves this conclusion: "If a given power moves a given mobile
through a given distance in a given time, half that power will move half
the mobile through an equal distance in an equal time, because, "analog-
ically," the relation of half the mover to half the mobile is similar to
that of the whole mover to the whole mobile." Such a statement, interpreted as referring to arithmetic proportionality, is discernibly false
(as has already been made sufficiently clear in the first argument
raised against the present theory). Moreover, regarding this same passage, Averroes says that the proportion will be the same "in the sense
that geometricians universally employ in demonstrations."

The above thesis of Aristotle may be demonstrated geometrically as
follows: As is the whole mover to half the mover, so is the whole mobile
to half the mobile. Therefore, permutatively, (by Axiom 7 of Chapter I):
As is the whole mover to the whole mobile, so is half the mover to half
the mobile. And this is what was to have been proved.

The reading of Aristotle proposed by the present theory does not
stand up, moreover, because, in Book VII of the Physics, Aristotle also
proves this conclusion: "If two movers, separately, move two mobilia
through equal distances in equal times, those two movers, conjointly,
will move those two mobilia, conjoined, through a distance and in a time

aequale spatium in aequali tempore cum priori," per idem medium." "Analogum enim est" (et per "analogum" intelligit proportionale). Sed non proportionalitate arithmetica, quia non secundum aequalem 85 excessum excedit simplex motor simplex motum et compositus compositum, ut ex secundo argumento contra hanc opinionem apparet. Et Averroes ibidem probat quod "erit eadem proportio, non aequalis excessus, per primam quinti Elementorum Euclidis dicentis: 'Si fuerint quarumlibet quantitatum aliarum totidem 90 aeque multiplicitates aut aeque maiores aut aeque minores aut singulae singulis aequales, necesse est quemadmodum una illarum ad sui comparem, totum quoque ex his aggregatum ad omnes istas pariter acceptas similiter se habere.'" Igitur glosa praedicta non poterit esse vera. 95

Quarto sic: Tunc sequeretur quod aliquod mixtum habens resistentiam intrinsecam velocius movetur in pleno quam in vacuo. Sit enim A grave mixtum habens potentiam motivam et potentiam resistivam in se, et descendat ex se in aliquo medio (quod sit B) et sit C terra pura, minoris potentiae quam excessus A super 100 totam suam resistentiam. Tunc A haberet ex se motum certae velocitatis in vacuo. Subtilietur igitur B medium donec C moveatur aequali velocitate in B cum A in vacuo. Et tunc ponatur A in illo medio cum C, et movebitur velocius illo; habet enim maiorem excessum. Et C movetur in illo medio aequali velocitate 105 cum A in vacuo. Igitur movetur velocius in illo medio pleno quam in vacuo. Quod autem B possit tantum subtiliari donec C movetur in illo velocitate praedicta, apparet; quia ad quamtamcumque velocitatem datam potest motus localis velocitari per subtiliationem medii, ut patet quarto Physicorum, capitulo de vacuo, ubi 110 supponitur quod per subtiliationem medii (manente eodem motore), possibile est devenire ad quamtamcumque velocitatem motus localis datam. Et per hoc concluditur quod, posito motu locali in vacuo, idem movetur localiter aequevelociter in vacuo et in pleno. 115

Quinto sic: Tunc sequeretur quod, si aliquis motor excederet suam resistentiam per minorem excessum quam alius suam, tardius moveret illam. Descendat igitur terra magna cum aliqua resistentia, quam secundum excessum magnum excedat, et descendat aliqua terra minoris potentiae excessu maioris terrae 120 ad suam resistentiam. Et maneat maior terra et sua resistentia non alterata et subtilietur medium in quo movetur minor terra, donec moveatur aequevelociter cum maiori. Tunc minor terra

by the same middle [proposition]:

equal to the former," if the medium through which the motions take
place remains the same, "for the motions are 'analogous'." By "analogous" he means a proportional, but not in the sense of arithmetic proportionality, for the simple mover does not exceed the simple mobile
by the same amount that the compound mover exceeds the compound
mobile, (as was made clear in the second argument against this theory).

Averroes, commenting on this passage, proves that, "although the proportion will be the same, the excess will not." He does this by employing
Theorem I of Book V of Euclid's Elements, which states that: "If the
members of a given set of quantities are either equal multiples of,
equally greater or less than, or exact equals of the members of a corresponding set, it follows that the relations between corresponding individual terms of the two sets will be the same as the aggregate relation of
the two sets." Therefore, the above-mentioned reading of Aristotle cannot be taken as valid.

The fourth criticism is as follows: It would follow, on the basis of the
present theory, that a mixed body, possessing internal resistance, could
move faster through a medium than through a vacuum. Let A, for example, be a heavy mixed body (possessing within itself both motive and
resistive power), and imagine it to descend of itself through some medium, B. Let C represent a quantity of pure earth, possessing less power
than the excess of motive power over resistance in A. A will, of itself,
move at a determinate speed in a vacuum. Now let the medium, B, be
rarified to the point at which C moves in it with a speed equal to that
of A in the vacuum. If A is now placed in the same medium with C, it
should move faster than C (for it possesses a greater excess of motive
power over resistance). C will move in that medium with a speed equal
to that of A, moving in the vacuum. Therefore A will move faster
through the medium than through the vacuum.

That it is, in fact, possible to rarify B to a point at which C would
move in it with the speed just specified is evidently true, for, by rarefaction of the medium, local motion can be accelerated to any desired
degree. This is shown to be the case in Book IV of the Physics (in the
chapter on the "void"), where it is stated that, with the moving power
remaining constant, it is possible to arrive at any given speed of local
motion by rarifying the medium.

Thus (positing that a local motion could take place in a void), we find
that the same body could move at the same velocity in both a medium
and a vacuum.

Our fifth criticism is that it would also follow that, if a given mover
exceeded its resistance by a lesser amount than another mover exceeded
its resistance, the former motion would be the slower one. Let a large
quantity of earth, possessing a given resistance which its downward
force greatly exceeds, be supposed to fall. Let also another quantity of
earth, possessing a lesser such excess of power, be supposed to fall.
Letting the larger quantity of earth and the resistance associated with
it remain constant, let the medium in which the smaller quantity of
earth moves now be rarified to the point at which its speed becomes
equal to that of the larger quantity. The smaller quantity now moves its

aequevelociter movet suam resistentiam sicut maior terra suam,
et tamen illam per excessum minorem excedit.   125

Sexto sic: Tunc sequeretur quod, si terra pura movetur in
aliquo medio quod in dupla proportione excederet vel maiori,
non posset moveri in duplo velocius in aliquo medio alio. Non
enim posset excedere aliquod medium per duplum excessum,
quoniam tunc totum esset excessus. Et tunc, manente eodem   130
motore, non in infinitum per subtiliationem medii posset velocitas motus generari (quod ex prioribus constat esse falsum).

Septimo sic: Tunc sequeretur quod, si aliquis motor excederet
suam resistentiam per maiorem excessum quam alius suam,   135
velocius moveret illam; et tunc quodcumque mobile fortis homo
per maiorem excessum excederet quam debilior motor (sicut
puer vel musca vel aliquid huiusmodi) excederet suum mobile,
moveret et illud velocius. Et cum homo fortis per maiorem
excessum excedit quodcumque mobile cum quo potest moveri   140
maius quam debilior motor excedit aliquod mobile, sequitur
quod fortis homo moveret quodcumque mobile cum quo possit
moveri velocius quam debilior motor moveret aliquod mobile
cum quo posset moveri, cuius contrarium declarat experimen-
tum. Videmus enim quod musca portando aliquod modicum vel-   145
ociter multum volat, et puer aliquod modicum velociter satis movet, et homo fortis unum magnum mobile (quod vix potest movere)
movet valde tarde. Et licet illi mobili apponatur maius quam
musca vel puer posset movere, movet totum non multum tardius
tunc quam prius.   150

Ex his igitur omnibus sufficienter ostenditur ista conclusio
negativa: <u>Proportio velocitatum in motibus non sequitur excessum potentiae motoris super potentiam rei motae.</u>

Contraria autem his non difficile est solvere, quoniam Aristoteles et Averroes commentator, quando dicunt quod velocitas in 155
motu sequitur excellentiam sive excessum potentiae motoris super
rem motam, vel aliquid huiusmodi, intelligunt per excellentiam
sive excessum proportionem maioris inaequalitatis qua potentia
motoris excellit sive excedit potentiam rei motae.

SECUNDA PARS CAPITULI SECUNDI

Sequitur de secunda opinione erronea ponente proportionem   160
velocitatum in motibus sequi proportionem excessus potentiae
motoris super potentiam rei motae. Et hoc videtur fundari in dicto
Averrois super septimo <u>Physicorum</u>, commento 36: ibi enim dicit
quod "velocitas motus est secundum proportionem excessus potentiae motoris super potentiam rei motae."   165

Haec autem opinio debet redargui tamquam falsa. Ponatur enim
quod excessus potentiae motoris super potentiam rei motae sit

$$\frac{N_2}{N_1} = log\left(\frac{F_1 - R_1}{R_1}\right)\left(\frac{F_2 - R_2}{R_2}\right)$$

resistance with the same speed that the larger moves its own, and yet exceeds it by a smaller amount.

Sixthly, it would also follow that, if a bit of pure earth were moving in some medium whose resistance its power exceeded by a ratio of two to one, or more, it could not move at double that speed in any other medium. It could not exceed any medium by double the first excess, for, in that case, the entire moving power would be excess, and, with the moving power remaining constant, it would consequently not be possible to increase the speed of the motion indefinitely by rarefaction of the medium. Such a consequence has already been established as false.

In the seventh place, another consequence would be that, if a given mover were to exceed its resistance by a greater amount than another mover exceeded its own resistance, the former motion would be the faster. Then, since a strong man exceeds anything he moves by a greater excess of power than a weaker mover (such as a boy, or a fly, or something of that sort) exceeds what it moves, he should move it more rapidly.

Experience, however, teaches us the contrary, for we see that a fly carrying some small particle flies very rapidly, and that a boy also moves a small object rather rapidly. A strong man, on the other hand, moving some large object which he can scarcely budge, moves it very slowly, and even if there were added to what he moves a quantity larger than either the fly or the boy can move, the man will then move the whole not much more slowly than he did before.

From all these considerations, therefore, the following negative conclusion is sufficiently well established:

The proportion of speeds in motions does not vary with the amount whereby the power of the mover exceeds that of the thing moved.

Objections to this conclusion are not difficult to dissolve, for Aristotle and Averroes, when they say that the speed of a motion varies in accordance with the amount by which the power of the mover excels or exceeds that of the thing moved, understand by "excellence," or "excess," a proportion of greater inequality whereby the power of the mover excels, or exceeds, the power of the thing moved.

CHAPTER TWO, PART TWO
[THEORY II]

Let us now turn to the second erroneous theory, which supposes the proportion of the speeds of motions to vary in accordance with the proportion of the excesses whereby the moving powers exceed the resisting powers. This idea is evidently based on Averroes' Comment 36 on Book VII of the Physics, for he there states that the speed of a motion is determined by the proportion whereby the power of the mover exceeds that of the thing moved.

This theory should, however, be refuted as false. For just imagine the case in which the excess of the power of the mover over that of the

suppose $F - R = R$, *then* $\frac{F-R}{R} = \frac{1}{1}$

aequalis potentiae rei motae. Tunc nullus motor potest movere
aliquod mobile velocius nec tardius illo motu; quia nullius motoris
proportio excessus suae potentiae ad potentiam rei motae potest   170
esse maior vel minor (ut per septimam conclusionem primi capituli patet). (p. 8¹)

   Secundo sic: Movens primo movet totum per totam suam potentiam et non per excessum suae potentiae. Igitur motus et velocitas
eius primo et essentialiter sequuntur habitudinem vel proportion-   175
em totius potentiae motoris ad potentiam moti, et non proportionem excessus, nisi fuerit accidentaliter et ex consequenti.

   Sic igitur patet ista conclusio negativa: <u>Proportio velocitatum
in motibus non sequitur proportionem excessus potentiae motoris
super potentiam rei motae</u>.   180

   Dictum autem Averrois, si quis glosare voluerit, potest sicut
alias auctoritates pro prima opinione adductas.

TERTIA PARS CAPITULI SECUNDI

   Sequitur de tertia opinione erronea, quae ponit proportionem
velocitatum in motibus (manente eodem motore vel aequali) sequi
proportionem passorum, et (manente eodem passo vel aequali)   185
sequi proportionem motoris.

   Et hoc videtur fundari quantum ad primam partem, in textu
Aristotelis et in multis locis. Nam quarto <u>Physicorum</u>, capitulo
de vacuo, textu commenti 71, sic dicit: "Sit enim B quidem aqua,
D vero aer; quanto vero subtilior aer aqua et incorporalior, tan- 190
to citius A," id est mobile, "per D movebitur quam per B. Habet
igitur eandem rationem," id est proportionem, "secundum quam
distat aer ab aqua, velocitas ad velocitatem; quare si duplex sub-
tile est aer, duplici tempore quod est ipsum B pertransibit quam D."
Et textus sequens manifeste supponit quod (manente eodem motore 195
et medio variato) proportio velocitatum in motibus sequitur proportionem mediorum, et etiam proportio temporum mensuran-
tium illos motus sequitur proportionem mediorum econverso:
scilicet quod maius tempus correspondet motui per medium den-
sius, et minus tempus motui per subtilius medium correspondet.   200

   Et primo <u>De caelo et mundo</u>, capitulo de infinito, sic dicit: "Ab
eodem," scilicet agente, "enim supponatur in pluri et minori tempore maius et minus pati, quaecumque proportionaliter tempori
divisa sunt."

thing moved is equal to the power of the thing moved. No mover will
be able to move any <u>mobile</u> either faster or slower than the speed produced by this proportion, because no other proportion can be either
greater or smaller than that whereby the excess of power of this mover
over its <u>mobile</u> is related to the power of the <u>mobile</u> as a whole (as is
demonstrable by Theorem VII, Chapter I).

In the second place, a moving power moves a whole <u>mobile</u> primarily
by means of its total strength, and not by means of a residuum of its
strength. A motion and its speed vary primarily and essentially, therefore, with the relation, or proportion, between the entire power of the
mover and that of the thing moved, and not (except accidentally and
secondarily) according to a proportion of excess.

This negative conclusion is therefore evident: <u>The proportion of the
speeds of motions does not vary in accordance with the proportion
whereby the excess of the moving power over its</u> mobile <u>is related to
the power of that</u> mobile. The above-mentioned statement by Averroes
may, if anyone were so to desire, be interpreted in the same way as
were the other authorities cited·in support of Theory I.

CHAPTER TWO, PART THREE
[THEORY III]

There follows the third erroneous theory, which claims that: <u>(with
the moving power remaining constant) the proportion of the speeds
of motions varies in accordance with the proportion of resistances,
and (with the resistance remaining constant) that it varies in accordance with the proportion of moving powers.</u>

With respect to its first part, this theory is seen to be founded on
many passages of Aristotle's writings. In Book IV of the <u>Physics</u> (in
the chapter on the "void") he speaks as follows: "Let B represent a
given quantity of water and D a given quantity of air. Now, by however
much air is thinner and more incorporeal than water, by so much will
A (that is, the moving body) move faster through D than through B. Let
the one speed bear the same ratio, or proportion, to the other as that
whereby air differs from water, and then, if air is twice as thin, the
body will traverse B in twice the time required to traverse D." Furthermore, the text immediately following manifestly makes the supposition
that, with the moving power remaining constant and the medium being
varied, the proportion of the speeds of motions varies in accordance
with the proportion of media, and that, conversely, the proportion of
the times measuring those motions varies also in accordance with the
proportion of media (namely, that the longer time corresponds to the
motion through the denser medium and the shorter time to the motion
through the rarer medium).

Further, in Book I of the <u>De caelo</u> (in the chapter on the "infinite") he
speaks as follows: "It is held to undergo a greater and less effect by
the action of the same agent, in a longer and shorter time, any such
effects are divided proportionally to the time."

Et septimo <u>Physicorum</u>, in fine, vult Aristoteles quod si aliqua   205
potentia moveat aliquod mobile per aliquod spatium in aliquo
tempore, eadem potentia movebit medietatem eiusdem mobilis
per duplum spatium in aequali tempore, et per idem spatium in
medietate temporis.

Tantum pro prima parte huius opinionis. Et pro secunda parte   210
huius opinionis supponit Aristoteles, quarto <u>Physicorum</u>, capitulo
de vacuo, quod gravia et levia diversa in quantitate (si alia similiter se habeant) ferantur per aequale spatium in eodem medio
velocius et tardius secundum proportionem gravium et levium
adinvicem.   215

Et in septimo <u>Physicorum</u>, in fine (secundum expositionem
Averrois) vult Aristoteles quod "si aliqua potentia moveat aliquod
mobile per aliquod spatium in aliquo tempore, dupla potentia
movebit illud mobile per duplum spatium in aequali tempore."

Et octavo <u>Physicorum</u>, versus finem, vult Aristoteles quod   220
potentia motiva dupla ad aliam moveat idem mobile in medietate
temporis quantum potentia minor in toto tempore; et universaliter
quod potentia motiva maior alia moveat idem mobile quantum
potentia minor in minori tempore proportionaliter secundum con-
versionem proportionis (scilicet quod maiori potentiae debetur   225
tempus minus et minori tempus maius).

Et idem vult Aristoteles primo <u>De caelo et mundo</u>, capitulo de
infinito, ubi loquens de gravibus quae debent descendere per
aequale spatium in eodem medio, sic dicit: "Analogiam," id est
proportionem, "quam gravitates habent et tempora econtrario   230
habebunt; puta si media gravitas in hoc, dupla in medietate eius."

Et tertio <u>De caelo</u> (ubi probat Aristoteles omne corpus motum
recte gravitatem aut levitatem habere) supponit quod gravia inaequalia in virtute pertranseunt spatia eis proportionalia in eodem
medio, in eodem tempore.   235

Idem patet per primam conclusionem <u>De ponderibus</u>, quae sic
dicit: "Inter quaelibet gravia est velocitatis in descendendo et
ponderis eodem ordine sumpta proportio."

Idem per rationem poterit sic ostendi: Si unus motor sit praecise in duplo maioris potentiae quam alius, praecise in duplo   240
plus potest movere idem mobile vel aequaliter duplum mobile.
Nam si sit praecise duplae potentiae, potest praecise duplum
facere (quia si posset plus quam duplum, esset potentiae maioris
quam duplae; et si non posset duplum, sed minus tantum, esset
potentiae minoris quam duplae).   245

Haec pro secunda parte positionis istius; et sic ista positio
quantum ad utramque partem videtur esse fundata.

Ista tamen positio est dupliciter arguenda: primo super insufficientia, secundo super mendacio consequentis.

Est autem insufficiens quia non docet proportionem velocita-   250

And, at the end of Book VII of the Physics, Aristotle wishes it to be understood that, if a given power moves a given mobile through a given distance in a given time, the same power will move half the same mobile through twice the distance in an equal time, and through the same distance in half the time.

Thus much in favor of the first half of the present theory.

In support of the second part of this position, Aristotle holds, in Book IV of the Physics (in the chapter concerning the "void") that, other conditions remaining constant, heavy and light bodies differing in quantity will move through a given distance in the same medium more swiftly and more slowly in accordance with the proportion of the heavy and light bodies to each other.

According to Averroes' exposition, at the close of Book VII of the Physics, Aristotle intends that, if a given power moves a given mobile through a given distance in a given time, double the power will move that mobile through double the distance in an equal time.

At the close of Book VIII of the Physics, Aristotle maintains that a motive power which is double another such power will move the same mobile in half the time required by the lesser power, and that, universally, a motive power greater than another will move the same mobile which the smaller power moves in a time that is less by converse proportion (that is, that less time is required by the larger power and more time by the lesser power).

Moreover, Aristotle intends the same thing in Book I of the De Caelo (in the chapter on the "infinite"), where, speaking of heavy bodies that fall equal distances in the same medium, he writes as follows: "The 'analogy' (that is, the proportion) between the weights will be the contrary of that between the times. For example, if the whole weight in a given time, then double the weight in half that time."

Further, in Book III of the De Caelo, where Aristotle proves every body to possess a rectilinear gravity or levity, he states that heavy bodies unequal in power will traverse, in the same medium and the same time, distances proportional to those powers.

The same is evident from Theorem I of the De Ponderibus, which states the following: "The proportion between the speeds of descent of any given heavy bodies is the same as that between their respective weights."

The theory may also be set forth by the following reasoning: If one mover has exactly twice the power possessed by another, it can move the same mobile exactly twice as much, or move twice the mobile the same amount, for, if it is exactly twice the power, it can accomplish exactly twice as much. If it could accomplish more than twice as much, it would be of more than twice the power; and if it were not capable of twice, but only of less, it would be of less than twice the power.

So much for the second part of this position, and thus we have seen what are the foundations of both parts of the theory.

The theory is, however, refutable on two grounds: first, on that of insufficiency, second, because it yields false consequences.

It is insufficient, because it does not determine the proportion of the

tum in motibus nisi in quibus est idem motor vel aequalis, seu
idem mobile vel aequale. De motibus autem ubi diversantur tam
moventia quam mota, penitus nihil dicit.

Est autem ista positio ex mendacio arguenda, quia aliqua
potentia motiva localiter potest movere aliquod mobile aliqua   255
tarditate, et potest movere dupla tarditate. Ergo (per istam positionem) potest movere duplum mobile. Et potest movere quadrupla tarditate: igitur quadruplum mobile, et sic in infinitum.
Igitur quaelibet potentia motiva localiter esset infinita.

Similiter autem potest argui de quolibet mobili. Nam quodlibet   260
mobile potest moveri aliqua tarditate et dupla et quadrupla et sic
sine statu: igitur ab aliquo motore, et a subduplo, et a subquad-
ruplo et sic sine fine. Igitur quodlibet mobile a quolibet motore
potest moveri.

Nec potest dici quod tarditas motus non potest in infinitum   265
duplari: quia si sic, sit A tarditas mobilis quae duplari non potest.
Volvatur igitur sphera, seu corpus columnare, super axem quiescentem. Tunc in aliqua parte iuxta polum spherae, seu axem corporis columnaris, est tarditas dupla ad A ut est satis notum et
facile demonstrare. Tunc cum ista parte colligetur corda fortis   270
et longa, in cuius extremo alligetur aliquod ponderosum, quod sit B.
Tunc tarditas motus B est dupla ad A tarditatem; et hoc est quod
volumus demonstrare.

Nec potest dicere cavillator quod motus B est motus per accidens, et in potentia tantum, ideo non facit ad propositum, quia   275
iste motus habet motorem in actu et motum seu mobile in actu,
terminos a quo et ad quem in actu, tempus in actu, et spatium
seu locum pertransitum in actu. Igitur est motus in actu.

Nec potest dici quod motor non est in actu sed in potentia quia
est pars spherae, vel corporis columnaris; quia totum movet   280
primo, et pars ex consequenti. Et etiam tunc, si homo traheret
illud ponderosum per cordam cum manu, illud moveret per accidens, quia per partem hominis. Et etiam quia tunc nullus motus
ab extrinseco esset motus per se vel in actu, quia nullum movens
extrinsecum potest per se totum applicari moto, sed secundum   285
partem tantum.

Tertio est ista positio super mendacio arguenda, quoniam experi-
mentum sensibile docet huius positionis contrarium. Videmus
enim quod, uno homine movente aliquod ponderosum (quod potest
vix solus movere motu valde tardo) si alius sibi adiungatur, illi   290
duo movent illud multo plus quam in duplo velocius.

Et patet manifeste de pondere suspenso ad axem circumvolu-
bilem, quod per suum descensum movet insensibiliter et volvit
axem seu rotam motu insensibili (sicut accidit in horologio) ad
quod si suspendatur tantum pondus, totum descendet et circum-   295
volvet axem seu rotam multum plus quam in duplo velocius (ut
sensui sufficienter constat).

speeds of motions except in cases where either the mover or the mobile are constant. Concerning motions in which the moving forces, as
well as the mobilia, are varied, it tells us almost nothing.

The theory is, on the other hand, to be refuted on the ground of falsity, for the reason that a given motive power can move a given mobile
with a given degree of slowness and can also cause a motion of twice
that slowness. According to this theory, therefore, it can move double
the mobile. And, since it can move with four times the slowness, it can
move four times the mobile, and so on ad infinitum. Therefore, any motive power would be of infinite capacity.

A similar argument may be made from the standpoint of the mobile.
For any mobile may be moved with a given degree of slowness, with
twice that degree, four times, and so on without end; and, therefore, by
the given mover, and by half of it, one fourth of it, and so on, without
end. Any mobile could, therefore, be moved by any mover.

Nor is it legitimate to object that slowness of motion cannot be
doubled indefinitely, for, supposing this to be true, let A represent some
slowness of a mobile that cannot be doubled. Now imagine a sphere or
cylinder, revolving about a fixed axis; then, at some point near the pole
of the sphere, or the axis of the cylinder, there is a degree of slowness
double that of A, as is quite clear and easy to demonstrate. Now, at
this point let there be attached a strong, long cord, at whose end is af-
fixed a given weight, B. Then the slowness of the motion of B is twice
that of A, and this is what we wished to demonstrate.

Nor can some quibbler properly claim that the motion of B is acci-
dental motion, merely motion in potentia, and that it really has no rele-
vance to the question; for this motion possesses a mover, a thing moved,
initial and final limits, a time and a space traversed...all in actu. Therefore, the motion is a real one. Nor can it be maintained that the mover
is not in actu, but only in potentia, inasmuch as it is part of the sphere,
or cylinder, and because it is the whole that moves primarily and the
part by consequence. In that case, if a man were to pull that weight by
hand, by means of the cord, it would move accidentally, because by
virtue of a part of the man; it would then follow that no motion, extrinsically caused, could be a "real" motion, (one which is in actu), since
no mover can apply itself wholly to the thing moved, but can only do so
by means of a part.

Thirdly, the present theory is to be refuted on the ground of falsity,
because sense experience teaches us the opposite. We see, indeed,
that if, to a single man who is moving some weight which he can
scarcely manage with a very slow motion, a second man joins himself,
the two together can move it much more than twice as fast. The same
principle is quite manifest in the case of a weight suspended from a
revolving axle, which it moves insensibly during the course of its own
insensible downward movement (as is the case with clocks). If an equal
clock weight is added to the first, the whole descends and the axle, or
wheel, turns much more than twice as rapidly (as is sufficiently evident
to sight).

Consimiliter autem accidit de tarditate (manente eodem moto
et diminuto motore, et etiam econtrario).

Et sic patet ista conclusio negativa: <u>Proportio velocitatum in</u>   300
<u>motibus</u> (manente eodem motore vel aequali) <u>non sequitur propor-</u>
<u>tionem passorum; nec</u> (manente eodem passo vel aequali) <u>sequitur</u>
<u>proportionem motorum</u>.

Pro rationibus autem quae istam positionem fundare videntur,
dicendum quod omnes auctoritates volentes quod (existente eodem 305
motore) proportio velocitatum in motibus sequitur proportionem
passorum, intelligunt quod sequitur proportionem passorum ad
sua agentia.

Et ideo pro prima auctoritate, quarti <u>Physicorum</u>, dicendum
quod Aristoteles intelligit quod quanto est minor proportio aeris   310
(propter maiorem subtilitatem et incorporeitatem) quam aqua, ad
illud quod debet utrumque dividere, tanto illud citius movebitur
per aerem quam per aquam; quoniam quanto proportio aeris ad
aliquid est minor proportione aquae ad illud, tanto proportio illius
ad aerem est maior quam ad aquam; et proportio velocitatum in   315
motibus sequitur proportionem moventium ad res motas (ut pos-
terius ostendetur). Et auctoritas alia allegata similiter est glosanda; et illa primi <u>De caelo et mundo</u> quae dicit: "Ab eodem enim
supponatur in pluri et minori tempore maius et minus pati quaecumque proportionaliter tempori divisa sunt," id est, quorum-   320
cumque proportiones ad illud idem agens, proportionaliter tempori
sunt divisae.

Conclusio autem allegata ex septimo <u>Physicorum</u>, quae dicit,
"si aliqua potentia moveat aliquod mobile per aliquod spatium in
aliquo tempore, eadem potentia movebit medietatem illius per   325
duplum spatium in aequali tempore," intelligit per, "medietatem
mobilis," partem mobilis habentem ad illam potentiam motivam
medietatem proportionis totius mobilis ad eandem. Et hoc bene
patet per Averroem, qui ibi probat conclusionem praedictam hoc
modo: "Cum diviserimus motum," id est, rem motam, "contingit   330
necessario ut proportio potentiae motoris ad motum," id est, rem
motam, "sit dupla illius proportionis." Quod tamen esset falsum
nisi intelligeret modo dicto, quoniam licet aliquod totum habeat
aliquam proportionem ad aliud totum, non sequitur quod habeat
duplam proportionem primae proportionis ad medietatem illius   335
(ut in sequentibus ostendetur). Et per ista auctoritatum sequentium
glosa patet.

Conclusio autem <u>De ponderibus</u> allegata similiter debet intellegi:

Since the situation regarding retardation is closely similar, whether the thing moved be constant and the mover be diminished or the reverse, we arrive at this negative conclusion: <u>With the mover remaining constant, the proportion of the speeds of motions does not vary in accordance with the proportion of resistances, nor, with the resistance remaining constant, does it vary in accordance with the proportion of movers.</u>

As for the reasons which seemed to support this theory, it should be pointed out that all authorities claiming that, with the mover remaining constant, the proportion of the speeds of motions varies in accordance with the proportion of resistances, really mean that the proportion of speeds varies with the proportion of the things affected to the things affecting them.

As a matter of fact, in the case of the first authority cited (that of Book IV of the <u>Physics</u>) it should be realized that what Aristotle means is that, to whatever extent the proportion of air to a given body which moves through it is smaller than that of water to that same body (due to the greater thinness and incorporeality of air), to that extent the body will move faster through air than through water; for to whatever extent the proportion of air to a given body is smaller than the proportion of water to that body, to the same extent is the proportion of the body to air larger than its proportion to water, and, as will later be shown, the proportion of the speeds of motions varies in accordance with the proportion of movers to things moved.

The second authority cited should also be construed in the same sense, together with that passage, from Book I of the <u>De Caelo et Mundo</u>, which reads: "It is held to undergo a greater and less effect, by the action of the same agent, in a longer and shorter time, and any such effects are divided proportionally to the time." In other words, the proportions of any given effects are divided proportionally to the time.

In the case, moreover, of the theorem drawn from Book VII of the <u>Physics</u> (which states that, if a given power moves a given <u>mobile</u> through a given distance in a given time, the same power will move half of it through double the distance in an equal time), Aristotle understands, by "half the <u>mobile</u>," a part of the <u>mobile</u> possessing a proportional relation to the given moving power which is half that of the whole <u>mobile</u> to that power.

This quite clearly appears to be Averroes' interpretation, for, regarding the passage in question, he proves the above-mentioned theorem as follows: "When we divide the motion (or the thing moved), it follows necessarily that the proportion of the power of the mover to the motion (or thing moved) is twice the former proportion. This would, nevertheless, be untrue, unless understood in the sense previously indicated, for, although a given whole may bear a given proportion to some other whole, it does not follow that it bears a proportion to half of the latter whole that is, half the original proportion (as will be shown in what follows)." It is in this sense that the following authorities should be interpreted.

The theorem drawn from the <u>De Ponderibus</u> must be read in the

"Inter quaelibet gravia," et cetera, id est, inter quaelibet gravia
est velocitatis in descendendo et proportionis ponderis ad suam   340
resistentiam eodem ordine sumpta proportio. Et hoc debet intellegi, resistentia existente aequali hinc inde. Auctor tamen non
ponit aliqua principia illam conclusionem probantia.

Potest autem obici contra glosam praedictam quod nullus commentator probat illam conclusionem ad intellectum praedictum,   345
sed ad alium quem habet ista positio: quod nulla est proportio nec
aliquis excessus potentiae motivae ad potentiam resistivam (et
ideo quem verba illius conclusionis praetendunt).

Dicendum quod nullus commentator quem nos vidimus probat
istam conclusionem ad intellectum praedictum, nec aliquem   350
alium. Nam unus commentator capit duo pondera inaequalia et
duas lineas inaequales istorum descensus designantes, et capit
primo tamquam datum ab adversario quod proportio maioris
ponderis ad minus est maior proportione maioris lineae ad minorem. Et ex hoc arguit proportionem minoris ponderis ad maius   355
esse minorem proportione minoris lineae ad maiorem: ex quo
concludit minorem esse proportionem ponderum quam descensuum,
cuius oppositum erat datum. Istud autem non obviat, quoniam primo
erat datum maiorem esse proportionem maioris ponderis ad minus
proportione maioris descensus ad minorem, et huic non repugnat   360
sed sequitur conversim esse proportionem minorem (scilicet
minoris ponderis ad maius) quam minoris descensus seu lineae
ad maiorem.

Alius autem commentator similiter cum primo capit duo pon-
dera inaequalia et eorum descensus inaequales, et apponit minori   365
ponderi aliud pondus ut ex ambobus compositum sit aequale
maiori. Et supponit quod descensus ponderis appositi per se, per
tempus aequale tempori priorum descensuum, appositus minori
descensui, maiori descensui, adaequatur. Et illud non est prius
probatum, nec per se notum, nec sequens, nec est universaliter   370
verum, sed in pluribus casibus est falsum quam verum (ut ex
sequentibus apparebit). Et ex isto supposito concludit quod minor
est proportio maioris ponderis ad illud pondus appositum quam
maioris descensus ad descensum illius ponderis appositi; cuius
contrarium asserit esse datum. Sed non est ita, quia non erat   375
prius datum universaliter: "quorumlibet ponderum inaequalium
esse maiorem proportionem maioris ad minus, proportione suorum
descensuum eodem ordine acceptorum," sed specialiter, "istorum
duorum ponderum prius acceptorum et suorum descensuum." Et
ideo illi non repugnat quod aliquorum aliorum ponderum inaequal-   380
ium sit minor proportio maioris ad minus quam suorum descensuum, eodem ordine acceptorum. Aliquorum enim ponderum
inaequalium est aequalis proportio maioris ad minus et suorum

pondera

same way. "Between whatever heavy bodies, etc. ...," that is, between whatever heavy bodies the proportion of speed of descent and that of the proportion of weight to resistance are taken in the same order. (And with the proviso that the resistance remains equal.)

The author of this work, however, proposes no principle in proof of this theorem, and it may well be objected against the above interpretation, that neither does any commentator prove the theorem in this sense, but rather in another, which the present theory supports (namely, that there is neither any proportion nor excess of motive power over resistive power) and which is, in fact, what the words of this theorem really mean.

The fact is that no commentator whom we have seen either proves this theorem according to our interpretation, or according to any other. One commentator, for example, takes two unequal weights and two unequal lines representing their descents, and then, first taking it as granted by his adversary that the proportion of the larger weight to the smaller is greater than the proportion of the longer line to the shorter, he argues from this that the proportion of the smaller weight to the larger is less than the proportion of the shorter line to the longer. From this he concludes that the proportion of weights is less than that of descents (the opposite of which had been stipulated).

This, however, presents no obstacle, for it was admitted that the proportion between the weights was greater than that between the descents, in the first place, and it not only does not invalidate the theorem, but it follows (conversely) that the proportion of the smaller weight to the larger will be smaller than that of the shorter descent, or line, to the longer.

Another commentator, also taking two unequal weights and their unequal descents, adds to the smaller weight a second, such that the two together are equal to the larger. He now posits that the descent of the added weight, by itself, through a time equal to that of the previous descents, when added to the descent of the lesser weight, is equal to the descent of the larger weight.

This had neither been previously proved, nor is independently known, nor follows logically, nor is universally true. In many cases it is, in fact, false (as will appear from what follows).

From this supposition, at any rate, he concludes that the proportion of the larger weight to the weight that was added is less than that of the descent of the larger weight to the descent of the additional weight (the opposite of what he states to have been given). Yet this is not the case, for it was not previously laid down as universally true that, "of any given unequal weights, the proportion of the larger to the smaller is in the proportion of their descents, taken in the same order," but only specifically that, "of these two weights, which have been chosen, and of their descents." This is, therefore, not incompatible with the thesis that, in the case of certain other weights, the proportion of the larger to the smaller should be less than that of their respective descents; for, in the case of some weights, the proportion of the larger to the smaller is equal to that of their respective descents, in other

descensuum, eodem ordine acceptorum, aliquorum autem maior,
et aliquorum minor (ut in sequentibus erit lucide demonstratum).   385

Ad rationem quae auctoritatibus plus movet, dicendum quod
prima consequentia non valet. Et principia causalis adducta ad
probationem illius est vera, quia semper dupla potentia minoris
potentiae potest movere duplum mobile mobili minoris potentiae
per aequale spatium in aequali tempore. Sed ex hoc non sequitur   390
quod posset movere idem mobile in duplo velocius, sed bene sequitur quod posset movere illud mobile tanta velocitate maiori
quanta est duplae difficultatis ad velocitatem priorem, et duplam
virtutem requirit. Et illa velocitas aliquando erit praecise dupla
velocitatis prioris, aliquando autem maior quam dupla, quandoque 395
vero minor (ut ex sequentibus erit clarum).

QUARTA PARS CAPITULI SECUNDI

Quarta vero opinio ponit quod nulla est proportio nec aliquis
excessus potentiae motivae ad potentiam resistivam, et ideo proportio velocitatum in motibus non sequitur aliquam proportionem
nec excessum potentiae motivae ad potentiam mobilis, sed quod-   400
dam dominium et habitudinem naturalem motoris ad motum.

Et haec positio videtur fundari super auctoritatem Averrois,
octavo Physicorum, commento 79, ubi in solutione eiusdem conclusionis dicit quod: "potentia non corporea non dicitur finita nec
infinita, quia finitum et infinitum tantum de corporibus dicuntur,   405
nec etiam una potentia incorporea potest dici maior alia." Maius
enim et minus solius est quantitatis. Nec etiam potentiae separ-
atae a corpore sunt proportionales, nec habent proportionem,
quoniam proportio solius est magnitudinis ad magnitudinem. Ex
istis videtur sequi quod nulla potentia motiva est finita vel infinita 410
nec maior vel minor, nec aliquo modo proportionalis potentiae rei
motae, quia omnis potentia motiva non est corpus, sed forma ex-
tensa in corpore vel a corpore separata.

Et haec positio, una cum dicto Averrois, per definitiones proportionis poterunt confirmari.   415

Primo: Proportio est comparatio rerum eiusdem generis (ut
patet per definitionem proportionis primo capitulo assignatam).
Sed potentia activa et passiva non sunt eiusdem generis, ut videtur.

Praeterea, si potentia activa et passiva haberent proportionem
adinvicem, tunc essent comparabiles. Igitur essent eiusdem spe-   420
ciei specialissimae: Igitur haberent subjectum vel substantiam
eiusdem speciei specialissimae. Consequens est falsum, quia
potentia dividitur per activum et passivum, ut genus per differentias repugnantes. Et consequentia patet per Aristotelem septimo

cases it is greater, and in yet other cases less (as will be clearly demonstrated, later on).

As for the argument which is most convincing to writers on this subject, it should be replied that, although the causal principle adduced in its proof is true, the first consequence drawn from it does not hold. Fundamentally, a power which is double another power can move a mobile which is twice that moved by the lesser power through an equal distance and time. Instead of it following from this that the greater power can move the lesser <u>mobile</u> twice as fast, it rather follows that the greater power can move the lesser <u>mobile</u> at a speed which is as much greater as that expressed by the proportion of double the resistance to the former speed, and that it requires twice the power to do it. That speed will, in some cases, be exactly double the former speed, in some cases more than double, and in some cases less than double (as will be clear from later portions of this work).

CHAPTER TWO, PART FOUR
[THEORY IV]

A fourth theory declares there to be <u>neither any proportion nor any relation of excess between motive and resistive powers.</u> It holds that, instead of there being some proportion or excess of motive power over thing moved, motions take place in accordance with some sort of "natural dominance" of mover over moved.

This contention may be seen as founded on the authority of Averroes, who (Comment 79, <u>Physics VIII</u>) in solution of the same problem, says that an incorporeal power is neither to be called finite nor infinite, because only bodies may be referred to in this way. Furthermore, one incorporeal power may not be referred to as greater than another, since the terms, greater and less, may be applied only to quantities. Moreover, powers separate from body can neither be proportionals nor possess proportional relations, since a proportion can only be between one magnitude and another.

From the above it is seen to follow that no motive power can be either finite or infinite, greater or lesser, or in any way proportional to the power of the thing it moves, because no motive power is a body, but is rather a form (either extensive within the body or separate from it).

This theory, together with Averroes' opinion, may be further confirmed by the definition of proportion, for a proportion is a comparison of two things of the same kind (as is evident on the basis of the definition of proportion set forth in Chapter I). It is obvious, however, that active and passive powers are not of the same kind.

Furthermore, if active and passive powers were to bear a proportion to each other, they would then be comparables. They would, therefore, be of exactly the same species and would consequently, have a subject or substance of exactly the same species. This consequence is false, because powers are divided into active and passive, as is a genus, by incompatible differences. That it nevertheless follows is shown by Aristotle, at the end of Book VII of the <u>Physics</u>, where he expresses

Physicorum, versus finem, ubi vult quod omnia quae debent ad   425
invicem comparari, tam subiectum sive substantia comparationis,
quam illud seu illa in quo vel in quibus est comparatio, erunt
eiusdem speciei individualis et differentiam nullam habentes.

Praeterea, si potentiae motivae esset aliqua proportio ad potentiam rei motae, illa esset proportio inaequalitatis maioris quia   430
deberet excedere potentiam rei motae. Et cum omne excedens aliud
dividitur in excellentiam et in illud quod excellitur (ut patet quarto
Physicorum, capitulo de vacuo) sequitur quod quaelibet potentia
motiva posset dividi isto modo. Quod falsum est, quia omnes potentiae motivae incorporeae sunt indivisibiles simpliciter, et aliqua   435
potentia corporea est minor secundum extensionem quam potentia
rei motae. Nec potest dici quod Aristoteles loquatur ibi tantum de
excellentia proprie (quae tantum in quantitatibus reperitur) quia
loquitur de excessu subtilitatis ad subtilitatem.

Ad idem, primo Rhetoricae Aristotelis, capitulo septimo (ubi   440
determinat de maiori bono et magis conferente) sic scribitur:
"Sit itaque excellens quidem tantum et amplius, excessum autem
quod inexistit." Non igitur dictum Aristotelis tantum de excellente
proprie est verum.

Ista autem positio poterit reprobari, quia si inter potentias non   445
esset proportio (eo quod non sunt quantitates) eadem ratione nec
inter voces. Et tunc totius musicae modulatio deperiret. Nam
epogdous seu tonus in sesquioctava proportione consistit: diatessaron autem in sesquitertia: diapente in sesquialtera: diapason
(quae ex diatessaron et diapente componitur) in duplo; diapason   450
cum diapente in tripla: et bis diapason in quadrupla proportione
fundatur (ut ex diversis locis Musicae satis patet).

Praeterea, Averroes, super septimum Physicorum, commento
36 et commento 38, probat quasdam conclusiones de proportione
velocitatum in motibus per quasdam geometricas conclusiones (ut   455
in tertio argumento contra primam opinionem apparet). Et primo
De caelo et mundo, commento 65, probat istam conclusionem in
textu: "Nullum infinitum potest movere finitum" (capiendo ab adversario quod infinitum posset movere finitum in tempore finito,
et quod agens finitum potest eodem tempore movere partem illius   460
passi finiti). Et tunc capit aliquod movens finitum, quod se habet
ad primum movens finitum acceptum sicut totum passum finitum
ad istam partem: et tunc arguit permutatim (scilicet, per duodecimam quinti Elementorum Euclidis) quod sic se habet maius
movens finitum ad totum passum sicut minus movens finitum ad   465
istam partem. Ex quo concludit maius movens finitum movere
illud passum totum in aequali tempore quo minus movens finitum
movet istam partem, et quo agens infinitum etiam movet illud
totum.

the opinion that all things which are to be compared must be of the same individual species and entirely without difference with respect to the subject or substance of comparison, as well as to that regard or those regards in which the comparison is made.

Further, if there were some proportion of a motive power to the thing it moves, it would have to be one of greater inequality, since it would have to exceed the power of the thing moved. And since everything which exceeds something else is divisible into what exceeds and what is exceeded (as appears from Book IV of the Physics, in the chapter on the "void") it follows that any motive power may be so divided. This is false, for all incorporeal motive powers are fundamentally indivisible, and an embodied motive power is smaller in extension than the power of the thing moved.

Nor can it be claimed that Aristotle is here speaking of excesses only in the strictest sense (the sense in which they are found among quantities), for he is actually referring to the excess of rarity of one medium over another. To the same effect, in Book I, Chapter 7 of Aristotle's Rhetoric, where relative good and relative utility are under discussion, there appears the following: "So let the thing that surpasses be as much as and more than the exceeded thing contained within it." Aristotle's dictum is, therefore, not true merely of the strict usage of "excellence."

This theory is, however, capable of disproof, for if there were no proportion between powers, for the reason that they are not quantities of the same kind, neither could there be such a proportion between musical pitches, and the entire science of harmonics would collapse, accordingly. For the epogdoös or "tone" is constituted in the proportion of nine to eight, the diatessaron in the proportion of four to three, the diapente in the proportion of three to two, the diapason (composed of diatessaron and diapente) in the proportion of two to one, the diapason and diapente combined in the proportion of three to one, and the double diapason in the proportion of four to one. This is sufficiently evident from various passages of the Music.

Furthermore, Averroes, in Comments 36 and 38 on Book VII of the Physics, proves certain theorems concerning the proportion of the speeds of motions by means of geometric theorems, as has already appeared in the third argument against Theory I. In Comment 65 on Book I of the De caelo, he also proves this theorem: It being granted that the infinite can move the finite in a finite time and that a finite agent can, in the same time, move part of this finite resistance, no infinite can move a finite. What he does is take a second finite mover which bears the same relation to the former as the whole finite resistance bears to this part. He then argues permutatively, from Definition xii of Book V of Euclid's Elements, that the proportion of the larger finite mover to the whole resistance is equal to that of the lesser mover to the part. And from this he concludes that the larger finite mover moves the whole resistance in a time equal to that in which the lesser finite mover moves the part and also equal to that in which an infinite mover moves the whole resistance.

Praeterea, secundum istam positionem et secundum veritatem,   470
potentia motiva dominatur super potentiam rei motae. Et secundum
Averroem, in multis locis, potentia motiva excedit potentiam rei
motae, et movens est maioris potentiae quam res mota. Igitur sicut
dominatur et excedit et est maioris potentiae, sic oportet quod hoc
sit secundum aliquam proportionem proprie communiterve accept- 475
am. Aristoteles etiam et Averroes supponunt, multis locis, aliquam esse proportionem potentiae motoris ad potentiam rei motae.

Et sic patet haec affirmativa conclusio: Cuiuslibet potentiae
motivae ad potentiam resistivam rei motae aliqua proportio reperitur.   480

Primae autem rationes pro opinione adductae faciliter solvun-
tur per definitionem proportionis primo capitulo praelibatam. Nam
inter potentiam motivam et potentiam resistivam proportio non
proprie dicta, sed communiter reperitur.

Alia autem ratio de comparatione solvitur per distinctionem   485
comparationis consimilem. Auctoritas autem allegata intelligitur
de comparatione propriissime et non communiter dicta. Notum
enim est quod in genere sit comparatio (ut virtuosior, et scientior
et similibus) et in genere generalissimo. Nam forma est magis
substantia quam materia, vel compositum ex ambobus; et etiam   490
in transcendente omne genus, quoniam substantia est magis ens
quam accidens.

Pro ultima ratione dicendum verum esse potentiae motivae ad
potentiam rei motae aliquam proportionem et excessum, communiter loquendo, reperiri. Et ad auctoritatem dicentem quod omne   495
excellens dividitur in excellentiam et in illud quod excellitur,
dicendum quod sicut excellens est duplex, ita et dividi in excellentiam et in illud quod excellitur est duplex (scilicet communiter et
proprie). Omne igitur excellens proprie dividitur proprie isto
modo.   500

Excellens vero communiter sic partitur. Omne enim excellens
communiter (quantum est de ratione excellentis) potest remitti
seu minorari ad similitudinem seu aequalitatem illius quod excellitur. Et sic potest capi tota latitudo qua excellit et similitudo seu
aequalitas quae in excellente virtualiter et in potentia continetur. 505

Vel sic: Omne excellens aliud, communiter dividitur in excellentiam et in illud quod excellitur (verum est non in se, sed in comparatione ad aliud extrinsecum, puta actionem vel passionem seu
resistentiam). Et sic potentiae moventis et moti et resistentiae
cuiuslibet possunt omnibus modis secundum excedens et excess-   510
um adinvicem comparari. Et ideo si capiatur potentia motiva
aequalis potentiae resistivae, eadem potentia motiva est dupla
medietatis istius potentiae resistivae (non quia duplum potest
movere, sed quia duplum istius est praecise tantae virtutis in

Further, according to the present theory and (as a matter of fact) in reality, the power of the mover "dominates" that of the thing moved. In many passages Averroes says that the power of the mover exceeds that of the thing moved, and that the mover is of greater power than the thing moved. If, therefore, it "dominates" and exceeds and is of greater power, this must necessarily take place according to some proportion, whether strictly or generally understood, and both Aristotle and Averroes, in many passages, suppose there to be some proportion of the power of the mover to that of the thing moved.

We thus arrive at this affirmative conclusion: <u>A proportion is found to exist between any motive power and the resistive power of the thing it moves</u>.

The first reasons which were brought forward in favor of the present theory are easily countered by means of the definition of proportion already given in Chapter I, for the proportion found to exist between motive and resistive power is not a strict, but only a general one.

The next argument concerning comparison is overthrown by a similar distinction in the meaning of the word, "comparison." The authority which was cited is to be understood as speaking of strict rather than general comparison. It is to be noted, indeed, that comparison is made: (1) within a genus (as, for example, indicated by the terms: "more virtuous," "wiser," etc.), (2) within the most general genus (for example, "form is substance rather than matter or a compound of the two"), and (3) also in transcendence of every genus (for example, "substance is being rather than accident").

As for the final argument, it is to be replied that it is true that there is, in the general sense, a proportion of excess between motive and resistive power. To the authority cited as saying that everything that exceeds is divided into what exceeds and what is exceeded, it must be replied that, just as "what exceeds" may be taken in two senses, so also "to be divided into what exceeds and what is exceeded" may be taken in two senses (i.e., generally and strictly). Everything that exceeds is, therefore, strictly divisible in this manner.

In the general sense, on the other hand, what exceeds may be divided as follows: In a general sense everything that exceeds may be reduced or lessened until equal to what was exceeded; and thus may be understood the entire latitude whereby it exceeds and likewise the similarity or equality which is contained virtually and potentially in the thing that exceeds.

Or it may be carried out thus: Everything exceeding something else is divided, in the general sense, into excess and what is exceeded, not, of course, in itself, but in comparison to something else outside itself (for example, action, and passion or resistance). In this sense, the powers of mover, moved and resistance can be compared to each other in every way in terms of excess and what exceeds. And if one were to take the example of a motive power equal to a resistive power, that motive power is twice half of the resistive power, not because it can produce twice the motion, but because twice the halved resistance has precisely the power of resistance that the motive power has of moving.

resistendo sicut ista potentia motiva in movendo). Et de omni   515
alia proportione motoris ad motum proportionaliter est ponendum.
　　Haec igitur opinio, una cum prioribus, erronea dicetur.

CAPITULUM TERTIUM

　　His igitur ignorantiae nebulis demonstrationum flatibus effuga-   1
tis, superest ut lumen scientiae resplendeat veritatis. Scientia
autem veritatis ponit quintam opinionem, dicentem quod proportio
velocitatum in motibus sequitur proportionem potentiae motoris
ad potentiam rei motae.   5
　　Et hoc est quod vult Averroes, super quarto <u>Physicorum</u>, commento 71, sic dicens: "Universaliter manifestum est quod causa
diversitatis et aequalitatis motuum est aequalitas et diversitas
proportionis motoris ad rem motam. Cum igitur fuerint duo motores et duo mota, et proportio alterius motoris ad alterum motum   10
fuerit sicut proportio reliqui motoris ad reliquum motum, tunc
duo motus erunt aequales in velocitate; et cum diversatur proportio, diversabitur motus secundum istam proportionem."
　　Et infra, in eodem: "Diversitas motuum in velocitate et tarditate est secundum hanc proportionem quae est inter duas poten-   15
tias" (scilicet motivas et resistivas).

　　Et secundo <u>De caelo</u>, commento 36, sic dicit: "Velocitas enim
et tarditas non fit nisi secundum proportionem potentiae motoris
ad potentiam rei motae; quanto igitur fuerit proportio maior, tanto
magis motus erit velocior; et quanto proportio minor, tanto motus   20
erit tardior."
　　Et septimo <u>Physicorum</u>, commento 35, ex duplicatione proportionis potentiae motoris ad motum, arguit duplicationem velocitatis
in motu, sic dicens: "Cum diviserimus motum contingit necessario
ut proportio potentiae motoris ad motum sit dupla istius propor-   25
tionis, et sic velocitas dupla ad istam velocitatem."
　　Et post, commento ultimo, dicit: "Haec duo," scilicet velocitas

alterationis et quantitas temporis, "sequuntur proportionem inter
alterans et alteratum. Si igitur proportio fuerit magna, velocitas
erit magna et tempus breve, et econtrario."   30
　　Ad idem Aristoteles et Averroes (ut patet tertio argumento
contra primam opinionem) volunt multis locis quod aequalitatem
proportionis motoris ad motum sequitur aequalis velocitas motuum.
Aequalitas igitur proportionis motorum ad mota est causa, qua
primo posita, ponitur primo aequalis velocitas motuum, et qua   35
primo remota, primo removetur. Ergo aequalitas proportionis
motorum ad mota est prima et praecisa causa aequalitatis veloci-

Concerning every other proportion of mover to moved this is proportionally true.

This theory, therefore, together with the former ones, is pronounced false.

CHAPTER THREE

Now that these fogs of ignorance, these winds of demonstration, have been put to flight, it remains for the light of knowledge and of truth to shine forth. For true knowledge proposes a fifth theory which states that the proportion of the speeds of motions varies in accordance with the proportion of the power of the mover to the power of the thing moved.

This is what Averroes intends when he says, in Comment 71 on Book IV of the Physics: "It is manifest that, universally, the cause of the diversity and equality of motion is the equality and diversity of the proportion of mover to thing moved. If, therefore, there are two movers and two things moved, and the proportions between these movers and the things which they respectively move are equal, then the two motions are of equal speed. If the proportion is varied, the motion is also varied in that proportion."

Further on in the same comment, he also says: "The difference between motions with respect to slowness and fastness varies in accordance with the proportion between the two powers (namely, motive and resistive)."

In Comment 36, on Book II of the De caelo, he says: "Fastness and slowness do not occur otherwise than in accordance with the proportion of the power of the mover to that of the thing moved. By however much, therefore, the proportion is greater, by so much will the motion be faster; and by however much the proportion is less, by so much will the motion be slower."

In Comment 35, on Book VII of the Physics, from a doubling of the proportion of mover to moved he argues a doubling of the speed of the motion, as follows: "If we divide the mobile in two, it necessarily comes about that the proportion of the power of the mover to the thing moved becomes double the former proportion, and thus the speed will be twice what it was before."

Further on, in the final comment, he remarks that: "These two (that is, the speed of alteration and the quantity of time) vary in accordance with the proportion between that which causes the alteration and that which undergoes it. If, therefore, the proportion is great, the speed will be great and the time short, and conversely."

Concerning this same problem, both Aristotle and Averroes (as is evident in the third argument against Theory I) express, in many passages, the opinion that, from an equality of proportion between mover and moved, there follows equality of speed. Equality of the proportion of movers to mobilia is, therefore, the causal condition which, when fulfilled, posits an equal speed of motions and which, when not fulfilled,

tatem in motibus; igitur ad variationem istius causae primo sequitur variatio proportionis in motibus.

Praeterea, non videtur aliqua positio qua potest rationabiliter   40
salvari proportio velocitatum in motibus nisi aliqua iam dictarum.
Sed quattuor primae sunt destructae; tantum igitur remanet quinta
vera.

Sic igitur patet ista conclusio: Proportio velocitatum in motibus
sequitur proportionem potentiarum moventium ad potentias resis-   45
tivas, et etiam econtrario. Vel sic sub aliis verbis, eadem sententia
remanente: Proportiones potentiarum moventium ad potentias resistivas, et velocitates in motibus, eodem ordine proportionales
existunt, et similiter econtrario. Et hoc de geometrica proportionalitate intelligas.   50

Secunda conclusio: Si potentiae moventis ad potentiam sui moti
sit dupla proportio, potentia motiva geminata movebit idem motum
praecise in duplo velocius.

Hanc ostensive demonstres. Sit enim A potentia motiva dupla
ipsius B potentiae resistivae, et sit C potentia motiva dupla   55
ipsius A. Tunc (per primam conclusionem primi capituli) proportio
C ad B est praecise dupla ad proportionem A ad B. Igitur (per
proximam) C movebit B praecise in duplo velocius quam A moveat
B. Et hoc est propositum.

Tertia conclusio: Si potentiae moventis ad potentiam sui moti   60
sit dupla proportio, eadem potentia movebit medietatem eiusdem
moti velocitate praecise duplata. Hanc, ut proximam, rationaliter
demonstrabis.

Quarta conclusio: Si potentiae moventis ad potentiam sui moti
sit maior quam dupla proportio, potentia motiva geminata motus   65
eiusdem duplam velocitatem nequaquam attinget. Hoc per quartam
primi capituli et per primam tertii concluditur ostensive.

Quinta conclusio: Si potentiae moventis ad potentiam sui moti
sit maior quam dupla proportio, eadem potentia movente medietatem eiusdem moti, velocitas motus nullatenus fiet dupla. Hoc   70
per tertiam primi et primam tertii concludetur ostensive.

Sexta conclusio: Si potentiae moventis ad potentiam sui moti
sit minor quam dupla proportio, dupla potentia movente idem
motum, motus ultra duplum velocitatem excrescet. Istam per sextam primi et primam tertii ostensione faciliter patebit.   75

Septima conclusio: Si fuerit potentiae moventis ad potentiam
sui moti minor quam dupla proportio, eadem potentia movente
medietatem eiusdem moti, motus ultra duplam velocitatem transibit. Hoc per quintam primi et primam tertii ostensive patebit.

makes impossible an equality of speeds. Equality of the proportion of movers to <u>mobilia</u> is, thus, the primary and precise cause of equality of the speeds of motions, and to the variation of this cause there directly corresponds the variation of proportion between different motions.

Furthermore, there does not seem to be any theory whereby the proportion of the speeds of motions may be rationally defended, unless it is one of those already mentioned. Since, however, the first four have been discredited, therefore the fifth must be the true one.

We, therefore, arrive at the following theorem:

Theorem I. <u>The proportion of the speeds of motions varies in accordance with the proportion of motive to resistive forces, and conversely.</u> Or, to put it in another way, which means the same thing: <u>The proportion of the proportions of motive to resistive powers is equal to the proportion of their respective speeds of motion, and conversely.</u> This is to be understood in the sense of geometric proportionality.

Theorem II. <u>If the proportion of the power of the mover to that of its mobile is that of two to one, double the motive power will move the same mobile exactly twice as fast.</u> This may be demonstrated by means of an example. Let A be a motive power that is twice B (its resistance), and let C be a motive power that is twice A. Then, (by Theorem I, Chapter I) the proportion of C to B is exactly double that of A to B. Therefore, (by the immediately preceding theorem) C will move B exactly twice as fast as A does. This is what was to be proved.

Theorem III. <u>If the proportion of the power of the mover to that of its mobile is two to one, the same power will move half the mobile with exactly twice the speed.</u> This you may demonstrate by an argument like that used for Theorem II.

Theorem IV. <u>If the proportion of the power of the mover to that of its mobile is greater than two to one, when the motive power is doubled the motion will never attain twice the speed.</u> This may be demonstrated by means of Theorem IV, Chapter I; and Theorem I, Chapter III.

Theorem V. <u>If the proportion of the power of the mover to that of its mobile is less than two to one, when the resistance of the mobile is halved the motion will never attain twice the speed.</u> This may be demonstrated by means of Theorem III, Chapter I and Theorem I, Chapter III.

Theorem VI. <u>If the proportion of the power of the mover to that of its mobile is less than two to one, when the power moving this mobile is doubled it will increase the speed to more than twice what it was.</u> This is likewise easily demonstrable, from Theorem VI, Chapter I and Theorem I, Chapter III.

Theorem VII. <u>If the proportion of the power of the mover to that of its mobile is less than two to one, when the same mover moves half that mobile the speed of the motion will be more than doubled.</u> This may be demonstrated clearly, from Theorem V, Chapter I and Theorem I, Chapter III.

Ex nulla proportione aequalitatis vel minoris inaequalitatis   80
motoris ad motum sequitur ullus motus.

Hanc per primam tertii, et septimam et octavam primi, demonstrative concludes (adiuncta hac suppositione, per se nota: "Omnis
motus eiusdem speciei secundum velox vel tardum possunt adinvicem comparari."). -   85

Omnis motus ex proportione maioris inaequalitatis producitur,
et ex omni proportione maioris inaequalitatis fieri potest motus.

Prima pars huius per primam et octavam tertii (suppositione
proxima coadiuncta) patebit. Secunda pars huius apparet eo quod
omnis excessus motoris ad motum sufficit producendum (ut erit   90
alibi demonstratum).

Quocumque motu dato, potest motus in duplo velocior et motus
in duplo tardior inveniri.

Hoc per primam tertii et secundam partem nonae eiusdem concluditur (auxiliante ista suppositione, per se nota: "Proportio   95
maioris inaequalitatis motoris ad motum in additione et diminu-
tione duplari poterit in infinitum.").

Quantumcumque gravius alio in eodem medio tardius et velocius
illo et aequali velocitate potest descendere.

Sit enim A grave mixtum ex gravi et levi quantumlibet habens   100
pondus, et B grave simplex ita parvi ponderis ut desideras. Et
subtilietur aliquod medium donec B habeat ad illud aequalem proportionem proportioni gravitatis A ad levitatem in eo, vel maiorem;
et ponantur ambo in illo medio. Tunc gravitas A habet minorem
proportionem ad totam suam resistentiam intrinsecam et extrin-   105
secam quam B habeat ad suam resistentiam. Igitur (per primam
tertii) A tardius movetur quam B.

Iterum econtra condensetur medium donec proportio B ad illud
sit minor proportione gravitatis A ad totam suam resistentiam
intrinsecam et extrinsecam. Tunc (per primam huius) A movetur   110
velocius quam B.

Tertio, adaptetur sic medium quod proportio B ad illud sit
aequalis proportioni gravitatis A ad suam resistentiam intrinsecam et extrinsecam. Tunc (per primam huius) A et B aequevelociter movebuntur.   115

Vel sic: A haberet ex se in vacuo motum certae velocitatis, quae
sit C. Et subtilietur aliquod medium donec B descendat in illo velocitate C, vel maiori. Tunc A, positum in eodem medio, tardius B
descendet. Rursus condensetur medium sicut oportet, et reliqua
duo provenient.   120

Unde manifestum est quod cuiuslibet gravis simplicis quaelibet
velocitas et tarditas, et cuiuslibet gravis mixti quaelibet tarditas,
per subtiliationem et condensationem medii, in infinitum poterit
duplicari; necnon quod cuiuslibet gravis mixti quaelibet velocitas
per subtiliationem medii geminari non potest. (Istud correlarium   125
ex praedictis sufficienter constabit.)

Theorem VIII. <u>No motion follows from either a proportion of equality</u> <u>of one of lesser inequality, between mover and moved</u>. With the addition of the following axiom, independently known:

Axiom 1. <u>All motions of the same species may be compared to each</u> <u>other with regard to slowness and fastness</u>; this theorem may be proved by means of Theorems VII and VIII of Chapter I and Theorem I, Chapter III.

Theorem IX. <u>Every motion is produced by a proportion of a greater</u> <u>inequality, and from every proportion of greater inequality a motion</u> <u>may arise</u>. The first part of this may be proved by Theorems I and VIII of Chapter III and the axiom just given. The second part is demonstrable from the fact that every excess of mover over moved suffices to produce motion, as will be shown elsewhere.

Theorem X. <u>Given any motion, one twice as fast and one twice as</u> <u>slow can be determined</u>. This may be proved by Theorem I and Theorem IX (Part 2) of Chapter III, with the help of the following axiom, independently known:

Axiom 2. <u>A proportion of greater inequality of mover to moved may</u> <u>be halved or doubled indefinitely.</u>

Theorem XI. <u>An object may fall in the same medium both faster,</u> <u>slower, and equally with some other object that is lighter than itself.</u>

Let, for example, A represent a heavy mixed body composed of heavy and light and having a certain weight, and let B represent some pure heavy body, as small as you please. Now let a given medium be rarified to the point at which B bears to it a proportion equal to, or greater than, that of the heaviness to the lightness in A. Then let both bodies be placed in the same medium. The heaviness of A will now be in a lesser proportion to its total intrinsic and extrinsic resistance than B is to its resistance. Therefore, by Theorem I, Chapter III, A moves more slowly than B.

Conversely, let the medium be condensed to the point at which the proportion of B to it is less than the proportion of the heaviness of A to its entire intrinsic and extrinsic resistance. Then, by Theorem I of this chapter, A moves faster than B.

Thirdly, let the medium be so determined that the proportion of B to it is equal to the proportion of the heaviness of A to its entire intrinsic and extrinsic resistance. Then, by Theorem I of the present chapter, A and B will move at equal speeds.

Alternately, let A be supposed to have a determinate speed, C, in a vacuum, and let some medium be rarified until B falls in it with speed C or faster; then A, placed in the same medium, will fall more slowly than B. Conversely, let the medium now be condensed as required, and the remaining two consequences will follow.

Corollary 1. It is manifest, from the foregoing, that <u>the fastness and</u> <u>the slowness of any pure body and the slowness of any mixed body</u> <u>may be doubled indefinitely, but that the fastness of a mixed body may</u> <u>not be so doubled by rarefaction of the medium</u>. This corollary is sufficiently well established on the basis of what has been said above.

Omnia mixta compositionis consimilis aequali velocitate in
vacuo movebuntur. Nam in omnibus talibus motores sunt proportionales suis resistentiis. Igitur (per primam huius) omnia talia
aequevelociter movebuntur.   130

Ex hoc quoque scies quod, si duo gravia mixta inaequalia, compositionis consimilis, in aequilibri in vacuo suspendantur, gravius
declinabit. Sint enim A et B duo talia gravia, A maius, B vero
minus, et sit C gravitas A, D vero levitas similiter eiusdem. E
autem sit gravitas B, F vero levitas sit eiusdem. Tunc C, D, E, F 135
sunt quattuor proportionalia, et C est maximum, F vero minimum.
Igitur (per octavam suppositionem primi huius) C et F pariter congregata excedunt D et E pariter adiuncta. Et C et F nituntur elevare B, et tantum D et E resistunt. Igitur (per secundam partem
nonae conclusionis huius) B ascendet, A vero descendet.   140

seems to imply that when two forces act together they are added.
If multiply forces together then would get equals + balance.

SECUNDA PARS CAPITULI TERTII

Nunc, in secunda parte huius capituli, superest quaedam praedictorum disputatione rimari.

Primo, contra istam positionem et contra huius primam conclusionem sunt omnia ista quae pro alia opinionum praedictarum
sunt adducta; de quibus est hic silendum, quia de eis prius suf-   145
ficienter est dictum.

Secundo, ex ista positione videntur sequi tria inconvenientia:
videlicet, quod ex aequali proportione motorum ad mobilia quandoque sequitur inaequalitas velocitatum in motibus, et quod ex
minori proportione unius motoris ad suum mobile quam alterius   150
ad suum quandoque sequitur aequalis velocitas in motibus, et
maior quandoque.

Sint enim A et B duae terrae purae inaequales, A maior, B minor;
et sint C et D duo aeres inaequales uniformes proportionales A
et B, et C maior, D minor. Et A, per suum descensum, dividit C,   155
B vero D. Vel ergo istae divisiones sunt aequales secundum tempus, vel non. Si sic, igitur A dividit et movetur velocius B; pertransit enim maius spatium in aequali tempore. Et sic patet
primum. Iterum, manente proportione B ad D, minoretur proportio A ad C donec movetur aequevelociter cum B: et tunc patet   160
secundum. Rursus, maioretur etiam econtra modicum proportio
A ad C, non tamen ad aequalitatem proportionis B ad D. Tunc A
dividit et movetur velocius quam in secundo casu. Igitur velocius
quam B; et sic sequitur tertium.

Ideo dicendum quod, stante primo casu, illae divisiones totales   165
non sunt aequales secundum tempus, sed A et B (propter aequali-

Theorem XII. <u>All mixed bodies of similar composition will move at equal speeds in a vacuum</u>. In all such cases the moving powers bear the same proportion to their resistances. Therefore, by Theorem I of this chapter, all such bodies move at the same speed. From this you must also understand that:

Corollary 2: <u>If two heavy mixed bodies of unequal weight, but similar composition, were balanced on a scale within a vacuum, the heavier would descend.</u>

Let A and B represent two such heavy bodies, A greater and B less; let C and D represent the heaviness and lightness of A, respectively, and let E and F represent the heaviness and lightness of B, respectively. Then C, D, E and F are four proportionals, C being the greatest and F the smallest. Therefore (by Theorem VIII, Chapter I) C and F, combined, exceed D and E, combined. Since C and F tend to raise B and only D and E resist, therefore (by Part ii of Theorem IX of the present chapter) B ascends and A descends.

CHAPTER THREE, PART TWO

Now, in the second half of this chapter, it remains to explore further, by disputation, some of the things which have just been set forth.

In the first place, against the present theory, and especially against Theorem I, may be alleged everything that was cited in favor of the preceding theories. Since enough has already been said about these objections, we will omit further discussion of them here.

Secondly, it may be objected that three inconsistencies follow from the present theory: namely, that (1) from equal proportions of movers to <u>mobilia</u> there may, on occasion, result unequal speeds, that (2) when the proportion of one mover to its <u>mobile</u> is less than that of another mover to its <u>mobile</u>, the speeds may, on occasion, be equal, and that (3) this may also happen when the proportion is greater.

For example, let A and B represent two unequal quantities of pure earth, A being the larger and B the smaller, and let C and D represent two unequal but uniform quantities of air equally proportional to A and B, C being the greater and D the lesser. In its fall A divides C and B divides D.

Now, these descents either occupy equal times, or they do not. If they do, then A falls faster than B, since it traverses a greater distance in an equal time. This is the first inconsistency.

On the other hand, with the proportion of B to D remaining constant, let the proportion of A to C be diminished until A moves at the same speed as B. Here is the second inconsistency.

In the other direction, let the proportion of A to C be increased a little, but not enough to become equal to the proportion of B to D. Now A falls faster than in the second case, and therefore faster than B. Here is the third inconsistency.

It should be pointed out in reply that while, in the first case, the total descents are not accomplished in equal times, A and B do nevertheless

tatem proportionum ad sua mobilia) moventur aequevelociter. Et
ideo dum B dividit totum D, A dividit de C partem aequalem D.

Contra: Sit ista pars E; tunc A movetur aequevelociter per E
sicut B per D. Ergo (per secundam partem primae huius) proportio 170
A ad E est aequalis proportioni B ad D; igitur est aequalis proportioni A ad C, quia istae sunt aequales per casum. Quod falsum est;
quia C est maius E, ergo (per quintam suppositionem huius primi)
quodcumque trium ad illa comparatum ad E habet proportionem
maiorem, ad C vero minorem.   175

Ad idem, primo De caelo et mundo, capitulo de infinito, ubi
probantur istae duae conclusiones: "Infinitum non potest moveri
a finito" et "Infinitum non potest movere finitum," supponit textus
quod, si agentia fuerint proportionalia suis passis, movebunt illa
per totum consimili motu in aequali tempore. Et de motu altera-   180
tionis loquitur ibi textus. Et Averroes ibidem, commento 63, dicit
expresse quod si agentia fuerint proportionalia suis passis (aequali
proportione aut alia) actiones istorum agentium et passa eis cor-
respondentia essent proportionales in temporibus aequalibus.
Igitur (eadem ratione in proposito) cum A et B sint agentia pro-   185
portionalia suis passis, movebunt illa per totum in aequali tempore; et secundum verbum Averrois, actiones illorum sunt
proportionales agentibus. Igitur, qua proportione A excedit B, et
actio A actionem B. Non igitur sunt aequales.

Pro primo istorum dicendum non esse inconveniens idem hab-   190
ere eandem proportionem qualitative (scilicet in virtute agendi) ad
totum et ad partem sed quantitative non; quia licet totum et pars
sint inaequalia in quantitate, possunt tamen esse aequalia in qualitate resistendi. Et ideo sicut non differunt in qualitate resistendi
sed in quantitate, sic nec motus per media differunt in qualitate   195
motus (quae est velocitas et tarditas) sed in quantitate motus (quae
est longitudo vel brevitas temporis).

Pro secundo dicendum quod aliqua agentia possunt esse proportionalia suis passis qualitative (scilicet in virtute agendi) et
ex ista proportionalitate sequitur aequalitas motuum qualitative   200
(scilicet in velocitate et tarditate); vel quantitative, quoad agen-
dum in suum passum per totam suam quantitatem, et ex tali proportionalitate sequitur aequalitas motuum correspondenter (videlicet quantitative), et hoc est in longitudine et brevitate temporali
motus. Et sic auctoritates allegatae procedunt.   205

move at equal speeds, by virtue of the equal proportion of movers to mobilia. While B divides the whole of D, A divides a part of C equal to D.

It may now be objected that, letting this part be represented by E, then A will move at the same speed through E as that with which B moves through D. Therefore, according to the second part of this objection, the proportion of A to E is equal to the proportion of B to D. It is then also equal to the proportion of A to C, since they have been posited as equal. This is, however, false, since C is greater than E, and (by Axiom 5, Chapter I) whatever third thing is compared to it will have a larger proportion to E and a smaller one to C.

To the same effect is that passage, from Book I of the De Caelo (in the chapter on the "infinite"), where the following two theorems are proved: (1) that the infinite cannot be moved by the finite, and (2) that the infinite cannot move the finite. The supposition is here made that, if acting powers are equally proportionate to the resistances against which they operate, these powers will move through the entire resistances with equal motions and in an equal time.

Concerning the motion of alteration, at the same point in the text (Comment 63) Averroes expressly states that, if acting powers are proportionate to their respective resistances (whether equally or otherwise), the actions produced by those powers and undergone by their corresponding resistances will be proportional in equal times. Therefore, by applying the same line of reasoning to our present example, since A and B are acting powers proportional to their resistances, they will move them throughout in an equal time. Since, according to Averroes, actions are proportionate to acting powers, therefore by whatever ratio A exceeds B will the action produced by A exceed that produced by B.

Concerning the first of these objections it should be replied that it is not inconsistent for a given power to bear the same proportion "qualitatively" (that is, from the standpoint of its capacity to do work) to both whole and part, while "quantitatively" it does not. Granted that whole and part are quantitatively unequal, they may nevertheless be equal in their quality of resisting, and, just as they do not differ in the quality but only in the quantity of their resistance, so neither do motions through a medium differ in quality (that is, fastness and slowness), but in quantity (that is, longness and shortness of time).

To the second objection it should be replied that acting powers may be considered as proportionate to the things upon which they act, either qualitatively (i.e., by virtue of their capacity to act), or quantitatively (i.e., with respect to action upon the entire quantity of what undergoes the action). It is from a qualitative proportion that qualitative equality of motions may arise (i.e., equality with respect to fastness and slowness); from a quantitative proportion there correspondingly arises quantitative equality of motions (i.e., equality with respect to the temporal length or brevity of the motion). This is the proper interpretation of the authorities cited.

Contra: Tunc nulla pars aeris est aequalis resistentiae simpliciter ad movendum motu divisionis cum aliqua parte terrae, cum
tamen aliqua sit maioris et aliqua minoris. Si enim aliqua sit
aequalis alicui, sit A pars aeris quae est aequalis B parti terrae.
Tunc A non est aequalis B quantitative nec minor illo, quia tunc B 210
esset maioris resistentiae simpliciter quam A. Nec A est maius B,
quia duobus divisivis omnino aequalibus in virtute dividendi simul
applicatis, uno ad A (quod sit C) et reliquo ad B (quod sit D) aeque-
cito dividentur quoniam agentia sunt omnino aequalia in virtute et
passa similiter. Igitur C velocius dividit et movetur quam D; per- 215
transit enim maius spatium in aequali tempore. Igitur A est minoris resistentiae quam B (quod per praedicta satis faciliter scies).
Nec potest dici quod dum D dividit B, C dividit de A partem aequalem B, ita quod C et D aequali velocitate moventur, quia tunc
pars aeris et pars terrae (aequales in quantitate) et totum A et   220
pars eius essent resistentiae aequalis simpliciter; quod non con-
sonat veritati.

Dicendum quod aliqua esse aequalis resistentiae est tripliciter:
scilicet qualitative, et quantitative, et utroque modo. Et qualitative tripliciter: scilicet intrinsece, et extrinsece, et utroque   225
modo. Et hoc est aequalitas resistentiae aliquorum simpliciter.
Intrinsece dicuntur illa esse aequalis resistentiae quae, quantum
ad densitatem et raritatem ac alias conditiones intrinsecas, sunt
aequefacilia ad movendum. Extrinsece dicuntur illa aequalis resistentiae quae, per sua iuvamenta extrinseca, sunt aequaliter   230
resistentia; (aliquid enim resistit per aliquid. extra ipsum). Et
ideo difficilius est dividere vel alterare partem inexistentem toti
quam si a toto esset separata.

Hoc autem ad propositum applicando, dicemus quod aliqua pars
aeris et aliqua pars terrae sunt aequalis resistentiae quantitative, 235
sed non qualitative intrinsece (qualitative tamen extrinsece tantum, vel intrinsece et extrinsece coniunctim). Unde possunt esse
tales partes divisiva aequalia in virtute. Divident celeritate consimili, sed aequali tempore non oportet. Et sic pars aeris et pars
terrae aequales quantitative, et totum et pars aequalis resisten-   240
tiae, possunt esse.

Tertio, obicitur contra eam per hunc modum. Tunc magnes velocius ferrum parvum traheret quam magnum; habet enim maiorem
proportionem ad illud. Quod tamen est falsum, quia moveatur
magnes contignatus ferro, quod potest movere cum eo tanta cel-   245
eritate quanta ipse movetur, quae celeritas sit A; et, dempto illo

It may now be objected that, on the basis of this interpretation, it follows that no portion of air possesses a power of resistance absolutely equal to that of a portion of earth, although it may nevertheless possess either a greater or lesser such power. If one thing may be said to be equal to another, let A represent a quantity of air equal to B, a quantity of earth. It follows that A is neither quantitatively equal to nor less than B, for if it were, then B would be of an absolutely greater resistance than A. Nor, on the other hand, is A greater than B, for if two dividing powers (C and D) exactly equal in their power of penetrating are simultaneously applied to A and B, respectively, then they will be divided at equal speeds, since the active and passive powers are exactly equal. C, therefore, produces a faster motion than does D, since it traverses a greater distance in an equal time. Consequently, A is of less resistance than B, as you can see easily enough from the foregoing.

Nor can it properly be objected that during the time that D traverses B, C traverses a part of A equal to B, with the result that C and D are shown to move at the same speed. In that case, the portions of air and earth would be quantitatively equal, and the whole of A would possess a resistance absolutely equal to that of a part of A. This cannot be true.

The proper rejoinder to this criticism is that three ways must be distinguished in which things may be said to be of equal resistance, namely, qualitatively, quantitatively and in both senses at once. Qualitatively, there may be equality of resistance in three further ways: intrinsically, extrinsically, and in both senses at once (this last being the sense in which there may be said to be an absolute equality of resistances). Intrinsically, those things are said to be of equal resistance which are moved with equal ease by virtue of equal density, rarity and other intrinsic conditions. Extrinsically, those things are said to be of equal resistance which are equally resistive by virtue of some external assistance (the case in which a thing resists by virtue of something outside itself). It should be noted, in this connection, that it is more difficult to divide or alter a part existent within the whole than one separate from it.

Applying the preceding distinctions to the present difficulty we should say that the given portions of air and earth are of equal quantitative resistance, but not qualitatively-intrinsically equal. They are, however, of qualitatively equal resistance either extrinsically alone, or intrinsically and extrinsically together. For this reason equal powers can divide such parts with equal speeds, though not necessarily in equal times. It is in this sense that portions of air and earth may be quantitatively equal and, at the same time, the whole and the part be of equal resistance.

A third major objection might be raised against our theory on the ground that, according to it, a magnet would draw a small piece of iron toward itself faster than a big piece. This ought to follow, because the strength of the magnet bears a greater proportion to the smaller piece. This is, however, false, for (since a piece of iron can be moved with whatever speed the magnet which attracts it moves), let a magnet with a piece of iron adhering to it move with speed A. Now, removing the

ferro, applicetur ferrum minus consimiliter eidem magneti sic
moto. Tunc illud movebitur velocitate A, non enim praecedet magnetem nec separabitur ab eodem. Nec potest dici quod ferrum
minus velocius moveretur nisi impediretur a magnete, quia tunc   250
appeteret separari ab eo. Et etiam ponatur tunc illud ferrum ad
latus magnetis, vel in medio magnetis perforati, et secundum
hanc positionem separabitur a magnete (cum tamen, si fuerit sep-
aratum, redeat ad eundem).

Dicendum cum Averroe, super septimo <u>Physicorum</u>, commento   255
10, quod magnes non trahit ferrum, sed cum ferrum dispositionem
certam a magnete suscipit, ex se movetur ad illud.

Contra: Idem magnes in aequali tempore fortius potest alterare
illa alteratione ferrum parvum quam magnum. Igitur ferrum minus movebitur velocius quam maius in casu praedicto (quod ex   260
praedictis cognoscitur esse falsum).

Dicendum quod hoc non sequitur, quia ferrum in tali dispositione
non movetur secundum ultimum suae potentiae. Si enim modicum
a magnete distaret, ad eum velocius moveretur quam movetur
coniunctus cum illo; nam, per dispositionem causatam in ferro   265
a magnete, ferrum tantum appetit coniungi cum illo; et ideo sive
illa dispositio fuerit fortior sive debilior, si fuerit ferrum coni-
unctum magneti quiescenti, vel moto per illum, si possit tenet se
cum eo.

Hic unum ausculta quod vulgus mirabile iudicabit: videlicet   270
quod aequefacile est elevare magnetem cum ferro contignato magneti (sive sit suppositum, sive suprapositum, sive sit inclusum)
sicut magnetem per se sine ferro. Non enim resistit ferrum ele-
vanti magnetem, nec elevans magnetem elevat ferrum, sed ferrum ex se movetur cum magnete. Et per hoc quoque patet quod   275
magnes in aequilibri cum ferro, et idem absque ferro, aequaliter
ponderabunt.

Contra secundam partem nonae conclusionis huius sic instatur:
Tunc (per primam huius) aliqua proportio moventis ad mobile sufficiet ad motum causandum, et aliqua in duplo minor, et sic sine   280
fine. Igitur aliqua proportio motoris ad mobile aequalis proportioni
subduplae, et aliqua minor illa, sufficiet ad motum causandum.
Igitur aliquid excessum ab aliquo in proportione dupla et maiori
quacumque, posset illud movere; quod huius sententia non patitur.

Ad idem: Si aliqua proportio motoris ad mobile, et aliqua sub-   285
dupla illius, et sic in infinitum, sufficiens sit ad movendum tunc,
existente aliqua proportione mobilis ad motorem, et dupla illius
et sic in infinitum, posset iste motor movere illud mobile. Quanto
enim est minor proportio motoris ad mobile, tanto est maior proportio mobilis ad motorem; et tunc, existente dupla proportione   290
mobilis ad motorem, vel quacumque maiori, fieri posset motus:
quod huius octava repugnat.

first piece of iron, replace it with a smaller piece, so that it in turn
adheres to the moving magnet. This second piece of iron will now move
with speed A, for it does not precede the magnet or become separated
from it. (Nor can it legitimately be objected that the smaller piece of
iron would move more rapidly, if it weren't prevented by the magnet,
for it would then be seeking to separate itself from the magnet.)

Now place the piece of iron on the surface of the magnet, or within
a hole in it, and, according to the present theory, it will become separated from the magnet, and yet, if already separated, will return to it.

To this it should be replied, in agreement with Averroes, in his Comment 10 on Book VII of the <u>Physics</u>, that a magnet does not actually
attract a piece of iron, but that when the iron has received a certain
"disposition" from the magnet, it moves toward the magnet, of itself.

On the other hand, it may be objected that, in a given time, a magnet
can alter a small piece of iron more strongly than a large one. In that
case, a small piece of iron would move faster than a large one under
the conditions specified above; this has already been shown to be false.

To this it should be replied that it does not follow, since a piece of
iron so disposed does not move in accordance with its greatest power.
If it is a short distance from the magnet, it moves faster than it does
when it is joined to the magnet; for, by virtue of the disposition induced
in the iron by the magnet, the iron seeks only to be united with it, whether that disposition is stronger or weaker, whether the iron is joined to
a quiescent or a moving magnet.

At this point, there is one thing worth attention which will seem
amazing to the average man, namely, that it is just as easy to lift a
magnet with a piece of iron adhering to it (whether it is underneath, on
top, or inside) as it is to lift the magnet alone and without the iron. As
a matter of fact, neither does the iron resist the raising of the magnet
nor does raising the magnet raise the iron. On the contrary, the iron
moves, of itself, along with the magnet. From this it is also evident
that a magnet, with or without the iron, weighs the same.

Against the second part of Theorem IX of this chapter, it is also urged
that, according to Theorem I, if a given proportion of mover to <u>mobile</u>
suffices to produce motion, then another half as great also suffices, and
so on <u>ad infinitum</u>. Therefore, a proportion of mover to moved equal to
that of one to two, and also another less than that suffice to produce
motion. Therefore, anything exceeded by anything else in a proportion
of two to one, or more, can move that thing by which it is exceeded; this
is not to be granted.

To the same effect, if a given proportion of mover to moved, another
half that, and so on <u>ad infinitum</u> suffice to produce motion, then, given
a certain proportion of <u>mobile</u> to mover, twice that, and so on <u>ad infini-
tum</u>, this mover can move that <u>mobile</u>. For by however much the proportion of mover to <u>mobile</u> is smaller, by so much is the proportion of
<u>mobile</u> to mover greater. Consequently, from a proportion of <u>mobile</u>
to mover of two to one, or more, motion may arise: which contradicts
Theorem VIII of the present chapter.

Pro istis dicendum quod proportio maioris inaequalitatis potest
minorari et subduplari in infinitum, et tamen numquam proportionem aequalitatis attinget, nec ad aequalitatem alicuius propor-   295
tionis inaequalitatis minoris perveniet. Et de additione et
duplicatione proportionis inaequalitatis minoris similiter est
dicendum: numquam enim ad aequalitatem proportionis aequalitatis nec alicuius proportionis inaequalitatis maioris poterit augmentari (ut per septimam et octavam primi huius evidenter   300
apparet). Et ideo consequentiae prius factae sunt negandae.

Igitur de obiectionibus talibus sufficiunt haec ad praesens. Haec
igitur sunt evidentiores instantiae contra conclusiones praedictas.

CAPITULUM QUARTUM

Declarato in generali de proportione velocitatum in motibus in   1
comparatione ad potentias moventes et motas, sequitur quaedam
specialia de proportione velocitatum in motibus localibus circu-
laribus, in comparatione ad quantitates motus et pertransiti spatii,
demonstrare. Primo autem oportet quasdam definitiones et suppo-   5
sitiones praemittere, et per eas quasdam conclusiones ostendere,
quae in aliis auctoribus minime sunt inventae.

Definitiones sunt istae:

Quadratum est figura superficialis plana aequilatera atque
rectangula (ut patet primo Elementorum Euclidis).   10

Superficies similes sunt quarum anguli unius angulis alterius
sunt aequales, et latera aequos angulos continentia proportionalia
sunt reperta (ut patet sexto Elementorum Euclidis).

Quadrangulus est figura superficialis plana rectangula cuius
tantum latera opposita adaequantur (ut potest haberi ex primo   15
Elementorum Euclidis).

Suppositiones sunt istae:

Omnes anguli recti invicem sunt aequales (ut patet primo Elementorum Euclidis).

Omnium duarum superficierum multiangularum similium est   20
proportio alterius ad alteram tamquam cuiuslibet sui lateris ad
suum relativum latus proportio duplicata (ut patet per duodevicesimum sexti Elementorum Euclidis).

Omnium duorum circulorum est proportio alterius ad alterum
tamquam proportio quadrati sui diametri ad quadratum diametri   25
alterius (et hoc est secunda duodecimi Elementorum Euclidis).

Quorumlibet duorum circulorum circumferentiae suis diametris
sunt proportionales. (Et hoc est quinta conclusio De curvis superficiebus.)

Omnium duarum spherarum est proportio alterius ad alteram   30
sui diametri ad diametrum alterius proportio triplicata. (Et hoc
est ultima duodecimi Elementorum Euclidis).

The reply to these criticisms is that, although a proportion of greater inequality may be lessened and halved indefinitely, nevertheless this series will never reach a proportion of equality nor attain equivalence to a proportion of lesser inequality. The same is true of the addition and doubling of a proportion of lesser inequality, for it can never be increased to the point at which it either becomes equal to a proportion of equality or to one of greater inequality. This is clearly true, on the basis of Theorems VII and VIII of Chapter I of this treatise, and the consequences just drawn are, consequently, to be rejected.

The preceding is a sufficient treatment of such objections for the present, since these constitute the more obvious arguments against the theorems developed at the beginning of this chapter.

CHAPTER FOUR

Having completed a general treatment of the proportion between the speeds with which motions take place with respect to both moving and resisting powers, it remains to demonstrate certain properties peculiar to the proportion of speeds in circular motions with respect to quantities both of motion and of interval traversed. It is, however, first necessary to begin by setting down certain definitions and axioms and, by means of these, to develop certain theorems rarely encountered in other works.

The definitions are as follows:

Definition 1. A square is a plane-surface figure having equal sides and right angles (as appears in Book I of Euclid's Elements).

Definition 2. Similar surfaces are those whose corresponding angles are equal and whose sides, enclosing these equal angles, are found to be proportional (as appears in Book VI of Euclid's Elements).

Definition 3. A quadrangle is a rectangular plane-surface figure of which only the opposing sides are equal (as may be gained from Book I of Euclid's Elements).

The axioms are as follows:

Axiom 1. All right angles are equal to each other (as is made clear in Book I of Euclid's Elements).

Axiom 2. The proportion between any two similar, multi-angular surfaces is equal to the square of the proportion between any two of their respectively corresponding sides (as is shown by Theorem XVIII, Book VI of Euclid's Elements).

Axiom 3. The proportion between any two circles is equal to the square of the proportion between their respective diameters. (This is Theorem II of Book XII of Euclid's Elements.)

Axiom 4. The proportions between circumference and diameter of any two circles are equal. (This is Theorem V of the De curvis superficiebus.)

Axiom 5. The proportion between any two spheres is equal to the cube of the proportion between their respective diameters. (This is the final theorem of Book XII of Euclid's Elements.)

Cuiuslibet spherae superficies aequalis est quadrangulo qui
sub lineis aequalibus diametri spherae et circumferentiae maximi
circuli continetur. (Et hoc est octava Archimenidis <u>De curvis</u>   35
<u>superficiebus</u>.)

Quorumlibet duorum circulorum est proportio unius ad reliquum proportio sui diametri ad diametrum alterius duplicata.

Sint duo circuli A et B, super quorum diametros constituantur
duo quadrata, quae (per primam definitionem et primam supposi-   40
tionem et per definitionem proportionalium et secundam definitionem) fore consimilia demonstrabis. Ex quo (cum secunda
suppositione) ostendes proportionem unius illorum quadratorum
ad reliquum esse proportionem lateris unius istorum ad latus
alterius duplicatam. Et ex illa (cum tertia suppositione huius et   45
quarta suppositione primi) concludes intentum.

Omnium duorum circulorum proportio unius ad alterum est
suarum circumferentiarum eodem ordine proportio geminata. Istam
per proximam conclusionem, (cum adiutorio quartae suppositionis,
adiuncta quarta suppositione primi) faciliter demonstrabis.   50

Omnium duarum spherarum proportio adinvicem demonstratur
circumferentiarum suorum circulorum maximorum eodem ordine
proportio triplicata. Ista ex quinta suppositione et quarta huius,
cum auxilio quartae suppositionis primi, sequitur ostensive.

Quarumlibet duarum spherarum, proportio superficiei unius ad   55
superficiem reliquae, proportionis sui diametri ad diametrum
alterius, ostenditur esse dupla.

Sint duae spherae A et B, et accipiantur duo quadranguli sub
lineis aequalibus istarum diametris et circumferentiis maximorum circulorum suorum contenti, quorum similitudo (ex tertia   60
definitione et prima suppositione et quarta, cum definitione proportionalium et secunda definitione huius) concluditur manifeste.
Ex quo (cum secunda suppositione huius et quarta suppositione
primi) propositum demonstratur.

Omnium duarum spherarum proportio superficiei unius ad super-   65
ficiem alterius, ad proportionem circumferentiae maximi circuli
unius ad circumferentiam maximi circuli alterius, ostenditur fore
dupla. Istam per proximam et quartam suppositionem huius, cum
quarta suppositione primi, ostensive concludes.

Quarumlibet duarum spherarum proportio ad proportionem   70
superficierum suarum eodem ordine sesquialtera comprobatur.

Sint duae spherae A et B. Proportio vero A ad B sit C; et sit D
proportio superficiei A ad superficiem B; et sit E proportio diametri A ad diametrum B. Tunc (per quartam conclusionem huius)
D est duplum E. Ergo D continet praecise duo E. Et (per quintam   75
suppositionem) C est triplum E. Igitur C continet tripla E praecise.
Igitur C continet D semel et eius medietatem. Igitur (per definitionem sesquialteri) C est sesquialterum D. Et hoc est quod ostendere volebamus.

Axiom 6. <u>The surface of any sphere is equivalent to that of a rectangle whose sides are equal to the diameter of the sphere and to the circumference of its maximum circle.</u> (This is Theorem VIII of Archimedes' De curvis superficiebus.)

Theorem I. <u>The proportion between any two circles is equal to the square of the proportion between their respective diameters.</u> Given two circles, A and B, on whose diameters squares are constructed, the squares may be demonstrated as being similar (by Definition 1, Axiom 1, the definition of proportionals, and Definition 2). From this (by Axiom 2) you may show that the proportion of one square to the other is equal to the square of the proportion between their respective sides; and from this (by Axiom 3 of this chapter, and Axiom 4 of Chapter I) you may conclude what was intended.

Theorem II. <u>The proportion between any two circles is equal to the square of the proportion between their respective circumferences.</u> This you may easily demonstrate by means of the preceding theorem, together with the help of Axiom 4 of this chapter, and Axiom 4 of Chapter I.

Theorem III. <u>The proportion between any two spheres is equal to the cube of the proportion between the circumferences of their respective maximum circles.</u> This (with the help of Axiom 4 of Chapter I) obviously follows from Axioms 4 and 5 of the present chapter.

Theorem IV. <u>The proportion between the surfaces of any two spheres is equal to the square of the proportion between their respective diameters.</u> Given two spheres, A and B, the two rectangles constructed of sides equal to their respective diameters and maximum circumferences are manifestly similar (by Definition 3, Axioms 1 and 4, the definition of proportionals, and Definition 2 of this chapter), from which (by means of Axiom 2 of the present chapter, and Axiom 4 of Chapter I) the theorem is proved.

Theorem V. <u>The proportion between the surfaces of any two spheres is equal to the square of the proportion between the circumferences of their respective maximum circles.</u> This you may clearly demonstrate by employing the preceding theorem, Axiom 4 of this chapter, and Axiom 4 of Chapter I.

Theorem VI. <u>The proportion between any two spheres is equal to the proportion between their respective surfaces raised to the power of</u> "sesquialtera" <u>[i.e. 3/2].</u> Given the two spheres, A and B; let the proportion of A to B be C; let the proportion of their respective surfaces be D; and let the proportion of their diameters be E. Then (by Theorem IV of this chapter) D is the square of E. Therefore, D contains E exactly two times, and (by Axiom 5) C is the cube of E. Therefore, C contains E exactly three times. Therefore, C contains D to the one and a half power. Therefore (by the definition of "<u>sesquialtera</u>") C is "<u>sesquialtera</u>" D [i.e. $D^{3/2}$], and this is what we wished to prove.

SECUNDA PARS CAPITULI QUARTI

Circa proportionem velocitatum in motibus in comparatione ad   80
spatium, diversis diversa videntur. Quibusdam enim videtur proportionem motuum localium in velocitate esse tamquam spatiorum
situalium corporeorum eodem tempore descriptorum. Quae redar-
guitur de facili, quia tunc quodlibet corpus motum sua medietate
in duplo velocius moveretur. Et etiam tunc, si totum corpus per-   85
transiret spatium situale corporeum pedalis longitudinis in hora
et subduplum corpus pertransiret spatium situale corporeum
duplae longitudinis in hora, illa duo aequevelociter moverentur.
Nec etiam tunc posset motus puncti nec lineae in velocitate ad
motum corporis comparari, quia nec spatia ab eis descripta in   90
quantitate conveniunt.

Alii autem ponunt proportionem motuum localium in velocitate
esse sicut proportionem superficierum eodem tempore descriptarum. Haec autem positio, sicut prima, poterit reprobari.

Auctor vero De proportionalitate motuum et magnitudinum, sub-   95
tilior istis multum, ponit quod linearum rectarum aequalium temporibus aequalibus motarum, quae pertransit maius spatium
superficiale et ad maiores terminos moveri velocius, et quae
minus et ad minores terminos tardius, et quae aequale et ad
aequales terminos aequevelociter moveri supponit. Et intendit,   100
per terminos maiores, terminos ad quos a terminis a quibus
magis distantes.

Ista autem positio videtur in aliquo contraria rationi. Nam secundum eam quaelibet pars semidiametri circuli circumducti non
terminata ad centrum, et etiam tota semidiametri, moverentur   105
aequaliter suo medio puncto (ut primi huius conclusio prima dicit)
et, per consequens, tardius suo puncto extremo. Et tunc circulus
aequinoctialis moveretur in sesquitertia proportione velocius suo
diametro (ut prima conclusio vult secundi) et, secundum illud,
semidiameter aequinoctialis non moveretur velocius nec tardius   110
nec aequevelociter cum aliquo mobili cuius nullus punctus quies-
cit. Non enim pertransit aliquod spatium ad aliquos terminos,
sed ad terminum unicum (quoniam unum extremum semidiametri
non movetur).

*× "superficiale" is added by Bradwardine to Gerard's statement,

√ Gerard says "magis movetur"

lines 100-1 . B: Et intendit per terminos maiores ad quos a quibus
a quibus magis. ?

CHAPTER FOUR, PART TWO

Concerning the proportion between the speeds with which motions take place, different men have different opinions respecting intervals traversed.

[THEORY I]

To some it would appear that the proportion between the speeds of local motions varies in accordance with that of the volumes of space traversed by the respective bodies in the same time. This view is easily refuted, because, according to it, any body would move twice as fast as its half. Moreover, if the whole body were to traverse a volume of space one foot in length in one hour and half the body were to traverse a volume of space of twice the length in an hour, these two would be moving at equal speeds. Nor, on the other hand, could the speed of motion of a point or line be compared to that of a body, because there would be no ground of quantitative agreement between the distances traversed by them.

[THEORY II]

Others claim that the proportion of speeds in local motions varies with that of the superficies described by the respective bodies in the same time. This theory, however, may be disproved in the same manner as the first.

[THEORY III]

The author of the De proportionalitate motuum et magnitudinum (truly much more penetrating than the others) claims that, of equal straight lines moving in equal times: that which traverses the greater area and to the greater termini moves faster, that traversing a lesser area and to lesser termini moves slower, and that traversing an equal area and to equal termini moves at an equal speed. (By, "greater termini," he means termini toward which the motion takes place that are farther removed from the termini from which it proceeds.)

This theory is, however, seen to be in some respects unreasonable. For, according to it, any part of the rotating radius of a circle not terminated at the center, as well as the whole of such a radius, would be moved at the speed of the radius' mid-point (as stated in Theorem I, Chapter I of this work), and hence at a speed slower than its outermost point. Consequently, the equinoctial circle would be traversed one and a half times faster than its diameter (as claimed in his Theorem 1, Chapter II). Moreover, according to that principle, the equinoctial radius would move neither faster, nor slower, nor equally with a moved body no point of which is at rest; for it does not traverse a given distance toward given "termini," but instead toward a single terminus, since one end of this radius remains static.

spatium l. 118, 120, 122

Ideo videtur magis rationabiliter dici quod velocitas motus   115
localis attenditur penes velocitatem puncti velocissime moti in
corpore moto localiter, quia velocitas motus est ex eo quod mobile
pertransit magnum spatium quiescens in parvo tempore, et hoc
vel verum vel imaginatum. Vel etiam velocitas motus est in eo
quod mobile pertransit vel pertransiret magnum spatium fixum,   120
si esset sibi applicatum, in parvo tempore. Et hoc intellige pro
suprema sphera, quae in sua convexitate nullum spatium describit.
Et illud spatium, penes cuius magnitudinem attenditur velocitas
motus localis, non est corporeum nec superficiale (ut prius est
probatum). Est ergo lineale. Et quia velocitas motus localis non   125
attenditur penes minimum nec medium spatium pertransitum (sed
penes maximum) ideo ista duo principia supponantur:
Cuiuslibet motus localis, velocitas secundum maximum spatium
lineale ab aliquo puncto sui moti descriptum accipitur.
Quorumlibet duorum motuum localium, velocitates et maximae   130
lineae a duobus punctis duorum mobilium eodem tempore descriptae, eodem ordine proportionales existunt.
Et istis duobus tertium adiungatur: Circulorum in sphera exis-
tentium, qui per centrum spherae pertransit aliis maior existit.
Et hoc per sextam primi Theodosii De spheris apparet.   135
Per ista autem principia, una cum prioribus, quarumdam con-
clusionum istius auctoris opposita ostendemus; sed in pluribus
conclusionibus convenimus cum eo, quas multum brevius et levius
ostendemus.
Omnium duorum punctorum circumferentias circulorum eodem   140
tempore uniformiter describentium, proportio velocitatum tamquam diametrorum illarum circumferentiarum, proportio reperitur. Quoniam (per primam suppositionem partis huius et secundam)
velocitas istorum motuum et circumferentiae per eos descriptae
proportionales existunt. Igitur (per quartam suppositionem huius   145
et definitionem proportionalium) propositum concludemus.
Omnium duorum diametrorum seu semidiametrorum eodem
tempore uniformiter circulos describentium, proportio velocitatum est tamquam proportio diametrorum seu semidiametrorum
illorum.   150
Istam, quantum ad primam partem, per primam suppositionem
huius partis cum conclusione proxima demonstrabis. Et quantum
ad partem secundam, similiter probatur eandem esse proportionem
diametrorum et semidiametrorum (quod faciliter, per capitulum
primum, scies).   155
Omnes duas circumferentias circulorum in eodem tempore uniformiter circumductas, sive in seipsis sive superficies spherarum

[THEORY IV]

It, therefore, seems more reasonable to say that the speed of local motion is to be determined by the speed of the most rapidly moving point of the body in question, for speed of motion consists in a body's traversal of a great, unmoving interval in a short time (whether that interval be real or imagined). Put in another way, speed of motion is constituted by the fact that a body either traverses, or would traverse (if it were matched against that body) a great fixed space in a short time. (An imagined interval would be required in the case of the highest sphere, which, at its outer surface, does not mark off any space.)

Now, that interval, according to whose magnitude the speed of local motion is to be determined is neither that of volume nor of surface (as was previously proved). It is, therefore, linear and, because the speed of local motion is to be determined by neither the minimum nor the mean of the interval traversed (but, instead, by the maximum) these two principles are to be considered as axiomatic:

Axiom 1. The speed of any local movement is to be understood as referring to the greatest linear interval described by any point of the body in motion.

Axiom 2. The proportion between the speeds of any two local motions is equal to the proportion between the greatest linear intervals described, during the same time, by two points of the two bodies in motion, respectively.

To these two a third may be added:

Axiom 3. Of the circles contained in a sphere, that which transects the center is larger than the others. (This is evident by Theorem VI, Chapter I of Theodosius' De sphaeris.)

By the use of these axioms, together with what has gone before, we arrive at the opposite of some of this author's theorems; but, in many theorems (which we prove much more easily and briefly) we agree with him.

Theorem I: The proportion between the speeds with which any two points uniformly describe the circumferences of circles in the same time is equal to the proportion between the diameters of those circles. For (by Axioms 1 and 2 of this part of the chapter) the speeds of these motions and the circumferences described by them are proportionals, and therefore (by Axiom 4 of this chapter, together with the definition of proportionals) we conclude what was proposed.

Theorem II. The proportion between the speeds with which any two diameters or radii uniformly describe circles in the same time is equal to the proportion between their diameters or radii. The first part of this you may prove by Axiom 1 of this part of the chapter, together with the preceding theorem; and, as for the second part, it is similarly proved that the proportions between the diameters and radii are the same (which can easily be done, on the basis of Chapter I).

Theorem III. Every two circular circumferences uniformly described in the same time (whether in a place, or describing the surfaces of

describentes sive unam in se et aliam per totam superficiem
spherae, suis velocitatibus proportionales ostendes.

Circumferentia enim circuli quaedam movetur in se, ut circum- 160
ferentia aequinoctialis, et quaedam describit totam superficiem
spherae, ut circumferentia telluris. Primam partem huius per
primam suppositionem partis huius et secundam probabis. Secunda
vero pars huius patet per eandem, adiuncto quod: Circumferentiae
superficiem spherae describentis, punctum terminans diametrum 165
eius motus (secantem orthogonaliter diametrum suum quiescentem) describat maiorem circulum quam aliquod aliud punctum
eiusdem circumferentiae. Quod, per tertiam suppositionem huius
partis, poterit demonstrari. Prima vero et secunda parte probatis,
tertia faciliter apparebit.   170

Quorumlibet duorum circulorum eodem tempore uniformiter
circumductorum, sive in seipsis motorum, sive spheras describentium, sive unius hoc modo et alterius reliquo, proportio est
velocitatum in motibus proportio duplata.

Prima pars ostenditur per primam et secundam suppositionem 175
huius partis, cum secunda conclusione primae partis huius et
quarta suppositione huius primi. Secunda autem pars demonstratur
similiter, supposito quod: Circuli spheram describentis, punctum
terminans diametrum motam (secantem orthogonaliter diametrum
quiescentem) describat maiorem circulum quam aliquod aliud   180
punctum eiusdem circuli. Quod, per tres suppositiones huius
partis, scies probare; et, his probatis, tertia latere non potest.

Quarumlibet duarum superficierum sphericarum eodem tempore
uniformiter super suos axes immobiles circumientium, proportio
est velocitatum in motibus proportio geminata.   185

Ista ex prima et secunda suppositione partis huius, et quinta
conclusione partis primae huius, cum quarta suppositione primi
capituli, concluditur ostensive (auxiliante suppositione tertia
partis huius).

Omnium duarum spherarum eodem tempore uniformiter super 190
suos polos immobiles revolutarum, proportio est velocitatum in
motibus proportio triplicata.

Ista per primam suppositionem et tertiam cum secunda partis
huius, et tertia conclusione huius capituli (adiuncta quarta suppositione primi) indubitanter apparet.   195

TERTIA PARS CAPITULI QUARTI

Quia per quaedam praedictorum, paucis aliis veris coassumptis,
proportio elementorum adinvicem faciliter sciri potest, et eius
scientia multum philosophiae congruit naturali, et hucusque latuit
cooperta (licet praesenti negotio non multum pertineat) eius laten-
tiam detegemus.   200

Vera assumenda sunt ista:

spheres, or one in a plane and the other throughout the surface of an entire sphere) are proportional to their respective speeds: for the circumference of one circle may move in a plane (as, for example, the equinoctial circumference) and that of another may describe the surface of an entire sphere (as does the circumference of the earth). You may prove the first part of this by means of Axioms 1 and 2 of this chapter. The second part is evident on the same basis, with the addition that: When a circumference describes the surface of a sphere, the point terminating the diameter of this motion (cutting its non-moving diameter at right angles) describes a larger circle than any other point on that circumference. This may be demonstrated by Axiom 3 of this part of the chapter. With the first and second parts proved, the third is evident.

/ Seems / ~ unlikely /

Theorem IV. Of every two circles uniformly described in the same time (whether moving in their own planes, or describing the surfaces of spheres, or the one in a plane and the other in the second manner) the proportion is equal to the square of the proportion between their speeds. The first part of this theorem is proved by Axioms 1 and 2 of this part of the chapter together with Theorem II of the first part of this chapter and Axiom 4 of Chapter I. The second part is proved similarly with the additional axiom that: Of a circle describing a sphere, the point terminating the moving diameter (cutting its non-moving diameter at right angles) describes a larger circle than any other point on that circle. This you know how to prove from the three axioms of this part of the chapter; and, with these two parts of the theorem proved, the third cannot remain unsolved.

Theorem V. The proportion between any two spherical surfaces, revolving uniformly and in the same time on their unmoving axes, is equal to the square of the proportion between their speeds. This is an evident conclusion on the basis of Axioms 1, 2 and 3 of the present part of the chapter, Theorem V of the first part, and Axiom 4 of Chapter I.

Theorem VI. The proportion between any two spheres, revolving uniformly and in the same time on their unmoving axes, is equal to the cube of the proportion between their speeds. This appears true beyond doubt, on the basis of Axioms 1, 2 and 3 of this part of the present chapter, Theorem III of the present chapter, and Axiom 4 of Chapter I.

CHAPTER FOUR, PART THREE

Since, on the basis of the foregoing, and by assuming only a few more propositions to be true, it is possible to find with ease the proportion of the elements to each other, and because the discovery of this is most appropriate to natural philosophy, and has, up to this day, remained unknown, therefore (although this is admittedly not too pertinent to the present undertaking) we will, nevertheless, uncover the secret of it.

The truths to be assumed are these:

Quattuor elementa continua proportionalitate iunguntur. Prima
suppositio patet secundo De caelo et mundo in textu commento 32,
dicentis proportionem habere quandam aqua ad terram et plus
super distantiam elementorum. Et tertio De caelo, commento 47,   205
ita dicitur: "Habent proportionaliter magnitudines quae similium
partium," adinvicem scilicet elementa, secundum Averroem, quia
satis patet ex textu.

Quattuor elementa occupant, vel naturaliter occupare debent,
corruptibilium spheram totam.   210

Semidiameter totius spherae corruptibilium continet trigesies
et ter semidiametrum spherae terrae et dimidium eius dimidii
et vigesimam eius partem.

Istud per Alphraganum, Differentia 21, apparet, ubi vult longi-
tudinem propiorem lunae a terra in proportione praedicta ad   215
terrae semidiametrum se habere, cum quo Thebit filius Chorae,
in Praeambulis Almagesti (dimissis minutiis) in integris concord-
atur. Illud autem referunt, sed non probant; sed eius demonstrativa probatio, ex quinto Almagesti Ptholemei·, et ex quinto Thebit,
poterit esse certa.   220

Eadem est proportio diametrorum totalium et medietatum
suarum, nam sicut una diameter ad suam medietatem, ita reliqua
ad suam. Est igitur permutatim. Diameter igitur totius spherae
corruptibilium diametrum spherae terrae trigesies et ter tenet
(nequaquam minutiis computatis).   225

Sit igitur diameter terrae tamquam unitas et diameter totius
spherae corruptibilium velut 33. Deinde assignetur alius terminus
qui sit trigintiplus triplus 33 (scilicet 1089) ad quem etiam trigintiplus triplus terminus adaptetur (scilicet 35937). Hi igitur sunt
quattuor termini continue proportionales. Igitur (per secundam   230
primi) proportio primi (scilicet maximi) ad ultimum (scilicet minimum) est tripla proportionis tertii ad ultimum. Igitur (per quintam suppositionem primae partis huius) tota sphera corruptibilium
35937 continet spheram terrae.

Igitur, haec est proportio quattuor continue proportionalium   235
(scilicet quattuor elementorum coniunctim) ad minimum. Inter
illa quaeramus ergo quattuor continue proportionalia, quorum proportio simplex sit nota, quae coniuncta habeant proportionem
praedictam ad minimum inter illa. Et tunc illa proportio simplex
et nota erit proportio elementorum quaesita. Non enim potest   240
esse maior nec minor; cui si quis contradixerit, per praedictam
faciliter convincetur.

Sint igitur quattuor termini continue proportionales (scilicet:
1, 32, 1024, 32768) qui coniunctim constituunt 33825. Huius ergo
termini compositi ad minimum terminorum est minor proportio   245
quam totius spherae corruptibilium ad spheram terrae. Igitur proportio 32 ad 1 est minor proportione aquae ad terram.

Rursum disponantur alii quattuor termini continue proportionales (scilicet: 1, 33, 1089, 35937, qui collecti 37060 perficiunt).

Axiom 1. The four elements are linked in continuous proportionality. This first axiom is made evident by the text of Comment 32 on Book II of the De caelo et mundo, where (among other remarks concerning the space occupied by the elements) it is stated that water has a certain proportion to earth. Further, in Comment 47 on Book III of the De caelo, Averroes says that: "They" (the elements, that is) "have the magnitudes of similar proportional parts," for this is sufficiently clear from Aristotle's text.

Axiom 2. The four elements either occupy, or naturally should occupy, the entire corruptible sphere.

Axiom 3. The radius of the whole corruptible sphere is equal to 33.3 times the radius of the earth. This is correct on the authority of Alpharganus, in the 21st of his Differentiae, where he claims that the shortest distance from the earth to the moon is related to the radius of the earth in the above proportion. Disregarding fractions, Thebit, the son of Chora, in his Preamble to the Almagest, agrees on the integers. Though they refer to this figure without proving it, its demonstrative proof may, nevertheless, be considered as certain, on the basis of Book V of Thebit's work and Book V of Ptolemy's Almagest.

Now, permutatively, the proportion between the whole diameters is equal to that between their halves, for the one diameter is related to its half in the same way that the other is related to its half. The diameter of the entire corruptible sphere is, therefore, (neglecting the fraction) 33 times the diameter of the earth.

Let, therefore, the diameter of the earth be as unity and the diameter of the whole corruptible sphere as 33. Then let another term be designated as 33 × 33 (namely, 1089), which is again multiplied by 33 (yielding 35937). Now, these four terms (i.e., 35937, 1089, 33, 1) are continuous proportionals, and (by Theorem II, Chapter I) the proportion of the first and greatest to the last and smallest is, therefore, the cube of the proportion between the third and the last. Therefore (by Axiom 5 of the first part of this Chapter) the whole corruptible sphere contains the sphere of earth 35937 times.

This, therefore, is the proportion of four continuous proportionals (namely, of the four elements combined) to a minimum term. Among them let us, accordingly, try to find four continuous proportionals, whose base proportion is known, and which, when added together, will yield the above-mentioned proportion to their minimum term. This base proportion will then be the proportion between the elements, for which we have been looking, for it cannot be either greater or less. If anyone were to deny this, he could be easily convinced by the foregoing.

Take the four proportional terms: 1, 32, 1024, 32768, whose sum is 33825. The proportion between the sum of these terms and the minimum term is now less than that of the whole corruptible sphere to the sphere of earth. The proportion of 32 to 1 is, therefore, less than the proportion of water to earth.

Take again four other continuously proportional terms (namely: 1, 33, 1089, 35937, whose sum is 37060). The proportion between the sum of

Huius autem termini sic collecti ad minimum praedictorum est   250
maior proportio quam totius spherae corruptibilium ad spheram
terrae. Proportio igitur 33 ad 1 est maior proportione unius
elementorum ad proximum sibi minus; et, licet Alphragani minu-
tias computemus, proportionem elementorum praedictam nullatenus in integris excedemus.   255

Disponantur enim quattuor termini proportionales continue
proportione diametri seu semidiametri totius spherae corruptibilium ad diametrum seu semidiametrum spherae terrae, secundum sententiam Alphragani. Et tunc maximus istorum minimum
continebit 36926^{es} et 296 ex 8000 partes eius. Haec igitur est   260
vera proportio quattuor elementorum coniunctim ad simplicem
spheram terrae, ut ex praedictis apparet.

Haec autem proportio minor est proportione 37060 ad 1. Igitur,
Alphragani minutiis numeratis, proportio elementi maioris ad
proximum sibi minus est modicum minor proportione 33 ad 1.   265
Igitur, secundum omnem sententiam est ista conclusio mani-
festa: Cuiuslibet elementi maioris ad proximum sibi minus proportio est maior proportione 32 ad 1 et minor quam 33 ad 1; et
hoc est quod ostendere volebas.

Proportio spherae ignis ad spheram compositam ex tribus   270
elementis residuis est maior proportione 31 ad 1. Nam (per proximam) quodlibet elementum maius trigesies et bis continet proximam sibi minus. Igitur, ad instar quattuor elementorum disponantur
isti quattuor termini continue proportionales proportione praedicta
(1, 32, 1024, 32768) quorum, si tres primi congregentur in unum,   275
1057 constituent: quod spheram ex inferioribus elementis compositam representat. Per quod congregatum, si quartus terminus (qui
ignem significat) dividatur, 31 exhibunt et remanet unitas dividenda.
Quartus igitur terminus congregatus praedictum, trigesies et
semel et amplius continebit. Et hoc est cuius demonstrationem   280
quaesivimus.

Et secundum eundem modum venandi, cuiuslibet et quorumlibet
elementorum proportio ad quodlibet et quaelibet eorumdem poterit
depraehendi.

Distantia convexitatis aeris a centro terrae plus decies et   285
minus undecies continet semidiametrum spherae terrae. Nam
distantia convexitatis aeris a centro terrae est medietas diametri
spherae ex tribus elementis inferioribus compositae, quae sphera
sit A. Haec autem medietas plus decies et minus undecies continet semidiametrum spherae terrae. Quod sic faciliter apparebit. 290

Si enim ponatur quodlibet elementum maius excedere proximum
sibi minus sicut 32, 1, sequitur semidiametrum A plus decies
semidiametrum terrae continere. Disponantur enim ad instar tri-

these terms and their minimum term is now greater than that of the
whole corruptible sphere to the sphere of earth. The proportion of 33
to 1 is, therefore, greater than that of any of the elements to the element immediately lesser, and, even if we were to take Alpharganus'
fractions into account, we would never exceed the above proportion of
elements by an integer.

For let us now take our four continuously proportional terms (which
represent the proportion between either the diameters or radii of the
whole corruptible sphere, and the sphere of earth) according to Alpharganus' figures. The greatest of these terms will then contain the
smallest $36926 + \dfrac{296}{8000}$ times. This, then, is the exact proportion of the
sum of the elements to the sphere of earth alone (as is evident from
the foregoing).

This proportion, however, is less than that of 37060 to 1. When Alpharganus' fractions are taken into account, the proportion of a greater
element to the one immediately lesser is, therefore, a bit smaller than
the proportion of 33 to 1.

From every standpoint, then, the following conclusion is manifest:

Theorem I. The proportion of any larger element to the element immediately lesser is greater than the proportion of 32 to 1 and less than
that of 33 to 1.

Theorem II. The proportion between the sphere of fire and that composed of the three remaining elements is greater than the proportion
of 31 to 1; for (by the above conclusion) each element contains the one
immediately lesser more than 32 times.

Corresponding, therefore, to the four elements, take these four
terms, continuously proportional in the aforementioned proportion: 1,
32, 1024, 32768, the sum of whose first three terms is 1057 and represents the sphere composed of the lower elements. If the fourth term
(which represents the sphere of fire) is divided by this sum, the quo-
tient is $31 + \dfrac{1}{1057}$. The fourth term, therefore, contains the above-
mentioned sum 31 times and a fraction, and this is what we were seeking
to demonstrate.

By the same method the proportions between any and all combinations
of the elements can be worked out.

Theorem III: The distance of the outer surface of the air from the
center of the earth is more than 10 and less than 11 times the radius
of the earth; for the distance of the outer surface of the air from the
center of the earth is equal to half the diameter of the sphere compris-
ing the three lower elements. Let us call this sphere, A. That this half
contains the radius of the earth between 10 and 11 times appears easily
by the following:

If it is supposed that one of the elements exceeds the one immediately smaller than it by a proportion of 32 to 1, it follows that the
radius of A contains the radius of the earth more than 10 times. Cor-

um elementorum inferiorum secundum proportionem praedictam
isti tres termini; 1, 32, 1024, qui si adinvicem coniungantur 1057   295
perficiunt. Igitur A 1057^{es} continet spheram terrae, cuius proportionis subtripla (per quintam suppositionem huius) erit proportio
diametri A ad diametrum spherae terrae. Disponantur ergo isti
quattuor termini proportione decupla continue proportionales (1,
10, 100, 1000); et tunc, secundum secundam conclusionem primi   300
huius, proportio maximi istorum ad minimum est tripla proportionis decuplae. Et illa est minor proportione A ad spheram terrae.
Igitur per septimam suppositionem primi, tertia pars illius est
minor tertia parte alterius. Igitur tertia pars proportionis A ad
spheram terrae (quae est proportio diametri A ad diametrum   305
spherae terrae) decuplam proportionem transcendit. Cum igitur
cuiuslibet elementi maioris proportio ad proximum sibi minus
est maior proportione 32 ad 1, sequitur a multo fortiori tertiam
partem proportionis A ad spheram terrae proportionem decuplam
superare; et eadem est proportio diametrorum et semidiamet-   310
rorum (ut patet per praedicta). Semidiameter igitur A plus decies
continet semidiametrum spherae terrae.

Rursum ponatur quodlibet elementum maius 33^{es} continere proximum sibi minus: et tunc ad instar trium elementorum inferiorum
secundum primam proportionem disponantur isti tres termini con- 315
tinue proportionales: 1, 33, 1089, qui congregati in unum 1123
perficiunt. Est igitur, secundum istud, proportio A ad terram sicut
proportio 1123 ad 1 (cuius tertia pars est proportio diametri A ad
diametrum spherae terrae).

Disponantur hi quattuor termini continue proportionales, pro-   320
portione undecupla: 1, 11, 121, 1331, quorum maximi ad minimum
istorum proportio tripla proportionis undecuplae demonstratur.
Et hoc est maior proportione A ad spheram terrae.

Cum igitur cuiuslibet elementi maioris proportio ad proximum
sibi minus est minor proportione 33 ad 1, et per consequens pro- 325
portio A ad spheram terrae est minor proportione 1123 ad 1,
sequitur, a multo maiori, proportionem 1331 ad 1 proportionem A
ad spheram terrae transcendere. Igitur tertia pars huius, quae
est proportio undecupla, est maior tertia parte alterius, quae est
proportio diametri A ad diametrum spherae terrae. Ergo propor- 330
tio diametri A ad diametrum terrae, et, per consequens, semidiametri A ad semidiametrum terrae proportione undecupla minor
erit.

Et secundum eandem viam, cuiuslibet et quorumlibet elementorum diametri et diametrorum proportio ad cuiuslibet et quorum-   335
libet elementorum diametrum seu diametros, una cum spissitudine
cuiuslibet et quorumlibet eorumdem, poterit inveniri.

Punctum medium distante concavitatis caeli a medio puncto
terrae multum supra convexitatem aeris situatur. Nam distantia
concavitatis caeli a centro terrae continet 33^{es} semidiametrum   340

responding to the three inferior elements, take, in the above proportion, these three terms: 1, 32, 1024, whose sum is 1057. Thus A will contain the sphere of earth 1057 times and the cube root of this proportion (by Axiom 5 of this chapter) will be the proportion between the diameter A and the diameter of the earth.

Take, therefore, the following four terms, continuously proportional in the ratio of 10 to 1: 1, 10, 100, 1000. Then (by Theorem II, Chapter I) the proportion of the greatest to the least of these is the cube of the proportion, 10 to 1. It is thus less than the proportion of A to the sphere of earth, and, therefore (by Axiom 7, Chapter I) the cube root of the one is less than the cube root of the other. The cube root of the proportion between A and the diameter of the earth (which is the proportion between the diameter of A and the diameter of the earth) exceeds the proportion of 10 to 1.

Since, then, the proportion between any larger element and that immediately lesser is greater than the proportion of 32 to 1, it follows the more certainly that the cube root of the proportion of A to the sphere of earth exceeds the proportion of 10 to 1. Since, then, the proportion of diameters is the same as that of radii (as was seen previously), the radius of A contains the radius of the earth more than 10 times.

On the other hand, let it be supposed that one of the larger elements contains the one immediately smaller than it 33 times. Then, corresponding to the three inferior elements, take these three continuously proportional terms: 1, 33, 1089, whose sum is 1123. According to this, therefore, the proportion of A to the earth is as the proportion of 1123 to 1 (whose cube root is the proportion of the diameter of A to the diameter of the sphere of earth).

Now take the following four terms, continuously proportional in the ratio of 11 to 1: 1, 11, 121, 1331 (the proportion between whose extreme terms is shown to be the cube of the proportion, 11 to 1). This is greater than the proportion of A to the sphere of earth.

Since, therefore, the proportion of any larger element to the one immediately lesser is less than the proportion of 33 to 1, and, consequently, the proportion between A and the earth is less than the proportion, 1123 to 1, it follows even more certainly that the proportion of 1331 to 1 exceeds the proportion of A to the sphere of earth. Therefore, the cube root of this (i.e., the proportion of 11 to 1) is greater than the cube root of the other (i.e., the proportion of the diameter of A to the diameter of the sphere of earth). Therefore, the proportion between the diameter of A and the diameter of earth (and, consequently, that between their radii) will be less than the proportion of 11 to 1.

By the same method the proportion between any and all combinations of the diameters of the elements, as well as the density of any or all of them, may be discovered.

Theorem IV. <u>A point half way between the inner surface of the heavens and the center of the earth will be much above the outer surface of the air</u>; for the distance between the inner surface of the heavens and the center of the earth is 33 times the radius of the earth.

spherae terrae. Igitur distantia medii puncti eius a centro praedicto eandem semidiametrum 16^{es} et semis inevitabiliter continebit. Sed, per proximam, distantia convexitatis aeris a centro
terrae non continet undecies semidiametrum spherae terrae.
Igitur punctum medium distante caeli a centro terrae convexitate   345
aeris multo altius situatur. Sic igitur quod volumus lucide demonstratur.

Perfectum igitur opus est de proportione velocitatum in motibus
cum illius motoris auxilio a quo motus cuncti procedunt, cuius ad
suum mobile nulla proportio reperitur; cui sit honor et gloria   350
quamdiu fuerit ullus motus. Amen.

Explicit tractatus de proportionibus editus a magistro Thoma de
Bradelbardin. Anno Domini M^o CCC^o 28.

The distance of this mid-point from the above center will, therefore, inevitably be 16 and a half times that radius. But (by the preceding conclusion) the distance from the outer surface of the air to the center of the earth is less than 11 times the radius of the earth. The mid-point between the heavens and the center of the earth will, therefore, be situated much higher than the outer surface of the air. Thus, what was desired is clearly demonstrated.

Thus comes to completion this work, concerning the proportion between the speeds with which motions take place, by the grace of that Mover—from whom all motions proceed and between Whom and the thing He moves there exists no proportion—to Whom be honor and glory as long as there is any motion. Amen.

- - - - - -

Here ends the Treatise on Proportions, written by Master Thomas of Bradwardine in the year of our Lord, 1328.

VARIANT READINGS

SIGLA

N   MS. 14576, Bibliothèque Nationale (Latin)

O   MS. 176, Vatican (Ottob. Coll.)

B   MS. 500, Bruges

D   MS. 228, Bodleian (Digby Coll.)

X   MS. 76, Bodleian (Digby Coll.)

C   MS. 177, Bodleian (Canon)

V   MS. 1108, Vatican (Latinus)

VARIANT READINGS

PROEMIUM

1 <u>ante</u> in <u>add.</u>D motui
2 quapropter: quia <u>D</u>
4 cognitio illius: eius cognitio <u>N</u>
4-5 est . . . difficilis: multum
   est necessaria et difficilis <u>D</u>
5 difficilis: desiderabilis <u>Q</u>
6 in: cum <u>B</u>
8 eum: ei <u>Q</u>
8 omnem: omnis <u>BQ</u>
10 <u>ante</u> praemisimus <u>add.</u>D ut
14 ante mathematicalia <u>add.</u>O
   quod
15-16 proportionis: proportionalitas <u>Q</u>, proportiones <u>B</u>
16 ceteras <u>om.</u>O
19 demonstrat: determinat <u>Q</u>
20 <u>ante</u> seu <u>add.</u>B erroneas
21 exortas: erroneas <u>D</u>
24 <u>ante</u> capitulum <u>add.</u>B vero
24 <u>ante</u> veram <u>add.</u>O vero
25 <u>ante</u> moventium <u>add.</u>D potentias
25 moventium: motuius <u>Q</u>
25-26 potentias <u>om.</u>D
28 et determinat <u>om.</u>B
28 et: atque <u>DO</u>
30 <u>ante</u> velocitatum <u>add.</u>D
   motuum et
32 <u>ante</u> in <u>add.</u>O etiam est, <u>ibid.</u>
   <u>add.</u>B etiam
33 similiter <u>om.</u>N
33 quarum <u>om.</u>D
36 magnitudines: magnitudinem
   etiam <u>N</u>
39 <u>post</u> transeamus <u>add.</u>N Incipit tractatus, <u>ibid. add.</u> D
   Iste est prologus istius opus

CAPITULUM PRIMUM

2 aequale: aequales <u>B</u>
2-3 vel minus: et minus <u>BON</u>
3 seu etiam: seu et <u>B</u>
3 vel etiam: vel <u>D</u>
3 minusve: et minus <u>N</u>
4 potest <u>om.</u>D
4 comparatio: proportio <u>Q</u>
5 <u>ante</u> est <u>add.</u>D potest
5 potest: ponitur <u>Q</u>, poterit <u>DB</u>
5-6 <u>post</u> comparatorum <u>add.</u>N
   adinvicem
8 autem <u>om.</u>B
9 definitur hoc modo: sic definitur <u>N</u>
9 <u>ante</u> hoc <u>add.</u>B in
11 nam: una <u>B</u>
11 proportionalitatis: proportionis <u>N</u>, proprietatis <u>D</u>
13 <u>ante</u> tripla <u>om.</u>NB et
13 sic: ita <u>QD</u>
13 secundum: secundo <u>DO</u>
13 gradum: gradu <u>DO</u>
14 non <u>om.</u>N
15 tantum <u>om.</u>DBO
15-16 ab. . . denominatur <u>om.</u>O
20 autem <u>om.</u>B
21 commensurabilibus: mensur-
   abilibus <u>Q</u>
21 <u>post</u> seu <u>add.</u>N etiam
22 <u>ante</u> in <u>add.</u>B vero
23 invenitur <u>om.</u>N
26 et <u>om.</u>B
26 utramque: quamlibet <u>B</u>
28 sunt <u>om.</u>O
28 aliqua: una <u>N</u>
29 communis <u>om.</u>D
29 praecise <u>om.</u>D
29-30 cuiusmodi: cuius <u>N</u>

31 autem: etiam B̲, om.D

31 ante aliis add.D in

32 vero: autem B̲, om.D

32 post non add.N est

33-34 autem arithmeticae: etiam arithmeticis B̲

35 mathematicis om.N

36 autem magis: ergo N̲

36 arithmetico: arithmeticae N̲

37 est om.D

39-40 adinvicem om.B

40-41 Proportio. . . habitudo om.O

41 ante inaequalium add.ON adinvicem

41 adinvicem om.B

42 enim om.BN

42 et om.N

42 post minoris add.D inaequalitatis

44 est om.DN

44 quantitatis om.D

45 autem om.O

46 superpartiens: superparticularis O̲

48-49 superpartiens: superparticularis O̲

51 continentis: continens N̲

52 partitur: dividitur N̲

53 nominatur: variatur O̲

53 triplex sive om.ON

53 post tripla add.N nominatur

54 proceditur om.D

55 post autem add.N vero

56-57 continentis: continens N̲

57 autem om.N

58 est illa om.D

59 nullatenus: nullotiens O̲

59 nullatenus aliquotiens: nullotiens D̲

59 aequaliter om.DN

60 quinarii: quarternarii O̲

62 et om.D

62 hemiolia: cunolea N̲, embolia D̲, emiola B̲C̲, emiolea O̲, enyolia V̲, hemola X̲, correxi

62 proportio om.B

64 sicut: et sic O̲

65 se habent om.D

68 post semel add.D continentis ut septem ad quinque

68-69 ex. . . Et haec om.O

69 post pars add.B eius

69 continentis: continens N̲

69 haec om.B

70 secatur: secantur D̲

70 tripliciter: dupliciter O̲

70 numeri: tenentis O̲

71-72 praedictarum . . . partium om.O

71 secundo: alio NBO

72 eorumdem: earumdem O̲

72 et tertio: tertio D̲

72 ambobus: ambabus OD

72 Et ideo: ideo D̲

73 quantitas om.N

73-74 ut . . . tria om.ODB

74 contineat om.D

74 proportio om.OB

74 si: ut scilicet N̲, scilicet D̲

76 semel om.OBD

76 post minorem add.N quantitatem

76 ante et add.N semel

76 tales om.N

76 post eius add.N tales

76 contineat: continentur N̲, contineant D̲

76 sunt: autem O̲

77 vel supertertia om.DBO

78 post si add.B vero

78 istae: vero O̲

78 quartae: quattuor O̲

80 ante ex add.N et

80 mixtione: multitudine O̲

81 post minorem add.N contineat

81 eius om.N

82 contineat: eius N̲

82 tertias: tres O̲

82 ante vel add.N vocatur

83 superbitertia: superbialterna O̲, superbipartiens tertia B̲

83 modi est om.N

84 tria: tres O̲

84 et om.B

84 et . . . partes: si vero tres partes O̲

84 istae: vero tales B̲

(N.B. Due to some uncertainty in
the establishment of the original
text, variant readings of all seven
manuscripts are given at the following points: page 70, lines 97-99
(dupla sesquialtera . . . tripla sesquitertia); lines 108-111 (secundo
. . . supertriquartas); lines 114-
119 (primo sic . . . superbiquarta).
Readings from MS. V have been
omitted in lines 114-119 and lines
116-119 (duplex . . . superbiquarta), since V is badly confused at
that point.)

85 superbiquinta: superbipartiens
   quinta B
86 post huius add.D modi
87 semel: super N
87 minorem contineat: particu-
   lariter pertineat O, pariter
   pertingat B
87 eius om.D
90 termino: fine D
91 autem om.D
91 superparticularis: superpartiens O
93 post quae add.N etiam
94 duplex superparticularis: duplex superpartiens O
94-95 triplex superparticularis:
   triplex particularis OB
95 sic semper: super N, sic ultima B
95 post proceditur add.D in infinitum
96 superparticularitatis: superparticularis NBD
96 sesquialtera: sesquitertium OB
96 post sesquialtera add.N et
97 tertio om.BO
97-98 dupla sesquialtera: duplex
   sesquialtera X
98 dupla sesquitertia, tripla
   sesquialtera om.N, transp.
   X sic: triplex sesquialtera,
   duplex sesquitertia
98-99 tripla sesquitertia om.OX

99 sic om.D
99 proceditur sine fine: in infinitum procedit N
103 ante aliquotas add.O ex quibus
103 una: aliqua B
103 pars om.D
103 continentis om.OB
104 autem om.OB
105 dividendo: dicendo B
106 superpartientis: superbipar-
   tientis B
107 superbipartiens: tripartiens O
107-8 multiplex supertripartiens
   om.O
108 superpartiens: superbipartiens ND, supertripartiens B
108 post tertias add.BO vel
109 superpartiens quartas: supertriquartas O
109-11 tertio . . . supertriquartas
   om.O
109 sic om.B
109 multiplex superpartiens om.C
109-10 multiplex superbipartiens
   tertias vel multiplex superbitertias om.C
109-10 superbipartiens: superpartiens B
110 tertias: quartas X
110 vel om.DBVX
110 multiplex superbitertias:
   multiplex superbipartiens
   tria D, multiplex superbipartiens tertias X, om.BV
110-11 multiplex supertripartiens
   quartas: multiplex superbipartiens quartas DV, multiplex
   superpartiens quartas B, om.X
111 vel om.VX
111 multiplex supertriquartas:
   multiplex supertriquarta NC,
   multiplex supertripartiens
   quartas B, multiplex superpartiens quarta D, om.VX
112 iterum: item N
114 post primo add.N modo
114 triplex supertripartiens: triplex superbipartiens CX, om.N

114-15 et conversim superbipartiens duplex superbipartiens
om.BO

115 superbipartiens duplex transp.
DC

115 superbipartiens: triplex DC

115 triplex: supertripartiens DC,
om.BO

116 superpartiens: superbipartiens NX, supertiens D

116 post tertias add.D et conversim

116-17 triplex superpartiens tertias: triplex superbipartiens
tertias N, duplex supertiens
tertias D, triplex superpartiens quartas C, duplex superbipartiens quartas X

117 et conversim om.ND

117 post et conversim add.C triplex superpartiens quartas

118 post duplex superbitertia add.
O et eius, add.C et conversim

118 triplex superbitertia: duplex
superbitertia OC, triplex
superbipartiens tertias X

118 et econtra: et conversim X,
om.OC

118-19 duplex superbitertia: triplex superbitertia O, triplex
C, om.X

119 duplex superbiquarta: duplex
supertriquarta D, et eius duplex superbitertia duplex
supertriquarta O

119 post sic add.N quaelibet, add.
D quolibet

119-20 numerorum interminabilis:
modorum indeterminabilis D

120 interminabilis: in collis B

120 omnium: omnes ND,omnibus B

121 praecedentibus: praedictis D

121 satis liquent: patent B

123 sunt species quot: species quot
sunt N

124 eisdem: eiusdem NDO

124 appellantur: appellatur B

125 subsuperpartiens: superpartiens OB, subsuperparticu-
laris N

126 aliis om.NO

126 eius om.B

126 eius: eius aliis O

128 quod om.O

129 etiam om.D

130 illa: illius D

130 dupla dupla: duplex duplex D,
duplus dupla B

131 si subdupla subdupla: subduplex subduplex D, si subdu-
plus subdupla B

131 una quantitas: proportio
unius quantitatis D

132 ante est add. D et

132 etiam om.D

133 post haec add.OB proportio

133 primo et proprie: et propria
OB

134 existant: existunt O

135 dicta communiter: communiter accepta B

135-36 divisione et: divisione et
etiam de B

137-38 proportionalitate: proportione O

141 eiusdem: eius D

142 in sua communitate om.O

142 sua: sui ON

143 decem: quattuor O

144 post locutiones add.O sunt

145 intelligenda om.ON

145 ante utilia add.B sunt

148 appellatur: nominatur D

149 appellatur: nominatur O

149-50 nominatur: vocatur OBD

150 quando om.D

152 tria duo unum: duo et duo O

152 arithmeticis: arsmetrico OB

154 autem om.D

155 isto: hoc D

155 isto modo definitur: definitur
hoc modo OB

156 quando: tantum O

156 duarum om.O

159 est in tribus terminis: scilicet harmonica est N
160 quando om.O
162 et medii ad differentiam medii
et: ad differentiam medii et
medii ad N
163 senarii: sex O
164 sex et: sex ad ND
165 etiam: et O, om.D
165 et: ad ND
165 dupla: duplex OB
167 abinvicem: adinvicem NB
169 numerus om.D
169 terminorum om.OB
170 reperitur: invenitur D
170 etiam: autem O, om.B
174 post continua add.N et
176-77 medium . . . terminum
om.D
177 ut om.B
177 ante sicut add.N ut
177 ita: vel N, si B, sic O
178 per: et D
178 sic om.D
180 nec: vel per B
180 post nec add. D per
180 ante communes add.NDO
aliquos
180 post communes om.N terminos
180-81 dicendo om.OBD
181 unum: duo D
182 continua om.OD
183 vel per: vel ND
184 medios om.D
184 ut om.N
186 proportionum om.D
187 nec: aut D
189 post autem add.BO non
189 medietatibus: mediis B
189 non om.BO
190 transsumptionem: translationem D
191 ante ad add.D sunt
191 communem: alium D
191 copulantur: copulatae D
192 coniunguntur: copulantur BD
194 ante et add.B reperitur
194 ante pluribus add.D in

194 pluribus: aliis B
194-95 discontinua . . . reperitur
om.D
194-95 in quattuor terminis ad
minus: ad minus in quattuor
terminis B
195 ad minus et: sed O
195 in om.B
195 pluribus reperitur: aliis invenitur B
195 reperitur: invenitur O
196 Ametum: Aymetum D
197 Iosephi: Josaphi NBD
198 quod in: quod N
198 omnes: communes N
199 convenire: conversari D
199 sed in: sed O
199 sive disiuncta om.B
199 aliqui om.D
200 diversari: diversificari DB
200 post gratia add.B ut
201 movens ad movens: motus ad
motum N, movens O
203 dicuntur: differunt D
205 aliqua: alia D
206 proportione: proportionalitate
OB
206-7 decem modis: quemadmodo D
207 similiter om.D
208 tractandi: pertractandi D
210 autem om.D
211 aequales vel om.O
211 vel similes om.B
212 post Euclidi add.B in quinto
214 similes seu aequales:
aequales vel similes N, vel
similes aequales B
214 ante haec add.B et
215 post praedicta add.D sed
216 quibus: quo N
217 post quibus add.D proportionalitas
218 post proportionalia add.N
etiam
219 quorum om.B
221 sic: sicut OB
221 illius: unius proportionis N
222 sunt om.O
223 sicut duo: et duo D

224 et ideo: ideo D
225 existunt: erunt D
226-27 sunt illa quorum proportionalium proportionalitate
  geometrica om.O
228 antecedens illius: suum antecedens D
230 econtrario: econtra N
232 sive simplex om.ND
232 geometrica om.D
232-33 quorumlibet: quotlibet D
233 proportionum: proportionalium NDO
235 geometrica om.D
235 quorumlibet: quotlibet D,
  quorum O
235 sive: cum O
236-37 proportionalitate: proportione N
237 illorum om.BD
238 consequens om.D
238-39 idem consequens, et
  cuiuslibet alterius antecedentis illorum cum suo
  consequente ad om.N
239 consequens: antecedens D
239 proportionum: proportionalium D
240 sicut om.D
241 quorumlibet: quotlibet O,
  om.D
242 in disiuncta om.O
242 simplici: simpliciter OB
242-43 proportionalitate: proportione NB
244 antecedens: consequens B
244 cuiuslibet: cuiuscumque N
244 illorum: eius D
245 proportionum: proportionalium ND
247 Aequa: Econtra ND
248 propositis: proportionis ND
248 quaecumque: quaelibet N
249 post alterius add.B quae
249 proportionales: proportiones NB
250 proportionum: propor-
  tionem N, proportionalium D

251 multitudinibus: multiplici-
  bus ND
252 post et add.N sicut
252-53 sicut quattuor: sic quattuor N
255 Elementorum om.B
256 etiam: enim N
256-59 Consimiles . . . videre
  om.B
256-57 proportionalitati: proportionalitate D
258 adaptari: aptari O
259 facile: facilius O
259 est: erint N
260 huius: istius N
261 praemittens: praemittentes
  BD
263 eaedem vel aequales: aequales sive eaedem N
264 est om.OB
264 ista om.NBO
264 quibuscumque: quotcumque
  O
265 est om.O
267 proportione om.D
268 tertia est ista om.O
268 est ista om.B
268 quotcumque: quibuscumque
  OB
269-70 proportione: provectione
  O
271 post extremum add.OB proportionibus
272-73 Harum . . . eiusdem
  om.X
272 post proportionibus add.V
  Euclidi
274 Quarta est ista om.O
274 est ista om.B
275 comparentur: comparantur
  N
275 istam erit: illud est D
275 iterum: habet ND, retinet O
276 illius: tertiae N
276 ad om.O
276 est om.DBO
277 quinta om.O
277 est ista om.BO

278 proportionentur: proportionem O
280 post vero add.N proportio
281 sexta om.O
281 est ista om.BO
282 ipsas om.D
282 unius: illius D
282 una om.D
283 post proportio add.D una
   illas est
283 esse om.OD
284 septima om.O
284 est ista om.BO
285 permutatim . . . erunt: proportionales erunt ipsas permutatim D
286 octava om.O
286 ante est add.N suppositio
286 est ista om.BO
286 fuerint om.B
286 quattuor om.D
287 et fuerit: fueritque D, fuerit O
287 illarum om.D
288 pariter: partem tunc O
288 maiores: maius OB
288 necesse om.D
289 comprobantur: comprobatur
   B, componitur O
291 post quinti add.N Elementorum
291 post autem add.D est
292 quidem: vero N
293 prima conclusio om.NO
293 maioris inaequalitatis: maior
   inaequalitas O
294 ut: et B
294 ante erit add.O erit proportio
   primi ad tertium
295 praecise: praecipue N, om.BO
297 similes: consimiles N
298 proportionum: proportiones OB
300 suppositionem proportio: proportionem seu suppositionem
   praecise B, proportionem et
   suppositionem O
301-2 est praecise dupla: praecise
   dupla est D
302 utramque: quamlibet D
302 illarum: proportio B, om.O

302 post quod add.N ostensive
302 volebamus: voluisti D
303 secunda est ista om.NO
305 ad proximum: a proximo O
305 sequentem: sequente O
305 sequentem est tripla: tertius
   illarum sequens erit tripla B
306 ita: illud cum O
306-7 ita quod om.D
307 ante quod add.B enim
307 denominatio: denominatione B
308 sic: et D, tunc O
308 sic istam: istud patet B
308 ante per add.N conclusionem
309 tripli et quadrupli: dupli et
   tripli D
309 sic: ita O
309-10 proximam: proxima OB
310 demonstrabis: demonstratum
   D
311 tertia conclusio om.NO
311 est ista om.NOB
312 et om.OB
312 fuerit: fueritque B
312 post fuerit add.D. quoque
313 dupla: duplae B
315 similiter: scilicet N
315 demonstrabis: demonstres OB
315 A om.O
316 et sit: et sicut N
316 aequaliter: erit N
316-17 duplum om.D
317 tertii: secundi OB
317 quod: quae D
317-18 est aequale: erit aequale N
318 propter quartam: per quartam N
318 maius propter: maius C per N
319 suppositionem om.OD
320 per: propter D
324 demonstrari per nunc: per
   nunc demonstrari B
325 inter: necessaria O
326 et: ad D
326 interponatur: interponitur B
329 A ad D: ad D O
329 proportioni: proportionum D,
   proportio B

329 ut: prout N
330 quam: proportione A ad D quod N
331 quod quaesivisti: quod concessisti O, quaesitum N, propositum B
332 quarta om.ON
332 conclusio est haec om.ONB
333 tertii: primi N
334 tertium: secundum N
334 dupla: duplae B
336 sortitur: sortietur N
337 quinta om.NO
338 ante duplum add.O et vel inaequaliter
339 dupla ad: dupla N
340 dupliciter om.D
340 demonstratur: demonstretur OB
340-41 ad quod: quod O
341 habet: habeat ad O
341 probetur: probatur D
341 D om.O
342 post hoc add.N propositum concluditur
342 propositum om.N
342 concluditur: concludatur B, om.N
344 demonstratur: demonstretur B
346 sexta om.NO
346 conclusio om.NOB
348 maior . . . tertium om.O
348 dupla: duplae B
349 proxima similem: proximo talem N
350 septima om.NO
350 conclusio om.NOB
352 nam: namque D
352 proportione: proportio D
352 aliqua proportio: alia proportione D, om.O
352 aequalitatis om.O
355 proportio: proproximo D
355 aliquam: aliam D
356 maioris: maiorem O
356 ante ab add.N excederetur
356 alia: aliqua ND, illa O
357-59 excederetur . . . inaequalitatis om.O

358 excedatur: exceditur D, exceretur B
359 inaequalitatis: inaequalitas B
361 ante esse add.O esse maiores
362 invicem: adinvicem D
362 adequari: aequari B
365 quadrupla: propter quadruplam D
366 minoris: minor D
367 interponatur: tunc ponatur OB
367 habeat: habet D
368 quarternario: quarternarius O
368 et om.DO
368 interponatur: tunc ponitur O
369 isti: ibi B, etiam O
370 dupla: duplae D, duplex N
372 subdupla: subduplae OBD
373 subdupla: subduplae OBD
373 quadruplae: subquadruplae D
374 subdupla: subduplae B, duplae O
374 proportionis: proportioni D
375 duplae: dupli O
376 aequales: quarta O
377 unitas: unum B
379 ergo om.D
380 proportione aequalitatis om.NO
381 aequalitatis: inaequalitatis BO
381 aliqua: alia D
382 aliquam: aliam D
383 detur: demonstratur D
385 post quod add.D sic
386 si: cum D
387 accipiatur: accipitur O
387 si om.O
387 qui om.N
388 unitati: unitatis OB
388 capiatur: capitur O
388 scilicet quarternarius: unitati capiatur terminus duplus sicut quarternarius quae est duplus D
389 quarternarii: quattuor B
391 quadrupla: quarternarii D
391 ante est add.D ad unitatem
391 dupla: duplum O
391 duplae et: binarii ad unitatem ergo proportio quadrupla est dupla proportionis duplae ergo D

392-93 similiter . . . aequalitatis
om.N
394 post eandem add.D conclusionem
394 aequale: aequaliter D
394 eidem: eiusdem N, illae D
395 aequalia: aequales D
396 sic om.O
397 praecise: praecipue N
398 quod est: consequens D
398 quotienscumque: quotiens D
399 semper om.D
402 aequalitatis: aequalis N
403 proportione om.D
403 inaequalitatis: aequalitatis O
403 quia: quando OB
404 consequens: quod est BO
405 quotienscumque: quotcumque D
406 non om.D
406 secundum: tertium ND
406 in aequali: inaequalia O
408 nec om.O
408 proportio: proportione O
408 aliqua: alia D
409 quod: quia D
412 tunc om.O
414 habet . . . minorem: habeat
A ad D minoris O
414 habet A ad B: habeat A B
414 aequalitatis: aequalis proportio D, aequalitatis proportio
BO
415 igitur et cetera om.BO
416 aequalia: aequales ND
416 utrumque: uterque N
417 ad om.O
418 sit . . . proportio: erit proportio aliqua N, est aequalis
proportio D
419-20 A ad B et B ad C: ad B C
D ad C O
421 proportio: proportione O
422 sint: sit O
422 et B: B D
422 et C: C OD
423 componitur: est composita NO
426 idem: ideo O
426 quintam: regulam OB
426 dicentis: dicentem OB

428 primae ad tertiam: primi ad
tertiam D
428 primae ad secundam: primi
ad secundam D
430 B om.O
430 una om.D
431 alia: aliqua NO, una alia D
434 ante eodem add.D in
434 illi om.B
435 in om.O
437 secundo: secundum NBD
437 ante quod add.D est
439 quoque: vero B
439 utroque: utrique O
441 tantum om.D
442 proportionalitate: solum proportione D, om.N
442 maioris: minoris D
443 omnis om.O
443 obiectio: obiecto D, obicio NB
444 Octava: ergo N, om.DO
444 maioris om.B
444 aliqua: alia D
446-47 post deduces add.D ad hoc
impossibile
447 ad hoc impossibile om.D
447 proportio: proportione D
448 sunt: sint O
449 quod om.BD
449 invicem: adinvicem D
451 de om.O
451 dicta: praedicta N
451 sufficiant: sufficiunt D

CAPITULUM SECUNDUM

1 ante Istis add.D Incipit prima
pars capituli secundi
2 initio: tanto O
2 reprobemus: reprobamus NBO
4 ante erroneae add.D proponunt
4 proposito om.ODB
4 pertinentes: proponendae O,
ponendae B
4 sunt quattuor om.N
7 et om.D
7 mundo om.ND
7 ex: in BO
7 dicente: habente O

8 proportionaliter om.D
8 post oportet add.B motori
8 excellentiam: excellentias O
8 motoris: motuum O, moveri
   commenti 52 D, om.B
9 commento 71 om.O
9-10 commento . . . quod: dicentis 6NIC (sic), commento 5 et
   commento 71 B, commento 7 in
   textu dicente D
10 quod om.O
11 ante rem add.D potentiam
   moti vel
11 35: 36 B
11-12 sic dicit: dicit quod D,
   dicat N
13 moti et: rei motae et plus dicit
   illud idem D
13 commento 39 om.BO
13-14 scilicet . . . sic: post dicit
   istud BO, om.D
15 erit: est ND
15 quantitas: quantitatis N
16 multis: in multis B, in istis N
17 poterit: potest D
18 istum modum: illud N, idem D
18 post aliquo add.N modo
20 ante medietatem moti add.D
   excedit
21 et: ita D
21 eius: huius OB
22 medietatem eius: sui medietatem D, unitates eius B
23 est om.D
23 et om.B
24 patet: apparet B
24 post fine add.B et commento
   36
25 istam om.N
25 moveat: movet B
26 post medietas add.N motoris
26 movebit: movebat O
28 probat: patet D
28 nam similiter: ista similiter
   O, scilicet istam B, similiter
   ista ratio D
29 medietas: mensura O
31 Tunc sequitur: tunc sequeretur
   B, oit sequitur D, sequentem N

31 quod: ex D
31 motoribus moventibus: motoris
   N
32 aequale: aliquod D
33 coniunctim non moverent: non
   moverent coniunctim D
33 ante non add.O motores
33 coniuncta om.D
34 semper per: semper N
36 ad ista: ab ista N
37 quilibet: cuius N, quibus O
38 autem: igitur D
38-39 quarternarium: quarter-
   naritatem B
39 ante faciunt add.O faciunt
39 faciunt om.D
39-40 ante constituunt add.B
   faciunt vel
40-41 super unitatem: similiter N
41 aliis om.D
42 exceduntur: excedunt N
43 ut: ubi NBO
43 ubi om.N
44 divisim: divisae D
45 spatia om.D
45 duae om.N
45 coniunctae: coniunctim D
46 movebunt: movebant N
46 duo om.D
46 coniuncta: coniunctim D
47 cum priori om.ND
49 motor: ita motus D
50 proportione: proportionalitate
   O
50 scilicet: scilicet ex D, sive N
51 proportionum: proportionalium
   O
51 ante aequalis add.B alia littera
   aliquis gradus velocitatis
52 motuum: mobilium O
52 excessuum: extremum O,
   excessus B
52 quoniam: quia N
53 tres: tria B
54 alius autem: et excessus alterius est D
55 et om.OB
55 post contra add.N est
55 septimo: sexto N

55 et: ex N, in D, om.O
56 post multis add.B aliis
56 post locis add.N in textu,
   commenti 35 et 36
56 proportionum motorum: proportionis moventis O
57 aequalitatem velocitatum:
   aequalem velocitatem ND
57 Idem: sicut D
58 loca praedicta om.B
58 et om.OB
58 similiter: super D, om.B
59 71: AR N, 7 O, 9 D
59 primum: primo O
59 et mundo om.ND
59 63: ultimo D
60 locis om.O
61 intelligunt: intelligant O
62 seu . . . proportionalitatem:
   seu analogam proportionem D,
   om.N
64 ante probat add.N textu commento 39
64 probat Aristoteles: philosophus
   probat B
68 motoris: moventis B
69 motor: motus B
69 proportionalitate: proportione
   O
70 quae . . . excessuum om.N
71 post in add.N isto
72 ibidem om.D
73 geometri: geometrice NOB
75 totum motum: totus motus B
75 ante ad add.N ita medietas
   motoris
76 septimam: aliam B
76-78 Igitur . . . hoc om.N
77 motor: motus B
78 post hoc add.N quod
79 etiam: autem D
82 coniunctim: coniuncti N
82 coniuncta: coniunctim D
83 priori: priore N
83 idem: istdem O
84 Analogum enim: analogus B,
   analogum D, om.O
84 est om.BDO
84 intelligit: intendit N

85 arithmetica: arsmetricam O
85 secundum: per D, om.O
86 simplex motum: simplicem
   motum D
88 quod om.O
88 ante non add.N sed
89 quinti om.B
89 Elementorum om.O
89 Euclidis om.B
90 quarumlibet: quotlibet O,
   quaelibet B
90 quantitatum: quantitates BO
90 totidem: pondere N
92 una om.O
93 comparem: comparationem B
93 aggregatum: aggregatur D
93-94 istas pariter: partes istas
   D, pariter BO
94 Igitur: ideo D
95 poterit: potest N
96 sequeretur: sequitur NO
97 movetur: moveretur B
99 descendat: descendet D
101 certae: terrae BO
102 velocitatis: velocioris N, vel-
   ociorem B
102 Subtilietur om.N
102-3 moveatur: movetur N
103 aequali velocitate om.D
103 A: D N
103 A om.BO
104 enim om.D
105 movetur: movebitur NB
105 in . . . medio om.N
105 aequali velocitate: tunc aequevelociter BO
106 ante movetur add.D A
106 movetur: movebitur B
107 possit: potest B
108 illo: illa ND
108-9 quamtamcumque. . .datam:
   quamcumque hac velocitate
   data D
109 localis: locale B
109-10 subtiliationem: similita-
   tem N
111-12 medii. . .motore: moven-
   tum eumdem motorem O,
   manente eumdem motorem B

112 possibile est: contingit D
112 devenire: vene similiter Q,
    tene fieri B
112 quamtamcumque: quamcum-
    que D
113 motus localis datam: datam
    motus localis N
113 posito: positu N
114 movetur: moveretur B
116 sic om.N
116 sequeretur: sequitur NO
116 quod om.O
118 post moveret add.N secundum
118 Descendat: descendit N
118 post terra add.B alia littera
    in aquam
118-19 aliqua: alia D
119 quam: quod D
119 post quam add.N habet
120 descendat aliqua: excedat
    aliquam O
120 aliqua: alia DB
121 resistentiam: insistentiam N
121 maneat: moveat D
121 et sua: cum sua D
122 subtilietur: subscribetur N
123 moveatur: movetur O
123 terra om.ND
124 terra om.ND
125 excessum om.D
125 post minorem add.B
    minor
126 sequeretur: sequitur DO
126 movetur: moveatur N
127 post quod add.N medium
127 quod in: quem B
127 excederet vel maiori: excedit
    maiorem D, excedat medium
    B
128 velocius om.N
128 alio om.NOB
128 non om.OB
129 medium: spatium D
130 quoniam: quia N
130 post totum add.N movens
130 Et tunc: Et D
131 post medii add.O motus
131-32 velocitas motus: motus
    velocitatis B

132 motus om.O
132 quod: quia O
134 sic om.D
134 sequeretur: sequitur O
134 si om.D
136 post fortis add.N fortis
136 fortis homo: forte ut homo B
137 post sicut add.ND sicut
138 excederet: excedit N
139 et illud: illud ND
139 cum: tamen BO
140 excedit: excedat D
140 moveri: movere BD
141 maius om.N
141 excedit: potest movere homo
    fortis per maiorem quam
    debilior motor excedat D,
    potest movere quam debilior
    motor excedat BO
142-43 quo possit moveri: motore
    maius quam debilior motor
    posset movere D, quo posset
    movere maius quam debilior
    motor posset movere BO
143 mobile: spatium D
144 cum quo posset moveri: quo
    posset movere D, om.BO
144 cuius contrarium declarat
    experimentum: quod experi-
    mentum declarat esse falsum
    D
145 post aliquod add.D mobile
145-46 velociter: velocius D
146 velociter satis: satis velo-
    cius D
148 tarde: lente BO
148 apponatur: opponatur D, ap-
    ponetur B
148 quam: quod O
149 posset: possit O, possint B
149 non: vel B
150 tunc: nec N
151 Ex his: et his D, Ex istis N
151 ostenditur ista conclusio:
    istis ostenditur ista ergo D
152 negativa: neganda B
153 motoris: maioris O
154 his: huic N
154 quoniam: quam D

155 commentator om.ND
158 maioris: maiorum D
158 qua: quam BDO
158-59 potentia motoris: motorum potentia D
163 ibi enim: ubi N, ibi D
165 motoris: motorum D
165 rei motae: moti DO
166-67 Haec . . . motae om.B
167 motoris: motorum D
167-68 sit . . . motae om.O
168 potest: posset N
169 nec: aut D
171 post ut add.N patet
171 septimam: aliam B
175 sequuntur: sequentur D
175-76 habitudinem vel proportionem: habitudinem et proportionem BO, habitudinem D
176 potentiae: primi motus N, potentiae et proportionem D
176 ad . . . moti om.B
177 post ex add.O hoc
181 autem: igitur D
181 glosare: allegare D
185 et om.BO
186 motoris: motorum D
187 videtur . . . partem: quantum ad primam partem videtur fundari D
188 et in om.BO
189 textu . . . 71 om.BDO
189 quidem: quaedam D
190 quanto . . . aqua: quanto subtilius aer aqua B, quanto subtilius aqua aer O, quanto igitur subtilius aer D
190 incorporalior: incorporalibus B
191 id est mobile: immobile N
191 movebitur: movetur D
191 Habet: Hanc N
192 eandem om.B
192 id est: primam O
192 post quam add.ND quidem
193 aer ab om.O
193 post aqua add.B et

193 ad . . . quare: distabit ab velocitate quia B
193 ante quare add.N subduplis habebit
194 duplici: duplicati N
194 tempore: spherae O, tertiae D
194 ipsum: ipsi N
194 pertransibit: transibit BD
197 mediorum: motorum D
197 et om.O
197 post etiam add.B quod
198 illos: aliquos BO
199 tempus om.O
200 subtilius . . . correspondet: medium subtilius B
201 et mundo om.ND
201 dicit: dicitur B
201 post dicit add.N in textu commenti
202 supponatur: supponitur NO
202 post et add.NDO in
203 quaecumque: quidcumque D
203 post quaecumque add.B alia littera
203 proportionaliter om.O
203 tempori: tempora B
206 aliquod mobile: mobile N
208 in . . . tempore om.O
210 post Tantum add.N sufficit
210 huius opinionis: opinionis istius sit O, istius opinionis B
211 huius opinionis: istius positionis O, positionis istius B
211 supponit: sumit D
211 quarto: septimo BO
211 ante capitulo add.O et etiam
212 post vacuo add.N textu commenti 25 et ultimum
212 alia: aliqua BO
213 ferantur om.D
213 ferantur per: semper moveantur per B
213 aequale: aliquod BO
216 Et in: Et BO
216 post fine add.N vult Aristoteles

217 <u>ante</u> Averrois <u>add.N</u> commentis
217 vult Aristoteles <u>om.N</u>
219 illud: idem <u>B</u>
221 potentia motiva: mobilia potentia <u>O</u>
222 <u>post</u> tempore <u>add.D</u> proportionaliter
224 minori: maiori <u>D</u>
225 quod: quia <u>O</u>
226 minori tempus: minoris <u>D</u>, minori maius <u>O</u>
227 <u>ante</u> primo <u>add.N</u> in
227 De <u>om.B</u>
227 et mundo <u>om.ND</u>
228 <u>ante</u> ubi <u>add.N</u> textu commenti 51
228 loquens: loquitur <u>D</u>
228 debent: deberent <u>N</u>
229 eodem: aequali <u>N</u>
229 medio: tempore <u>NOB</u>
230 gravitates: gravius <u>O</u>
230 et <u>om.B</u>
230 tempora: corpora <u>OB</u>
231 si media: scilicet medii <u>D</u>
231 gravitas: gravitatis <u>BO</u>
231 <u>post</u> hoc <u>add.N</u> et, <u>add.O</u> in hoc
232 De caelo <u>om.B</u>
233 recte: ratione <u>B</u>
233 aut: ac <u>D</u>
233-34 inaequalia in virtute: aequalia in verticie <u>N</u>, inaequalia in velocitate <u>O</u>, inaequalia virtute <u>B</u>
235 <u>post</u> medio <u>add.BO</u> et
237 <u>post</u> dicit <u>add.BO</u> quod
237 velocitatis: velocitas <u>NBD</u>
238 ponderis: ponitis <u>BO</u>
238 proportio: proportione <u>B</u>
239 sit <u>om.B</u>
239-40 praecise in duplo: praecipue in duplo <u>N</u>, praecise a duplo <u>O</u>, praecise ad dupla <u>B</u>
240 praecise in duplo: in duplo praecise <u>D</u>, praecipue in duplo <u>N</u>
241 mobile: mobilis <u>O</u>

243 facere: ferre <u>BO</u>
243 posset: possit <u>D</u>
244 si: sic <u>B</u>
244 posset: possit <u>D</u>
244 sed: quia <u>BO</u>
246 parte . . . istius: huius postionis <u>N</u>
246-47 et . . . fundata <u>om.B</u>
248 arguenda: arguta <u>BO</u>
248-49 insufficientia: insufficientiam <u>ND</u>
249 secundo: et <u>N</u>
249 consequentis: consequente <u>N</u>
250 proportionem: proportionalitatem <u>D</u>
252 <u>post</u> De <u>add.D</u> talibus
252 autem <u>om.BD</u>
252 ubi: in quibus <u>N</u>
253 moventia: mobilia <u>N</u>
253 nihil: ubi <u>O</u>
254 ista: haec <u>BO</u>
256 et . . . tarditate <u>om.O</u>
257 mobile . . . movere <u>om.N</u>
258 <u>post</u> mobile <u>add.N</u> dupla tarditate
259 <u>post</u> quaelibet <u>add.N</u> potentia
260 Similiter autem: aequaliter <u>B</u>
261 et dupla: dupla <u>B</u>
262-63 igitur ab . . . sine fine iter.<u>B</u>
262 et a <u>om.N</u>
262 et a: et <u>D</u>, <u>om.N</u>
265-66 potest in . . . duplari: est infinitum duplum <u>B</u>
266 sit <u>om.N</u>
267 Volvatur: Volvetur <u>N</u>, velocitatur <u>D</u>
268 aliqua: alia <u>D</u>
269 A: supra <u>N</u>
269 ut est: potest <u>BO</u>, id est <u>D</u>
270 facile: faciliter <u>B</u>
270 demonstrare: est demonstrari <u>N</u>, demonstrari <u>B</u>
270 Tunc: et <u>Q</u>, etiam <u>B</u>
271 alligetur: colligetur <u>O</u>
275 et: vel <u>D</u>, <u>om.N</u>
275 ideo: et <u>BO</u>

276 et <u>om</u>.D

277 <u>post</u> quo et <u>add</u>.N terminos

278 locum: longum <u>N</u>, latum <u>O</u>, locus <u>B</u>

278 pertransitum <u>om</u>.B

278 Igitur . . . actu <u>om</u>.B

281 etiam: primo <u>N</u>

281 <u>ante</u> si <u>add</u>.D et

282 per cordam cum manu: cum manu per cordam <u>D</u>

283 <u>ante</u> quia per <u>add</u>.BO et

283 per <u>om</u>.BO

283 hominis: huius <u>N</u>

285 per: secundum <u>N</u>

285 <u>ante</u> moto <u>add</u>.B toti

287 positio: opinio <u>N</u>

287 arguenda: arguendo <u>N</u>

288 positionis: positionem <u>N</u>

290 solus <u>om</u>.BDO

290 adiungatur: coniungatur <u>BO</u>

291 multo: multum <u>DO</u>

292 Et: illud <u>D</u>, idem <u>B</u>

292 ad: super <u>B</u>

293 movet: movetur <u>BO</u>

293 insensibiliter: insensibili <u>O</u>

293-94 et volvit. . . insensibili <u>om</u>.BO

295 tantum: totum <u>O</u>

295-96 circumvolvet: circumvolvit <u>D</u>

296 multum: multo <u>B</u>

297 sensui: sensibili <u>B</u>

297 constat: constabit <u>BO</u>

299 etiam <u>om</u>.B

300 ista <u>om</u>.BO

300 velocitatum: velocitatis <u>N</u>

304 autem <u>om</u>.B

304 <u>ante</u> quae <u>add</u>.N ille

304 istam: ille <u>D</u>, <u>om</u>.N

304 fundare videntur: fundaverunt <u>B</u>

305 volentes: velocitates <u>D</u>

306 motibus: mobilibus <u>B</u>

307 intelligunt: intendunt <u>BO</u>

307 quod sequitur <u>om</u>.D

308 agentia: agenda <u>N</u>

309 quarti: quarto <u>B</u>

310 intelligit: intendit <u>N</u>

310 quod quanto: per quanto <u>BO</u>

311 propter: per <u>N</u>

311 incorporeitatem: incorporalitatem <u>D</u>

313 <u>post</u> quanto <u>add</u>.N est

314 illud: idem <u>BO</u>

315 quam: proportione illorum <u>D</u>

316 moventium: motuum <u>N</u>

317 ostendetur: ostenditur <u>N</u>, ostenderetur <u>O</u>

317 Et <u>om</u>.N

317 alia: autem <u>N</u>

317-18 similiter est glosanda: est glosanda similiter <u>B</u>

318 et illa: illa <u>B</u>

318 primi: primo <u>D</u>

318 et mundo <u>om</u>.D

318 enim <u>om</u>.B

319 supponatur: supponitur <u>BO</u>

319 <u>post</u> pluri et <u>add</u>.NBOD in, <u>correxi secundum textum latinicum Aristotelis</u>

319 tempore: tempus <u>N</u>

319 <u>post</u> pati <u>add</u>.D tempora

321 illud <u>om</u>.BO

323 quae dicit <u>om</u>.BO

323 <u>post</u> dicit <u>add</u>.NBO quod

330 Cum <u>om</u>.D

330 id est: et <u>N</u>

331 id est: id est ad <u>D</u>, et ad <u>N</u>

332 sit: sicut <u>B</u>

333 intelligeret: intelliget <u>N</u>, intelligitur et <u>D</u>

334 aliud: aliquod <u>N</u>

336-37 ista . . . patet: istam patet glosa sequentium auctoritatum <u>D</u>

338-40 allegata . . . ponderis <u>om</u>.BO

339 Inter . . . id est <u>om</u>.D

339 quaelibet <u>CVX</u>: quaedam <u>N</u>

340 velocitatis: velocitas <u>NDVCX</u>, <u>correxi</u>

342 tamen: autem <u>BO</u>

343 ponit: proponit <u>BO</u>

343 probantia: probantem <u>N</u>

344 autem: tamen <u>ND</u>

344 quod: quia <u>BD</u>

345 <u>ante</u> ad <u>add</u>.N praedictam

346 quod: et quod <u>O</u>, et quem <u>B</u>

346-48 nulla est . . . ideo quem om.BO

347 excessus: accessus D

347 et om.D

348 illius: istius D, ita N

348 conclusionis om.N

348 praetendunt: praecedunt D

350 intellectum praedictum: intellectum datum N, praedictum intellectum D

352 designantes: distinguentes N

353 primo om.N

357 minorem esse: maiorem esse O, esse maiorem B

358 Istud . . . obviat: illud non obviat autem B

358-59 primo erat datum: primo datam B

360 proportione: proportionem D

360 maioris: maius N

362 quam minoris: quam minor D

362 seu lineae om.N

364 capit: capto B

364-67 duo . . . maiori om.BO

365 eorum: illorum D

366 ante aliud add.D ad

366 compositum: oppositum BNO

367 appositi: oppositi O, appositus B

367-68 per tempus: quia tempus BO

369 descensui maiori descensui: descensu maiori descensu B

370 est om.B

372 supposito: opposito D

374 maioris: maior D

374 cuius om.BO

375 ita quia: quod D

375 erat: est D

376 quorumlibet: quorumdem D

376 inaequalium: inaequalia N

377 suorum: duorum BO

379 prius: primo BDO

380 illi: hoc N

381 suorum: duorum BO

383 maioris: maiori D

383 suorum: duorum BO

384 ante autem add.D aliquorum

385 erit . . . demonstratum: apparebit B

386 dicendum om.D

388 ante est vera add.B adducta

388 semper dupla: propter dupla quod dupla O

388 minoris: minori D

389 mobili: mobilis O

390 in . . . tempore: inaequalitate N

391 posset: possit B

391 movere: moveri D

391-92 idem . . . movere om.D

391 idem: vel illud BO

392 posset: possit BO

392 illud: idem N

394 virtutem: velocitatem BO

394 aliquando: alteri NO

395 velocitatis prioris: velocitati priori N, velocitas priorum D

395 autem om.D

396 vero om.B

396 ex om.D

396 clarum: declaratum N

397 vero om.B

397 post opinio add.B est quae

397 est om.O

397 nec: neque N

397 aliquis: aliquid est D

398 potentiae om.N

398 et om.D

399 non: nec B

400 mobilis: mobilem N

400-1 quoddam: quod N

401 habitudinem: hereditatem D

401 motoris: moventis BO, motorum D

402 super: per D

402 auctoritatem om.DBO

402 ante Averrois add.DO super

402 Averrois: Averroem BO

403 79: 7 D

403 eiusdem: cuiusdam N

403-4 conclusionis: quaestionis N

404-5 nec infinita om.B

405 corporibus: corporalibus N

407 enim: vero BO

407 et om.N

408 proportionem: proportiones
  N
410 sequi om.ND
410 post quod add.D sequitur
410 est: sit N
411 nec maior: maior B
411 vel: nec ND
411 ante rei add.N moti et
412 non: vel B
412 sed: vel B
412 forma om.N
414-15 definitiones proportionis:
  definitionem proportionum N
421-22 Igitur . . . specialissimae
  om.BO
421 Igitur: et D
421 substantiam: substantia N
422 est om.ND
423 per activum: in activum N
424 Et om.D
425 versus finem om.B
425 debent: habent N
426 comparari om.N
426-27 comparationis quam:
  corporis tam O, tam B
427 seu: quam BO
428 nullam: naturam D
428 habentes: habent BO
429 motivae om.D
430 quia: quae N
431 aliud: ad excessum D
432 excellitur: exceditur D
434 motiva om.N
435 simpliciter: similiter NDO
436 ante est add.D una
437 tantum om.N
438 excellentia: excellentibus
  ND
438 quae: quod D
440 Ad idem: praeterea Aristoteles B
440 Aristotelis om.B
440 septimo: octavo NBOD, correxi
441 determinat: determinatur N
441 conferente: cum felicitate B
442 itaque: itacumque B
442 excellens quidem: excedens
  quod D

442-43 autem quod inexistit:
  autem quod inexcedit D, aliquam vim excedit N
444 est: esset BO, erit D
445 positio om.DO
446 quod non: quod OB
447 tunc: tantum BO
448 epogdous: opogidus O, ap-
  podeus D, opodisus B, epo-
  dus N, correxi
449 diapente in: diapente OB
450 quae: qui B
450 duplo: dupla B
451 in tripla: est tripla O
452 fundatur: fundari NO
454 38: 28 N, 368 O, 37 B
454 post probat add.N quod
455 per: propter B
456 in om.N
456 apparet: apparuit N
456 Et: similiter B, Et universaliter O
457 et mundo om.NDO
457 65: 6 id est O
459 posset: potest BD
459 finitum: infinitum B
460 post finitum add.B acceptum
  sicut totum
460 post potest add.D in, add.B
  movere in
460 movere om.B
460 partem: partis D
460 illius: huius N, istius D
461 habet: habens D
462 post movens add.BO et
463 scilicet om.N
463 per om.NBO
463-64 duodecimam: 16 OBD,
  om.N, correxi
464 quinti: quinto N, om.D
464 Elementorum: et B, om.O
464 Euclidis om.B
464 sic: sicut ND
465 sicut: sic N
466 ante Ex add.B et tunc arguit
467 in . . . tempore: inaequaliter
  BDO
470 secundum istam: si istam O,
  si secundum istam B

470 ante veritatem add.N rei
471 Et om.BO
472 in om.D
475 aliquam: aliam D
475-76 acceptam: accepta BO
476 Aristoteles . . . Averroes:
     Et Averroes et Aristoteles N
476 ante multis add.N in
477 motoris . . . motae: rei
     moventis ad rem motam vel
     ad potentiam rei motae N
478 Et om.D
478 post patet add.N quod
479 rei motae om.BO
479 aliqua: alia D
481 post autem add.D opiniones
     vel
481 post pro add.D illa
481 adductae om.BO
482 praelibatam: allegatam D
483 ante proportio add.N non est
483 non om.N
484 proprie: propria N
484 dicta om.N
484 post communiter add.N
     dicta
485 distinctionem: definitionem
     N
486 intelligitur om.D
487 ante et add.N dicta
487 et om.D
487-88 Notum . . . quod: Notum
     est enim N, non tamen in
     quod D
488 sit: fit N
488 et scientior: subtilior N
489 et similibus: similibus D
489 et in: in D, cum B
490 vel: nec O
493 ante verum add.BO quod
494-95 communiter: naturaliter
     N, om.D
496 dividitur in: dividitur per N,
     dividitur D
496 et in: et D, et etiam B
496 post excellitur add.D in ex-
     cedens et in excessum
497 quod om.D
497 ita et: ita N, sic etiam D

498 in illud: illud D
498 duplex: duplum N, dupliciter D
499 proprie isto: isto N
501 Excellens iter.BO
501 communiter iter. BDO
501 partitur: percipitur D
502 communiter om.B
503 illius: eius N
504 qua: quam NDO
505 post quae add.D etiam
505 ante excellente add.N poten-
     tia, add.D potentia et
505 virtualiter . . . potentia
     om.ND
505 continetur: continentur O
507 in illud: etiam in illud N,
     illud D
508 extrinsecum: excessum BO
509 Et sic: Et sicut N, sic D
509 moventis: motae N, motoris
     D
509 et resistentiae: resistentis
     BO
510 excedens: excellens BO
511 capiatur: accipitur N
513 duplum potest: dupla potest
     BDO
516 motoris: motorum maioris D
516 ponendum: dicendum N,
     illeg. BO
517 Haec . . . dicetur om.BO

CAPITULUM TERTIUM

1 ante His add.D Prima pars tertii capituli
1 His: Eis B
1 igitur: autem N
1 ante nebulis add.O affugatis,
   add.B effugatis
1 flatibus: per logibus D, flacti-
   bus O
1 effugatis om.OB
2 lumen: lumine D
3 post scientiae add.N ut
3 veritatis: veritati DO
4 motoris: motorum D
9 fuerint: fiat D, om.N
11 reliqui: relati qui O

11 reliquum: relatum O
12 diversatur: diversabitur N, diversitatur O, diversarum diversabitur B
13 diversabitur om.B
13 istam: dictam B, dimidiam O
14 infra in: infram NBO
14 eodem: eadem NB
14 diversitas: diversitatis O
14 post et add.O cum diversatur proportio diversabitur motus
16 motivas et resistivas: motivam et resistivam ND
17 Et: Etiam Aristoteles D
19 rei motae: moti DO
19 quanto: quando N
20 et om.D
20 proportio om.O
22 ex: de N
22 duplicatione: duplatione D
23 motoris: motorum D
23 duplicationem velocitatis: du-plationem esse velocitatis D, duplam velocitatem N
26 dupla: erit dupla B, sit dupla D, erit duplum O
27 post om.ND
27 ante dicit add.N sic
27 post dicit add.N quod
31 tertio om.DO
32 primam: tertiam N
32 volunt: ponunt D, voluntin N
33 motoris: motorum BD
33 sequitur: sequatur D
33 aequalis velocitas: aequalitas velocitatis N
34 Aequalitas: aequaliter O
34 igitur: autem D
34 mota: motam D
35 posita . . . aequalis: positam potest primo talis N, ponitur aequalis BO
36 primo remota: prima remota D
36 primo removetur: removetur BO
36 aequalitas: aequalis BO
38 ante in add.D proportionis
38 istius: huius N
39 proportionis: proportionum D, proportionalis O

40 positio: opinio D
40 potest: videtur B
41 velocitatum: velocitatis D
41 iam: istarum N
42 post sunt add.B iam
42 tantum om.D
42 remanet: manet N
43 vera om.B
45 sequitur: sequeretur B
45 proportionem: proportio O
45-46 resistivas: resistentiarum D
46 et: vel BO
46 econtrario: econtra NO
48 velocitates: velocitas N
49 econtrario: econtra ND
49 hoc: haec B
49-50 proportionalitate: propor-tione NB
51 secunda conclusio om.ODB
51 Si: sed O
51 moti: motus N
52 ante potentia add.D tunc, add.O autem
52 geminata: duplata N, duplicata D
54 Hanc: hac B
54 ostensive: ostensione BDO
54 demonstres: demonstras D
54 Sit: si O
55 ipsius om.BO
55 potentiae om.N
56 A om.BO
58 proximam: maximam N
58 praecise. . . velocius: in duplo velocius praecise N
58 moveat B: movebit N
60 Tertia conclusio om.BDO
60 potentiae: potentia O
60 moventis: motoris BO
61 eiusdem: ipsius N
62 post moti add.O in
62 duplata: dupla ND
62 rationaliter: rationem N
64 Quarta conclusio om.BOD
64-67 Si potentiae . . . ostensive om.BO
66 attinget: attingit D
67 capituli om.N
67 per om.N
68 Quinta conclusio om.DBO

68 post Si add.D fuerint
69 sit om.D
71 tertiam: quartam NB
71 et: ad O, et per D
71 concludetur ostensive: ostensione concluditur D
72 Sexta conclusio om.BDO
73 dupla potentia: duplata potentia N
74 duplum: duplam D
74 excrescet: excresceret O
74 istam: ista O
75 ostensione. . . patebit: ostensive satis patebit N, similiter
   patefiet faciliter B, similiter
   patefiat faciliter O
76 Septima conclusio om.BDO
77 minor: maior BO
79 ostensive: ostensione D
79 patebit: parebit O
80 proportione: proportio N
80 inaequalitatis: aequalitatis O
82 octavam: secundam D
83 suppositione: propositione B
83 nota: vera O
84 vel: et N
87 fieri om.O
88 ante suppositione add.D cum
90 sufficit producendum: ad producendum motum est sufficiens D
90 erit: est N
92 ante et add.N dari
94 post Hoc add.B patet
95 suppositione: propositione B
95 nota: vera O
96 in: et N
97 Quantumcumque: quantumlibet BO
99 et: in D
99 potest: posset N, posse DBO,
   correxi
100 enim om.N
100 post levi add.OB et
100 quantumlibet: quantumque D,
    quamlibet O
100 habens: habet D
101 parvi: parvum NBO
101 ut desideras: sicut desideratur N
101-2 Et subtilietur: subtilietur B

103 proportioni om.N
104 ponantur illeg.N
104 illo: eodem D
104 minorem: maiorem NO
106 habeat om.N
106 post resistentiam add.N habeat
108 Iterum: item N
108 condensetur: quidem sequitur
    BO
108 B: A BO
109 proportione: proportio N
110 movetur: movebitur B
113 proportioni: proportio D
113 A: B OB
114 huius: habet N
114-15 aequevelociter: aequali-
    ter N
116 haberet: habebit motum N
116 in . . . motum: in vacuo N, in
    medio motum D
117 aliquod: ad NO
117 B om.OB
117 illo: illa NDO
118 maiori: maioritate N
118 positum: possit BO   ,
119 descendit: descendet O
119 ante medium add.N illius
120 duo om.NB
121 simplicis: simpliciter O
122-23 tarditas per: tarditas D,
    gravitas per N
123 subtiliationem et condensa-
    tionem: subtilitatem et con-
    densitatem O
124 duplicari: duplari D
124 quod: quidem B, ut D, om.N
125 subtiliationem: subtilitatem
    NBO
125 correlarium: corporeum O,
    quo relatium D, correlarium
    sufficienter B
126 post praedictis add.N satis
126 sufficienter om.B
128 motores: moventes N
129 suis om.BO
131-133 compositionis . . . talia
    gravia om.B
132 in aequilibri: inaequali NBO,
    in aequilibri ubi O
132 suspendantur: suspendatur O

134 et: C O
134 levitas: levitatis O
134 similiter: sit BO, om.D
135 autem: ergo D
135 sit eiusdem: eiusdem D
137 octavam: sexti B
137-38 congregata: aggregata D
138 adiuncta: adunata O
139 secundam: tertiam N, quartam O
140 conclusionis om.DBO
141 in: de D
141-42 praedictorum disputatione: praedictarum disputative N
143 istam: primam BO
143 positionem: opinionem N
144 omnia om.B
144 alia opinionum: aliqua opinionem NBO
145 sunt: fuerint B
145 silendum: soloendum D, sciendum O
145 quia: quod O
145 eis prius: his per DB, his per primum O
147 videntur: videtur B, visum N
147 inconvenientia: inconsequentia NB
148 post ad add.B sua
149 sequitur: detur D
149 quod: quia BO
153 ante minor add.N vero
154 et sint: sint D
154 inaequales om.BO
154 post uniformes add.B sumas, add.O sumes, add.D vero
155 et C: et sit C BO
155 ante minor add.BO vero
155 dividit: dividat B
156 istae om.B
156 divisiones: termini OB
156-57 tempus: tempore O
157-58 pertransit enim: et pertransibit N
159 Iterum: item N
159 manente: manifeste B
159-61 minoretur . . . secundum om.B

160 movetur: moveatur D
160 et om.D
161 ante Rursus add.B tunc A dividit et movetur velocius quam in secundo casu
161 Rursus: sive BO
161 etiam: tunc D
163 movetur: movebitur DO
162-63 Tunc . . . casu om.B
163 secundo: primo D, alio O
165 ante quod add.N est
166 tempus: tempore O
167-69 Et ideo . . . aequevelociter om.BO
168 dividit de C: de C dividit D
170 primae om.NOB
173 C est maius E: est maius C igitur B, om.O
173 ergo: et N, om.B
173 huius om.DB
173 post primi add.O ad
174 trium . . . comparatum: iterum comparetur N, trium ad illa comparativa BO
176 et mundo om.ND
176 capitulo de infinito om.BO
177 probantur: probat N
177 duae: tres OB
178 et om.N
179 proportionalia: proportionabilia B
181 ibi: in N, om.O
181 Et: ibi et O, om.N
182 proportionalia: proportionabilia B
182 aequali: econtra N, est O
183 aut alia: ad aliquas D
183 et: in D
184 essent: erunt DO
184 proportionales: proportionalia O
185 B: C BDO
185 sint: sicut N, fuerint D
188 proportione: proportio BO, ratione N
189 Non . . . aequales om.ND
190 ante non add.N quod
190 esse: est N
191 in om.N

191 agendi: agentis <u>O</u>
191 ad <u>om.N</u>
192 sed . . . non: si quantitative <u>BO</u>, secundum quantitatem <u>N</u>
194-95 resistendi . . . qualitate <u>om.B</u>
195 sic: sicut <u>NDB</u>
195 media: ipsam <u>D</u>
196-97 quae est: est <u>OB</u>
197 vel: et <u>N</u>
197 temporis: temporalis <u>N</u>
198 <u>ante</u> quod <u>add.N</u> est
200 proportionalitate: proportione <u>NDB</u>
201 et: vel <u>BO</u>
201 vel: et <u>N</u>
201 <u>ante</u> quoad <u>add.O</u> scilicet
202 in: et in <u>N</u>
202-3 proportionalitate: proportione <u>NDB</u>
203 correspondenter: correspondentium <u>D</u>
203-4 videlicet: scilicet <u>BO</u>
205 auctoritates allegatae: auctoritas allegatorum <u>N</u>
206-7 simpliciter: similiter <u>NB</u>
207 aliqua: alia <u>O</u>
208 <u>post</u> tamen <u>add.BO</u> alii
208 maioris: maior <u>D</u>
208 et <u>om.B</u>
208 minoris: minor <u>D</u>, minoris sit <u>O</u>
209 alicui: illi <u>N</u>, aliae <u>B</u>, aliteri <u>D</u>
209 pars: scilicet <u>N</u>
209 quae est: sit <u>D</u>, <u>om.BO</u>
210 est <u>om.BO</u>
212 <u>post</u> duobus <u>add.D</u> agentibus
212 aequalibus: aequaliter <u>B</u>
213 sit: est <u>D</u>
214 dividentur quoniam: divideretur quandoque <u>N</u>, dividuntur quoniam <u>DB</u>
214-15 et passa: et passiva <u>O</u>, activa et passiva <u>B</u>
215 Igitur: autem <u>D</u>
215-16 pertransit: pertransivit <u>D</u>, pertransibit <u>O</u>

216 enim <u>om.O</u>
216-17 est minoris: maioris <u>D</u>
217 quod <u>om.BO</u>
217 satis . . . scies: faciliter satis scies <u>DO</u>, satis scies faciliter <u>B</u>
218 C dividit: C <u>O</u>
218 de: dum <u>N</u>
219 moventur: movebuntur <u>BO</u>
219-20 tunc pars: tunc scilicet <u>N</u>
220 <u>post</u> terrae <u>add.N</u> facient
221 essent: esset <u>NB</u>
221 simpliciter: similiter <u>B</u>
223 tripliciter: dupliciter <u>BO</u>
224-25 Et . . . tripliciter: in aequalitative dupliciter <u>BO</u>
225 et utroque: in utroque <u>BO</u>
226 hoc <u>om.N</u>
226 est <u>om.DBO</u>
226 aequalitas: aequalitatis <u>BO</u>
227 Intrinsece: in virtute <u>D</u>
227 esse <u>om.BO</u>
228 ac: et <u>N</u>, aut <u>D</u>
228 intrinsecas <u>om.BO</u>
229 aequefacilia: aequefacilis <u>N</u>
229 <u>post</u> illa <u>add.N</u> esse
230 sua <u>om.N</u>
231 aliquid enim: aliquod enim <u>D</u>, enim <u>B</u>
231 per aliquid: per aliquod <u>D</u>
233 esset: fuerit <u>ND</u>
234 dicemus: dicetur <u>N</u>
235 aliqua <u>om.D</u>
236 intrinsece qualitative <u>om.O</u>
236-37 tantum: tamen <u>D</u>
237 et <u>om.N</u>
237 coniunctim: iunctim <u>D</u>
237-39 Unde . . . oportet <u>conferimus mss. tota</u>
237 Unde: dum <u>D</u>, <u>om.V</u>
237 possunt: possint <u>N</u>
237 esse: et <u>OBNCV</u>, <u>om.D</u>
238 partes: et tunc talia <u>X</u>
238 divisiva: divisive <u>ND</u>, divisi <u>C</u>, divisae <u>V</u>
238 aequalia: aequales <u>NV</u>, inaequalia <u>X</u>, aequalitate <u>D</u>
238 in virtute: divise <u>C</u>

238 Divident: dividatur <u>N</u>, dividendi dividerent <u>X</u>, dividentur <u>V</u>

238 celeritate: velocitate <u>V</u>, celeritati <u>C</u>

238-39 consimili: consimile <u>D</u>

239 aequali: aequalitate <u>V</u>

239 tempore <u>om.V</u>

239 sic pars: sit pars <u>D</u>, sic supposita <u>N</u>

239 et pars: et supposita <u>N</u>

240 aequales: aequalis <u>ND</u>

240 quantitative: quantitatis <u>D</u>

242 obicitur . . . eam: contra hanc obicitur <u>N</u>

242 Tunc: et etiam <u>BO</u>

243 ferrum . . . magnum: traheret ferrum parvum quam magnum <u>D</u>, traheret ferrum magnum quam parvum <u>BO</u>

243 enim <u>om.D</u>

244 tamen <u>om.N</u>

244 moveatur: motus <u>O</u>, movetur <u>B</u>

245 contignatus: cum <u>B</u>

245 quod: quia <u>BO</u>

245 eo: ea <u>B</u>

246 ipse: ipsa <u>B</u>, ipsum <u>N</u>

247 ferro <u>om.N</u>

247 eidem: ei <u>N</u>

248 moto: motae <u>BO</u>

248 illud: illo <u>D</u>

251 Et etiam: Et tunc <u>N</u>, etiam <u>O</u>, <u>om.B</u>

251 tunc: igitur <u>BO</u>, <u>om.N</u>

251 illud: idem <u>O</u>

252 latus magnetis: latum magnetum <u>N</u>

252 secundum: tunc per <u>D</u>

253 si <u>om.N</u>

255 cum Averroe: quod Averroes <u>BO</u>

255 septimo: octavo <u>O</u>

256 trahit: attrahit <u>BO</u>

256-57 cum . . . certam: cum praedictam suppositionem <u>BO</u>

257 suscipit: suscepit <u>O</u>

257-58 movetur . . . tempore: movebitur ad illum quam idem magnes in aequali tempore <u>BO</u>

257 illud: illum <u>D</u>

258 Idem <u>om.N</u>

258 alterare: alterari <u>D</u>

259 <u>ante</u> illa <u>add.N</u> vel

260 movebitur: movetur <u>D</u>

262 quod <u>om.BO</u>

263 movetur: moveatur <u>D</u>

265 causatam: tantam <u>O</u>

265 ferro: ferrum <u>BO</u>

266 tantum: tamen <u>BO</u>

266 coniungi: contingi <u>ND</u>

266 illo: eo per definitionem tantam in ferro a magnete ferrum tantum appetit coniungi cum isto <u>D</u>

267 illa <u>om.D</u>

267 dispositio: dispositione <u>N</u>

268 vel: ut <u>BO</u>

268 <u>post</u> possit <u>add.D</u> se

268 se <u>om.D</u>

269 eo: illo <u>N</u>

270 videlicet: videt <u>N</u>

271 <u>post</u> quod <u>add.N</u> vulgus, <u>add.</u> <u>D</u> est

271 est <u>om.D</u>

271 elevare: levare <u>N</u>

272 sive sit suppositum: cum sit sibi suppositum <u>D</u>

272 sit inclusum: inclusum sive non <u>D</u>

273 <u>ante</u> per <u>add.B</u> ponitur

273 <u>post</u> se <u>add.DO</u> penitus

275 Et . . . quoque: Ex hoc <u>N</u>, ex hoc quoque <u>D</u>

276 aequilibri: aequali virtuti <u>BO</u>

276 idem: illud <u>D</u>

276 absque: sine <u>N</u>

277 ponderabunt: ponderabit <u>D</u>

278 nonae conclusionis: instantiae <u>BO</u>, decimi <u>D</u>

278 instatur: movetur <u>O</u>

279-80 sufficiet: sufficienter <u>DO</u>

280 causandum: causandi <u>D</u>

280 <u>post</u> minor <u>add.DO</u> ita

280-81 sine fine: in infinitum <u>N</u>

281 motoris: moventis <u>D</u>

281 proportioni: proportionis sive <u>D</u>, proportio <u>O</u>

282 subduplae: quadruplae <u>B</u>

282 causandum: causandi D
284 illud: huius B
285 proportio motoris: potentia
motiva D
286 et . . . infinitum om.D
286 post infinitum add.B movere
286 movendum: motum DO
286-87 tunc existente: inexistente
B, etiam auxiliante O
288 posset om.D
288 motor: maior posset D
290 mobilis ad motorem om.N
291 maiori: motori N
291 ante fieri add.ND mobilis ad
motorem
292 octava: sententiae O
293 istis: isto N
293 dicendum: dicitur N
294 subduplari: subduplicari BO
294 numquam om.N
295 ante attinget add.N numquam
295 nec om.D
295 alicuius: alius D, om.N
297 proportionis om.N
298 ante numquam add.N quod
298 aequalitatem: aequalem D
299 alicuius: alius D
299 inaequalitatis: inaequalitas N
299 maioris: maius D
299-300 augmentari: augeri D
300 post ut add.B patet
300 septimam: primam D
300 evidenter om.N
302 obiectionibus: omnibus D
302 sufficiunt: sufficient N, sufficiant BO
302-3 Haec . . . praedictas om.N
303 praedictas: prius dictas O,
om.B

CAPITULUM QUARTUM

1 ante de add.B per praedictas
2 sequitur: sequuntur D
3 velocitatum: velocitatis D
4 comparatione: comparationes
N
4 quantitates: quantitatem D

4 motus: moti ND
5 autem: enim N
5-6 et suppositiones om.N
6 eas quasdam: eos N
7 sunt inventae: inveniuntur N
9 figura: linea BO
10 patet om.N
10 post Euclidis add.N patet
11 quarum: quorum B
12 continentia: contingentia BO
13 sunt reperta: reperiuntur N
13 Elementorum om.BO
13 Euclidis: capitulo O
15 opposita: omnia O
15 potest: patet NB
15 haberi: habere B
15 ex om.O
16 Elementorum om.BO
16 Euclidis: capitulo O
17 sunt istae: autem sunt istae D,
om.N
18 invicem om.N
18-19 Elementorum om.B
19 Euclidis om.DO
20 multiangularum: multiangular-
ium N, multiangulorum B, mul-
torum angulorum D
21 alteram: alterum N
21 sui om.N
22 post latus add.D alterius
22 per: primus O, om.B
22-23 duodevicesimum: undevice-
simum ND, om.OB, correxi
23 Elementorum om.B
23 Euclidis om.DO
25 quadrati: quarti B
25 sui: suae DO
25 quadratum: quarti B
26 est om.D
26 duodecimi: primi B, om.N
26 Euclidis om.BO
28 Et om.N
28 De curvis: ceteris BO
31 sui: suo BO, suae D
31 proportio triplicata: proportione tripla D, om.BO
32 duodecimi: tredecimi N
32 Euclidis om.O

34 aequalibus om.BO
34 diametri: diametro D
35 Archimenidis: Euclidis BO
35 De curvis: de terminis O
38 sui: suae DO, om.N
40 duo: duorum N
40 per primam: per unam BO
40 et primam: et unam BO
42 consimilia: similia ND, con-
  similium B
43 quadratorum: quattuor B
45 duplicatam: duplatam D
45 illa: illo N
46 concludes: concludetur O
48 ante geminata add.N triplicata
  ista ex ex quinta
48 Istam: ista BO, om.D
49 per . . . conclusionem: conclusionem proximam N, proxima conclusio BO
49 adiutorio: adiuncto BO
49 quartae: quintae N
50 adiuncta: adiunctae N
50 suppositione om.N
50 demonstrabis: demonstrabi-
  tur D
51 proportio: primo O
51 demonstratur: ductarum B
52 circumferentiarum: circumferentia BO, circumferentiae
  D
53 triplicata: triplata D
53 post quarta add.D scilicet
54 sequitur: demonstratur N
56 superficiem: proportionem O
56 reliquae: alterius D
56 proportionis: proportionalis O
56 sui: suae DBO
58 Sint: sicut O
58 duo om.BO
59 aequalibus: quadralibus BO
59 diametris: diametri O
60 suorum om.O
60 similitudo om.N
61 et prima suppositione: primae
  suppositionis BO
61 quarta: secundo D
61-62 proportionalium: proportionum N

62 secunda: tertia D
63 ante Ex quo add.N Ex quo cum
  secunda definitione huius concluditur manifeste
63 suppositione huius: supposita
  huius N
65-66 unius. . .alterius: alterius N
66 circumferentiae om.N
67 ante unius add.N circumferentiae
67 ante maximi add.N alterius
67-68 ostenditur. . .dupla: invenitur dupla N, coniunctim
  fore duplex B, coniuncitur
  fore dupla O
68 per om.N
69 suppositione . . . concludes:
  concludes suppositione BO
72 vero A: vero BO
74 huius om.BN
75 Ergo D: Ergo C B, Ergo N
75 praecise: praecipue N
76 triplum E: tripla E NO, triplum B
76 E praecise: A praecise D
77 C om.N
77 semel: solum O
78 sesquialteri: sesquialterae N
78 D om.B
80 motibus: motibus et N
81 spatium: spatia N
81 enim om.BO
82 tamquam: tam O
83 eodem: et eodem BO
83 tempore: ordine D
83 Quae: qui BO
85 moveretur: moveret N
86 pedalis: duplae N
87-88 et . . . hora: subduplum
  non pertransiret nisi subduplum in ea et D, om.NB
88 duplae: duplic O, correxi
88 aequevelociter: aequaliter D
89 nec . . . tunc: non tamen BO
89 puncti nec: punctus vel B
90 corporis om.N
92 Alii: aliter O
93 sicut: secundum N

93 tempore: ordine <u>BO</u>
93-94 descriptarum: descriptam <u>BO</u>
94 autem <u>om.BO</u>
94 positio: opinio <u>D</u>
95 vero: enim <u>N</u>
95 proportionalitate: proportione <u>D</u>
96 multum: multis <u>OB</u>
96-97 temporibus: cuibus <u>B</u>, cuilibet <u>O</u>
97 motarum: motorum <u>O</u>
99 minus et: minus <u>BO</u>
99 aequale et: aequale <u>BO</u>, aequales et <u>D</u>
100 aequevelociter: aequaliter <u>D</u>, velocitas <u>B</u>
100-1 intendit per: intelligit ad <u>N</u>
101 terminos ad: ad <u>NBO</u>
101 a terminis: terminus <u>D</u>, a quibus <u>B</u>, <u>om.N</u>
102 distantes: distant <u>N</u>, <u>om.BO</u>
104 semidiametri circuli: semicirculi vel semicirculi <u>B</u>, semicirculi vel semitercirculi <u>O</u>
105 terminata: terminatae <u>B</u>
105 moverentur: moveretur <u>ND</u>
106 suo: sua <u>O</u>
106 huius: istius <u>D</u>
106 <u>post</u> conclusio <u>add.D</u> prius
106 prima <u>om.DB</u>
107 suo: suus <u>N</u>, suo medio <u>B</u>, suo modo <u>O</u>
108 <u>post</u> velocius <u>add.B</u> moveretur
108 suo: sua <u>OD</u>
109 diametro: diametri <u>D</u>
109 secundum illud: per idem <u>N</u>, <u>om.D</u>
110 moveretur: movetur <u>D</u>
110 velocius <u>om.B</u>
111 nullus punctus: nullum punctum <u>DO</u>
112 Non: Nec <u>N</u>
113 terminum unicum: unum terminum <u>B</u>, unicum tantum <u>O</u>
114 movetur: magis <u>O</u>
115 Ideo: quinto <u>O</u>

116 velocissime: vehementissime <u>BO</u>
117 ex: in <u>B</u>, <u>om.DO</u>
118-19 hoc vel: hoc nihil <u>B</u>, hoc videtur <u>D</u>
119 verum vel: visum <u>O</u>, verum <u>B</u>
119 est in: est <u>N</u>, in <u>OD</u>
120 magnum: maximum <u>BO</u>
121 sibi: ibi <u>N</u>
121 intellige: intelligas <u>N</u>, intelligere <u>B</u>
121 pro: in <u>O</u>
122 suprema: summa <u>O</u>
123 illud: istud <u>O</u>
124 localis: mobilis <u>N</u>
125 Est ergo: ergo <u>B</u>, igitur <u>O</u>, ergo est <u>D</u>
126 <u>post</u> attenditur <u>add.B</u> velocitas motuum
126 sed: oportet <u>N</u>
128 spatium <u>om.N</u>
129 moti: motus <u>D</u>, motus modo <u>BO</u>
130 localium <u>om.BOD</u>
130 velocitates et: velocitatem et <u>BO</u>, velocitas <u>N</u>
131 duorum: suorum <u>ND</u>
132 ordine: tempore <u>N</u>
134 pertransit: transit <u>BO</u>
135 per sextam: sexta <u>O</u>
136 autem <u>om.N</u>
138 levius: facilius <u>N</u>
141-42 <u>ante</u> tamquam <u>add.D</u> est
144 velocitas: velocitates <u>O</u>
145 existunt: erunt <u>O</u>
146 propositum: proportionem <u>D</u>
147 duorum: duarum <u>DB</u>
147 seu semidiametrorum: seu diametrorum <u>O</u>, <u>om.B</u>
149 diametrorum: diametri <u>BO</u>
149 semidiametrorum: semicirculorum <u>BO</u>
150 illorum: istarum <u>NO</u>, suarum <u>D</u>
151 per: et <u>BO</u>
152 quantum: ipsum <u>BO</u>
153 similiter: oportet <u>D</u>
153 probatur: probare <u>D</u>, proportio <u>OB</u>

153 eandem: est O̲B̲
154 et: seu D̲
154 semidiametrorum: semicir-
    culorum B̲O̲
154 quod: quia B̲
154 capitulum: casum D̲O̲
154 scies: scias O̲
156 ante Omnes add.D̲ tertia
156 duas: tres B̲O̲
156 circumferentias: circum-
    ferentes N̲
156 in eodem: eorumdem N̲
158 describentes: descriptarum
    B̲O̲
158 in: per D̲
160 enim om.B̲
160 quaedam: quidam O̲
161-62 aequinoctialis . . . circum-
    ferentia om.N̲
162 telluris: toluris D̲, telluri O̲,
    telluri al colub N̲
162 primam: unam B̲O̲
163 et om.B̲O̲
164 vero om.D̲
165 superficiem: superficiei N̲,
    om.D̲
165 describentis: describentes
    superficiem D̲, describantur O̲
166 eius: huius N̲
166 motus: motam D̲O̲
166 suum: suam D̲O̲
167 describat: describit N̲
167 circulum: circulorum N̲B̲
167 aliud om.D̲
167 punctum: puncti O̲, punctum
    puncta B̲
168 tertiam suppositionem: tres
    suppositiones B̲
169 parte: partis B̲
169 probatis: probati N̲, om.B̲
170 apparebit: apparebunt O̲
171 uniformiter: uniformes O̲
172 circumductorum: conductor-
    um B̲O̲
173 reliquo: recto O̲, reliquo
    modo D̲
174 proportio: proportione D̲
174 duplata: est duplicata B̲O̲
175 secundam: tertiam D̲

175 suppositionem om̲.N̲
177 demonstratur: demonstretur
    D̲
178 similiter: super D̲
178 describentis: describentes D̲
180 maiorem: minorem B̲
181 tres: tertiam N̲D̲
181 suppositiones: suppositionem
    D̲
182 scies: sciens N̲, scis B̲O̲
183 duarum om̲.N̲
187 suppositione om̲.B̲
188 concluditur: ostenditur B̲O̲
188 ostensive: ostensione D̲
189 partis om̲.B̲O̲
191 suos: duos B̲O̲
193 Ista: et istam D̲
193 partis: parte N̲B̲O̲
195 primi om̲.D̲
195 apparet: appareat B̲
197 faciliter om̲.O̲
198 post congruit add̲.B̲O̲ et
198 hucusque: hoc usque N̲
201 assumenda: assumpta B̲O̲
202 proportionalitate om̲.D̲
202 iunguntur: coniunguntur B̲O̲
202-3 Prima. . .textu: ut patet
    secundo Caelo, in commento
    dicente, habet auctor quan-
    dam proportionem aquam
    ad terram; et tertio De caelo,
    commento 42, dicit habent
    per se proportionaliter mag-
    nitudines consimilium par-
    tium satis, scilicet elementa
    adinvicem. Secundum auc-
    torem quod satis patet ex
    textu V̲, om̲.D̲N̲C̲, M̲S̲. X̲ i̲s̲-
    t̲a̲m̲ p̲a̲r̲t̲e̲m̲ c̲a̲p̲i̲t̲u̲l̲i̲ q̲u̲a̲r̲t̲i̲
    n̲o̲n̲ c̲o̲n̲t̲i̲n̲e̲t̲
204 habere quandam: habet quam
    de B̲, habere quam O̲
208 patet om̲.B̲O̲
209 debent: deberent D̲
212 terrae om̲.B̲O̲
212 eius: eiusdem O̲
213 vigesimam: tergesimam B̲O̲
213 partem: partis B̲, partes O̲
214 Alphraganum: Alfarabium O̲

214 Differentia: dicitur B, dictum O, scilicet differentia D
214 ubi: igitur B
215 propiorem lunae: propinqui-
tatem lineae B, propinquita-
tem lunae D, proportionalitatem liniae O
215 in: in tanta O, om.N
215 praedicta om.O
216 terrae: semicirculum B,
om.O
216 semidiametrum om.B
216 Thebit: Theolus B, Thebis N,
Thebius O
216 Chorae: Chori N, Thore B
217 dimissis: divisis N
217 in integris: integris DB
218 post autem add.B hi
218-19 demonstrativa om.B
219 probatio: primo O
219 Ptholemei: Tholomei N,
potest haberi BO
219 Thebit: gebis BO
221 est: enim BO
221 diametrorum: diametri N
222 ante ita add.O et
223 Est igitur: Est autem ND
224 diametrum: diameter NB
224-25 tenet nequaquam: tamen B
226 Sit: sicut BO, om.N
226 terrae om.N
226 tamquam: sicut D
227 velut: velit N, vel O, videlicet B
227 deinde: demum B
228 triplus om.NBO
228 scilicet: 6 O
228 etiam: igitur DBO
229 triplus om.N
229 igitur: autem N
231 post ultimum add.ODB et
232-33 quintam: septimam N
235 igitur haec est: haec igitur
est N, igitur est haec B
236 scilicet   om.N
236 coniunctim: coniunctorum BO
236 minimum: motum N, unum
BO
237 proportionalia: proportionabilia B

238 nota: vero O
238 habeant: habeat N, habent O
239 minimum: minus N
239 Et om.N
240 nota erit: non erit NB, nota
est D, vero erit O
240 post proportio add.N proportio
240 enim: autem O
243 igitur: quattuor O
243 continue om.ND
243 proportionales: proportion-
abiles B
244 1: 5 B
244 32: 33 N
244 32768: 33768 BO
244 coniunctim: coniuncti O
244 Huius: His B
245 compositi: comparati BO
247 32: 33 BO
247 proportione: proportio O
248 Rursum: rursus B
249 scilicet om.O
249 1089, 35937: 1889, 359737 B
249 37060: 37860 N, 37030 O,
37838 B
249 perficiunt: perficiant B
250 Huius autem: Huiusmodi
autem N, autem huius BO
251 maior: minor B
252 igitur om.N
252 proportione: proportio O
254 proportionem: proportione N
255 in om.N
257 proportione om.BO
257 seu: per BO
259 tunc: etiam BO
260 et: 8 et N, 4 et B, ·C· et O
260 8000: 8000 ad B, 8026 N
261 vera: quanta B
263 37060: 37860 B
264 Alphragani . . . numeratis:
Alphragani minutiis naturaliter N, secundum Alphra-
ganum minutiis numeratis B,
secundum Alfraganum min-
uties numeratis O
265 post ad 1 add.B et hoc est
quod ostendere volebamus
268 32: 33 O

268 et minor . . . 1 om.O
268-69 et hoc . . . ostendere om.
    NB
269 volebas: volebamus O, om.NB
270 ante spherae add.D igitur
    scilicet
271 31:33 O
271 post ad 1 add.N Hoc est quod
    ostendere volebamus
272 elementum: elementi NB
272-73 proximam: proximum O
274 isti om.ND
275 32, 1024, 32768: 33, 3024,
    33768 B, 23, 2024, 33768 O
275 si om.N
275 post tres add.N termini, add.
    D terminus
275 congregentur: congregetur D
276 constituent: constituet N
276 spheram: spheram composi-
    tam D, om.N
277 representat: representant DO
277 congregatum: aggregatum BO
277 si om.ND
277 quartus: quattuor D
278 dividatur: dividitur O
278 31 . . . et: 32 exhibit et N,
    31 existenti B, 33 existenti O
278 remanet: remanebit NBO
279 Quartus: cuius B, eius O
279 congregatus: congregatum D
282 quorumlibet: quorum O
283 quaelibet: quilibet O
283 eorumdem: eorum NB
285 Distantia: distantiam B
285 convexitatis: convexitates O
285 et om.O
286 continet: continebit B
286-88 Nam . . . spherae om.B
287 aeris om.O
288 ante ex add.O terrae
288 compositae: composita B
292 32: 33 BO
292 sequitur om.BO
293 disponantur: disponatur DO
294 inferiorum: infinitorum O
295 1057: 1857 B
298 A: 1 B
299 termini om.BO

299 proportionales: proportion-
    abiles B
299 1: in N, om.D
300 secundum secundam: per con-
    sequens BO
301 tripla: triplae DN
302 illa: ita ND
302 proportione A: proportio 10
    B, proportio 10, 1 O
303-5 Igitur . . . terrae om.D
304 minor tertia: maior secunda
    BO
304 tertia: secunda BO
306 Cum: cuius N, tamen B
308 proportione: proportio BO
309 proportionem decuplam: pro-
    portione decupla O
310 proportio: proportione O
310-11 diametrorum et semidia-
    metrorum: diameter semi-
    diameter B, diametri semi-
    diametri O
311 A plus: septemplus B
313 quodlibet: quod O
313 continere: continet NBO
314 post sibi add.B proximum
314 post tunc add.N ad
314 post elementorum add.N ele-
    mentorum
315 primam: istam BO, ultimam D
315 termini om.BO
316 congregati: aggregati N
316 1123: 11331 B, 1133 O
317 A om.BO
317 sicut: sive O
318 1123: 1133 BO
318 pars om.NB
320 hi: huius B, om.O
320-21 proportione undecupla:
    indecupla B
321 121, 1331: 12, 11331 B
321 maximi: maximum D
322 istorum: istarum O
325 est om.D
326 proportione: proportio O
326 1123: 1133 BO, 123 N
327 sequitur . . . ad 1 om.O
327 sequitur: sequeretur D
327 maiori: maior NB

328 transcendere: transcendent NO
328 huius: istius D
329 tertia om.O
330 spherae: spherae recte O, om.N
330-31 Ergo . . . terrae om.NBO
331-32 et . . . terrae om.BO
334 eandem om.BO
335 diametrorum: diametrum O
335-36 ante quorumlibet add.D ad
337 eorumdem: correspondenter BO
338 Punctum: potest tamen BO
339 multum: multis BO
339 convexitatem: convexitatis NB
339 situatur: situari BO
341 eius om.N
342 inevitabiliter: ineffabiliter N, inevidenter O

343 convexitatis om.B
345 Igitur . . . terrae om.B
345 distante: distantiae NO
346 multo: multum BO
346 lucide om.N
348 Perfectum . . . de om.B
348 ante igitur add.O est
348 est om.O
349 illius om.BO
349 motoris: moventes O
350 reperitur: invenitur vel reperitur B
351 Amen om.BO
352-53 Explicit. . .28: Expliciunt proportiones Bradelbardyn D, Explicit tractatus de velocitate motus O, om.B

APPENDIX

NOTES

BIBLIOGRAPHY

APPENDIX [1]

This is Proposition I, of the Liber de ponderibus ascribed to Jordanus Nemorarius, extant in several versions, of which only one, entitled "Elementa Jordani super demonstrationem ponderis" appears to be by Jordanus Nemorarius (the mathematician). The only printed edition, Jordani Nemorarii . . . De Ponderibus Propositiones XIII. . . editus . . . Petro Apiano, Nuremberg 1533, contains a version quite different from the "Elementa Jordani," to which is added a commentary which, though showing influence of the Elementa Jordani, is probably of mid 14th century origin. In both versions, however, the theorems themselves are identical, the variations being in the explanations and proofs (or "commentary").

Prop. I, of the version printed by Apianus (corrected from Cod. Vat. Latinus 2185), reads as follows:

Inter quelibet gravia est velocitatis in descendendo proprie, et ponderis, eodem ordine sumpta proportio; descensus autem, et contrarii motus, proportio eadem sed permutata.

Prop. I, of the "Elementa Jordani super demonstrationem ponderis," as given in MS. Bibl. Nat. (Paris) f. lat. 10252, reads as follows:

Inter quelibet gravia est velocitatis in descendendo, et ponderositatis, eodem ordine sumpta proportio; descensus autem et contrarii motus proportio eadem sed permutata.

The proof which Bradwardine ascribes to "unus commentator," is substantially that which is given in the Elementa Jordani; the version represented by Cod. Vat. lat. 2185, and printed by Apianus together with a later commentary, would seem to be the version which Bradwardine had in mind, when he said that the "auctor" gave no principles in proof of the theorem—since in this version there is no attempt at a proof. Thus Bradwardine's statements would seem to indicate that Jordanus Nemorarius was not the author of the Liber de ponderibus, but a commentator on it.

An edition of the various versions of the De ponderibus, together with numerous other associated treatises on statics found in mediaeval manuscripts along with the treatises ascribed to Jordanus, has been published by Ernest Moody and Marshall Clagett under the title, The Medieval Science of Weights, Madison, Wis., 1952. (See pp. 286-87 for a discussion of the question raised in this appendix.)

The principal modern study of the De ponderibus treatises, before that of Moody and Clagett, was Pierre Duhem's Les Origines de la Statique, Vol. I, Paris, 1905.

1. This Appendix concerns lines 236-38, page 96.

179

NOTES

INTRODUCTION

1. Spelled variously as Bragwardin, Branduardinus, Bredwardyn, Bradwardyn, de Bredewardina, Bernardinus, Bladvardinus, Brivardinus, Bradewardyn, Bradelbardin, Bredvardin, Bracwerdin, Bragberdino, Brabarbin, Bradualdus, Brabornardinus. There were yet other variants.
2. "Per similem etiam rationem, quicquid nunc scribo Oxoniae, scriberet pater meus Cicestriae, quia genuit me scribentem, imo avus et proavus, et ceteri genitores, ipsi quoque primi parentes nunc facerent omnia facta nostra." — De causa Dei contra Pelagium et de virtute causarum, ad suos Mertonenses, p. 559. Stephen Birchington (in Anglia Sacra, I, 42) says he was born at Hertfield in the Chichester diocese; William de Dene (Historia Roffensis, ibid., p. 375) gives Condenna (probably Cowden, in the Diocese of Rochester). Neither writer gives any supporting evidence.
3. W. R. W. Stephens, in The Dictionary of National Biography, s.v. Bradwardine.
4. This date apparently has, as its original authority, Sir Henry Savile's estimate appended to his 1618 edition of the De causa Dei. Savile suggests 1290 as a likely approximation, on the basis of Bradwardine's Proctorship at Merton in 1325. George C. Brodrick (Memorials of Merton College, p. 188) claims that Bradwardine "was an M.A. of some years' standing in 1323, when he first appears in the College books." It has been impossible to verify this earlier date, since Brodrick's work, though very possibly reliable, contains neither footnotes nor bibliography.
5. Munimenta academica, Part I: "Libri cancellarii et procuratorum," p. 113.
6. Walter F. Hook, Lives of the Archbishops of Canterbury, IV, 93; Thomas Rymer, Foedera, conventiones, literae..., IV, 190.
7. Stephens, in D.N.B., s.v. Bradwardine; John Pits, De illustribus Angliae scriptoribus, pp. 470-71.
8. Savile's edition, at the close of the text, gives the date and place of composition as 1344, London. H. Denifle and A. Chatelain (Chartularium Universitatis Parisiensis, II, 590) assign 1344 as the date of the De causa Dei on the basis of two manuscripts: Bibliothèque Mazarine, MS. 389, and Padua, Biblioteca Antoniana, MS. 170.

9. Stephens, in D.N.B., s.v. Bradwardine.
10. Rashdall speaks of Bradwardine as "the original and vigorous exponent of that Augustinian predestinarianism which so deeply colored the Wyclifite and Hussite movements." — The Universities of Europe in the Middle Ages, III, 268. John Wyclif was himself a Merton College man in the University generation immediately following that of Bradwardine, and it is perhaps of some interest to note that in his Logica he treats of local motion in the manner characteristic of the fourteenth-century natural philosophers of Merton. See Sebastian Hahn, "Thomas Bradwardine und seine Lehre von der menschlichen Willensfreiheit," Beiträge zur Geschichte der Philosophie des Mittelalters, V, 2.
11. Pits, p. 470; Bacondorpius, a contemporary and friend of Bradwardine at Merton College, is mentioned as having been a Carmelite theologian of some prowess. See Rashdall, op. cit., III, 267.
12. Henry Knighton, a contemporary, also writes in his Chronicon (II, 63): "Hic [Bradwardine] erat famosus prae ceteris clericis totius Christianitatis, in theologia praecipue, similiter et in ceteris scientiis liberalibus."
13. For an outline of Bradwardine's influence on contemporary and immediately succeeding theorists, see Anneliese Maier, "Der Funktionsbegriff in der Physik des 14. Jahrhunderts," Divus Thomas; see also Sec. 3 of this Introduction.
14. See Rashdall, op. cit., I, 449; II, 243.
15. Denifle and Chatelain suggest, on what appears to be very little ground, that the "Thome" mentioned among "Masters of Theology who, with Benedict VII, examined the question of Beatific vision" at Pont de Sorgue may have been Thomas Bradwardine. The record in question is dated, "1335, October 4, Avignon." — Op. cit., II, 453.
16. Stephens, in D.N.B.; Edwin Burton, in The Catholic Encyclopedia, s.v. Bradwardine, Thomas.
17. Stephens, in D.N.B., s.v. Bradwardine.
18. Continuatio historiae Dunelmensis, in Anglia Sacra, I, 765.
19. Ibid.
20. Stephens, in D.N.B., s.v. Bradwardine.
21. Ibid.; Burton, in Cath. Ency., s.v. Bradwardine. Birthington (in Anglia Sacra, I, 42) writes: "He was first Confessor to the King of England, with whom he was in France and Normandy and taught the King himself and the army also with salubrious advice and example, to the effect that by the power of God alone, and not by multitude of arms, the King of England finally vanquished his enemies."
22. Adam of Murimuth, Continuatio chronicarum, p. 201.
23. Historical Papers and Letters from the Northern Registers, p. 379.

24. Stephens, in D.N.B.; Burton, in Cath. Ency., s.v. Bradwardine.
25. Anglia Sacra, I, 375.
26. Canonici Lichfeldensis indiculus de successione Archiepisco-
    porum Cantuariensium, in Anglia Sacra, I, 119; Birchington,
    op. cit., p.42. Joshua Barnes, on evidence best known to him-
    self, presents a slightly different version of the election: "He
    [Bradwardine] was so far from being ambitious that he could
    hardly be prevailed upon to accept the prebend of Lincoln when
    it was offered, he then being chancellor of St. Paul's in Lon-
    don [sic]. He made no attempt to become archbishop, the Con-
    vention electing him, the king allowing the choice, and the
    pope (not knowing what went on) independently appointing him.
    He could have had the post at any time he wished, and the rea-
    son given by the king for turning down his earlier election was
    that he could not spare him from his person and could not see
    that Bradwardine wished it otherwise." — History of Edward III,
    p. 439.
27. Anglia Sacra, I, 42.
28. Stephens, in D.N.B., s.v. Bradwardine.
29. Anglia Sacra, I, 42.
30. See, e.g., ibid.
31. Ibid.
32. Konrad Gesner, Bibliotheca Universalis, I, 617.
33. George Sarton, Introduction to the History of Science, III, 669.
34. Barnes (op. cit., p. 439,) speaks of Bradwardine as "Doctor de
    Profundis"; Burton (in Cath. Ency., s.v. Bradwardine) and Ges-
    ner (loc. cit.) also refer to Bradwardine's De causa Dei as
    Summa Doctoris profundi. This usage is of some interest,
    since the work does not have the usual scholastic form of
    disputed Quaestiones or Distinctiones, but is, instead, of a
    mathematical form more closely akin to Spinoza's Ethica more
    geometrico demonstrata; Savile, in his preface to the 1618
    edition of the De causa Dei, claims that the title "Profundus"
    is recorded in the "old Merton Register" as having been im-
    posed by the Pope.
35. The present attempt to identify and describe Bradwardine's
    works suffers unavoidably from the fact that it is based al-
    most wholly on the evidence of secondary sources rather than
    on an examination of the works themselves. Among the long
    list of works attributed to Bradwardine by various authors,
    many must remain undescribed, several are undoubtedly no
    more than alternate titles for the same works, some may
    well be spurious, and some, perhaps, no longer extant. Be-
    cause of the inaccessibility of manuscripts and early printed
    editions, the present bibliography can, therefore, be little
    more than a critical resume of other biographical sources
    which are, all too often, themselves no more than transcrip-
    tions.

36. For a more complete description, see Hahn, op. cit.; J. F. Laun, "Thomas von Bradwardine, der Schüler Augustins und Lehrer Wiclifs," Zeitschrift für Kirchengeschichte, XLVII, (1928), 333, 356.

37. In addition to Gesner's use of the term, Summa, MS. Vat. Lat. 1040 (See Codices Vaticani Latini, Vatican City, 1931, II, i.) is also written under the title, "Summa de causa Dei contra Pelagium" (signed: 1411). Both Pits and Sarton attribute a Summa scientiarum to Bradwardine, Sarton identifying the Summa theologica with the Summa scientiarum. Without further substantiating evidence, it would seem less likely that the two Summae are the same work than that Summa theologica is an alternate title for the De causa Dei. No printed edition exists under either Summa title.

38. "Geometria speculativa Thome bravardini recoligens omnes conclusiones geometricas studentibus artium et philosophie aristotelis valde necessarias simul cum quodam tractatu de quadratura circuli noviter edito . . . ."—British Museum Catalogue of Printed Books (London and Beccles, 1938), s.v. Bradwardine, Thomas.

39. "Praeclarissimum mathematicarum opus in quo continentur . . . thome Bravardini arismetica et eiusdem geometria necnon et sapientissimi Pisani carturiensis perspectiva quae communis inscribitur cum acutissimis ioannis d'assia [i.e., Henrici de Hassia] super eadem perspectiva quaestionibus . . . acuratissime emendatum reverendum fratrem thomam duram." —Ibid. The British Museum Catalogue also lists two, later, Paris reprints of the Geometria speculativa. The earlier (1516) is interesting in that it gives a variant title for the work: "Breve compendium geometriae theoretice a Thoma bravardino primum ex libris Euclidis Campani Archimedis et aliorum compilatum: deinde nonnullis additionibus. P. Cirvelus Darocensis aliquantisper dilatatum." The later is listed as follows: "Geometria speculativa Thome Bravardini . . . . simul cum quodam tractatu de quadratura circuli noviter edito. Elementale geometricum ex euclidis geometria a Ioanne Voegelin . . . decerptum. Apud R. Chauldiere; Parisius 1530." Johann G. Graesse (Trésor de livres rares et précieux, I, 222) speaks of the 1495 Paris edition as having been reprinted there in the years 1505 and 1511, as well as in 1530; Lynn Thorndike and Pearl Kibre (Catalogue of Incipits of Mediaeval Scientific Writings in Latin, s.v. Bradwardine, Thomas) also list a Paris edition for the year 1503; Johan A. Fabricius (Bibliotheca Latina mediae et infimae aetatis, I, 248) lists Paris editions for the years 1504 and 1512; Pits (p. 470) cites a Venice edition for the year 1530.

40. See Moritz Cantor, Vorlesungen über die Geschichte der Mathematik, pp. 113-20; Sarton, III, 669.

41. Pits wrongly presents the title, <u>Geometrica principia</u>, as though it were a separate work, but includes an incipit, which, when compared with Thorndike and Kibre (<u>op. cit</u>., <u>s.v.</u> Bradwardine), shows it to be the same work as that ordinarily called <u>Geometria speculativa</u>.

42. <u>B. M. Cat.</u>, <u>s.v.</u> Bradwardine, Thomas.

43. The title page of this edition, as given by the <u>Gesamtkatalog der Wiegendrucke</u> (ed. Hiersemann, Leipzig, 1925—, Vol. I, cols. 389-90, Item 792, s.v. Albert of Saxony), is as follows: "Tractatus proportionum Alberti de saxonia. Tractatus proportionum Thome braduardini. Tractatus proportionum Nicholai horen. Venales reperiuntur Parisius in vico divi Jacobi. Juxta templum sancti yvonis sub signo Pellicani."

44. Quaestio de modalibus bassani politi. Tractatus proportionum introductorium ad calculationes suisset. Tractatus proportionum thome barduardini. Tractatus proportionum nicholai oren. Tractatus de latitudinibus formarum eiusdem nicholai. Tractatus de latitudinibus formarum blasii de parma. Auctor sex inconvenientium."—<u>B. M. Cat.</u>, <u>s.v.</u> Bradwardine, Thomas. Sarton (III, 671) cites a Vienna 1515 edition of the <u>De proportionibus</u>: it is spoken of as being in an abridged form and is, presumably, the <u>Tractatus epitomatus</u>; Pits (p. 470) also mentions a Venice 1503 edition of the <u>Tractatus epitomatus</u>.

45. Überweg, apparently misled by Pits, wrongly supposes the title, <u>De velocitate motuum</u>, to indicate a separate work.—F. Überweg, <u>Grundriss der Geschichte der Philosophie</u>, ed. Bernhard Geyer, II, 622.

46. The "short" form of the <u>Tractatus</u>, often referred to in records of both editions and manuscripts, omits the Proemium and all of Chapter IV.

47. "Arithmethica [sic] thome bravardini. [Ends as follows:] Explicit arithmethica speculativa thome bravardini bene revisa et correcta a Petro sanchez Cirvelo . . . A Guidoni Mercatoris: Parisius . . . 1495."—<u>B. M. Cat.</u>; it is apparently this same edition which was reprinted in Paris in 1502. "Arithmetica Thome Bravardini. [Ends as follows:] Explicit Arithmetica Thome Bravardini, bene revisa et correcta a Petro Sanchez Cirvelo Aragonensi, mathematicas legente Parisius, impressa in Campo Gaillardo, a.d. 1502 . . . pro Dionisio Rosse."—<u>Catalogue Générale des livres imprimés de la Bibliothèque Nationale</u>, <u>s.v.</u> Bradwardine, Thomas.

48. See Note 39 above.

49. "Arithmetica Speculativa Thome Bravardini nuper mendis Plusculis tersa et diligenter Impressa."—<u>B. M. Cat.</u> To the above editions Sarton (III, 669) adds several others: Paris 1498, ca. 1500, 1504, 1505, ca. 1510, 1512, 1530, and Wittenberg 1534, 1536.

50. This edition is, unfortunately, imperfect, lacking the title page. It has been marked, by the library, as having been printed in 1505.

51. It seems quite certain that the title, Arithmetica, is equivalent to Arithmetica speculativa. Thorndike and Kibre (op. cit., s.v. Bradwardine) list a manuscript under the title, Arithmetica (Bodleian Library, Digby MS. 190), which has substantially the same incipit as that ascribed by Pits to the Arithmetica speculativa. The Amplonian Collection at Erfurt also contains a manuscript designated as Arithmetica, whose incipit is identical with that given by Pits. See Beschreibendes Verzeichniss der Amplonianischen Handschriften-Sammlung zu Erfurt, MS. F375.

52. It is not easy to imagine why the titles, Arithmetica practica and Arithmetica speculativa, should be used for the same work. Sarton apparently identifies the two, failing altogether to mention the Practica. Fabricius (op. cit., I, 248) lists the two titles separately and mentions a Venice 1505 edition, not listed by Sarton, for the Practica. Again, Thorndike and Kibre list an Arithmetica practica, but this turns out to be the Amplonian MS. F375, which is described in the library catalogue simply as Arithmetica. Tanner (Bibliotheca Britannico-Hibernica) does not seem, in the face of the foregoing considerations, to be sufficient reason for supposing the Practica to be a separate work. Most likely, it represents either an inauthentic work or a variant title.

53. This edition is cited by Sarton, III, 669.

54. Listed by Hahn, Überweg, and Pits, this title could conceivably indicate a separate work. In view of the close similarity between the two, however, this would seem extremely unlikely.

55. Given by the Codices Vaticani Latini for MS. 813, Xiberta's title is the incipit of this manuscript, attributed, at the close, to "Beaduard."

56. Maximilian Curtze, Zeitschrift für Mathematik und Physik, pp. 85-91; Cantor, op. cit.; E. Stamm, in Isis, XXVI, 13-32.

57. Stamm's reading, "cathetice" and "syncathetice," is presumably in error.

58. Stamm, in Isis, XXVI, 13-32; Sarton, op. cit., III, 669.

59. Stephens, in D.N.B., s.v. Bradwardine.

60. This title is given by Thorndike and Kibre (op. cit.) for MS. 169, McClean Collection, Cambridge. It seems unlikely that Bradwardine should have written two independent works on this rather specialized topic.

61. See Sarton, op. cit., III, 671.

62. Anneliese Maier, "Der Funktionsbegriff in der Physik des 14. Jahrhunderts," Divus Thomas, pp. 158-59. This article contains not only an able summary analysis of the De propor-

tionibus but also a useful sketch of the later development of "Bradwardine's function" in the minds of the Merton "Calculatores"—Swineshead, Heytesbury, Dumbleton and others, and of its use by the Parisian founders of the new physics: Buridan, Oresme, Albert of Saxony, Marsilius of Inghen, and Burleigh (who early moved from England to Paris). Marshall Clagett (Giovanni Marliani and Late Mediaeval Physics, pp. 100 ff.) also presents a sound description of the De proportionibus, but being more occupied with certain possible misunderstandings of the meaning of Bradwardine's theory which arose among Italian theorists toward the close of the fourteenth century, than with Bradwardine's Tractatus, itself, he does not develop so adequate an account of the significance of this work.

63. Pierre Duhem, Études sur Leonard de Vinci, III, 298-99.
64. Cf., Section 4, p. 53 ff. of this Introduction.
65. Maier, "Der Funktionsbegriff," Divus Thomas, pp. 158-59.
66. The reader of the De proportionibus will find in it, too, a clear instance of the independent and penetrating spirit with which the best of the scholastics studied and interpreted the "authorities." Aristotle and Averroes, for example, figure not simply as oracles of appeal but as sources from which arguments and conclusions may be developed.
67. For further information concerning the history of this controversy, see E. A. Moody, "Galileo and Avempace," Journal of the History of Ideas, XII, 163-93, 375-422.
68. Dumbleton, Swineshead, and Hentisberus (all of Merton College, Oxford) appear to have published independently statements of this law during exactly the same period. That this occurred before the year 1335 is attested by an Erfurt manuscript of Hentisberus' De motu locali. See Anneliese Maier, Die Vorläufer Galileis im 14. Jahrhundert, p. 303.
69. A partial disagreement is outlined in the fourth erroneous theory concerning velocities, which Bradwardine undertakes to refute in Chapter II. This theory would retain the thesis that there is a certain proportion between mover and moved, but maintains that it is only "quoddam dominium et habitudo naturalis" and not a mathematical proportion.
70. See David E. Smith, History of Mathematics, II, 378 ff.
71. Campanus de Novara, Euclidis Megarensis . . . Opera a Campano interprete fidissima tralata [sic] . . . Lucas Paciolus . . . detersit: emendavit . . . Scipio Vegius . . . diligentiam: et censuram suam praestitit. Book V, Definition 3.
72. Campanus, Euclidis . . . Opera . . . , Book V, Definitions 10 and 11.
73. Clagett, op. cit., 135 ff.

74. Abu Ja'afar Ahmad ibn Jusuf ibn Ibrahim ibn Al-Daya al Misri (floruit ca. 912), known to the West under the Latinized form of his name, Ametus filius Josephi, was a notable mathematician at the Tulunid court in Egypt. His Epistola de proportione et proportionalitate, done into Latin by the voluminous translator of Arabic works, Gherardo of Cremona (1114-87), is said to have influenced western thought mainly through the medium of Leonardo of Pisa and Jordanus Nemorarius. Only one of his works, the De arcubus similibus, has ever appeared in printed form (ed. Max Curtze, Mitteilungen des Copernikus Vereins, pp. 48-50). Although the only manuscript of the Epistola, microfilm of which has been seen by the present author (Bodleian, Ashmole MS. 357), is in such poor condition and so sloppily written that it is most difficult to read, the work is impressive in its full-length treatment of the subject (29 quarto faces) and it has at least been possible to decipher the passage to which Bradwardine here refers (f. 78). For criticism and bibliography, see Sarton, op. cit., I, 598.

75. Because of the extreme brevity with which "disiuncta proportionalitas" is defined in the text of the De proportionibus, it might appear that the above interpretation is not legitimate, but that, instead, Bradwardine's "disiuncta proportionalitas" is distinguishable from his "aequa proportionalitas" (given in his Definition 6). An examination of Campanus' definition of "disiuncta proportionalitas" (op. cit., Definition 14) shows, however, that "disiuncta" is to be thought as the opposite of "coniuncta," and that, consequently, "disiuncta proportionalitas" indicates the subtraction, from the antecedents of two proportions, of quantities equal to their respective consequents. Campanus' example is: if $\frac{A+B}{B} = \frac{C+D}{D}$, then, "disjunctively," $\frac{A}{B} = \frac{C}{D}$.

76. In the edition of Campanus to which we refer, because, apparently, of a printer's error, Definitions 14, 13, 15, and 16 are called "Propositions," even though grouped among the "Definitions."

77. Both the Maruef edition of ca. 1500 and the Vatican MS. lat. 1108 give Euclid as the author, and it is conceivable that this unknown treatise was sometimes falsely attributed to him. Of the remaining six MSS consulted, five omit Euclid's name, and one (Bodleian, Digby MS. 76) omits the reference to the De proportionibus altogether.

78. "Non diffinit autem proportionem extremorum continuae proportionalitatis inter plures quam quattuor terminos constitutae, propter id quod dimensiones in rebus naturalibus repertae non excedunt ternarium." Cf. Definition 11.

79. ". . . semper proportio extremorum in terminis continue proportionalibus totiens contineat proportionem primorum quot
sunt omnes termini minus uno." _Cf_. Definition 11.
80. It will be noted that Theorems I and II are essentially the same
as Axioms 2 and 3, aside from the fact that the theorems in
question bring out the meaning of "duplum," "triplum," etc.,
as designating the result of "compounding" successive proportions in a geometric series. What, in Campanus' commentary
on Euclid (Definitions 10 and 11), was given in definitional
form, Bradwardine proves from his second and third axioms,
drawn from the unknown <u>De proportionibus</u> and revealing a
more general principle than do Euclid's two definitions, taken
in themselves.
81. The attempt has been made throughout to stay as close as possible to the original mode of formulation of the theorems,
while abbreviating them through the use of modern notation.
In the case of Theorems VII and VIII, however, it is, perhaps,
worth noting that a much simpler statement can be given:

$$1^n \text{ (or } \left(\tfrac{1}{1}\right)^n) = 1$$

$$\sqrt[n]{\left(\tfrac{1}{1}\right)} + m > 1$$

$$\left(\left(\tfrac{1}{1}\right) - m\right)^n < 1$$

82. In other works, though $\frac{4}{1} = \left(\frac{2}{1}\right)^2$, $\frac{2}{1} \neq \left(\frac{1}{1}\right)^n$; and, more generally,
$\frac{x}{y} = \left(\frac{x}{y}\right)^{\frac{n}{m}}$, $\frac{x}{y} \neq \left(\frac{z}{z}\right)^{\frac{n}{m}}$.
83. This theory would indicate fairly clearly the formulation:
$kV = F - R$.
84. Anneliese Maier ("Der Funktionsbegriff," <u>Divus Thomas</u>, p. 153)
interprets Theory I as $V:V' = (F-R) - (F'-R')$. Though this
reading might seem, at first glance, to be supported by the
fact that the text speaks of a proportion of velocities but not
explicitly of a proportion of forces, it is significant that velocities are spoken of in the plural, while the "excess" of the
power of mover over moved is spoken of in the singular. "Sequi excessum" must mean "to vary in accordance with the excess," that is, to be in equal proportion to. There might be
some argument for supposing that an arithmetic, rather than
a geometric, proportion is intended, but even in that case, the
formula should read $V - V' = (F - R) - (F' - R')$ and not $V:V' = (F-R) - (F'-R')$.
85. Pierre Jean Olivi (<u>Quaestiones in secundum sententiarum</u>,
Quae. XXVI, p. 461) provides a nice illustration of that independent spirit which is such an important aspect of scholastic
philosophy, and the following quotation shows anything but that

slavish adherence to the teachings of Aristotle which has too often been wrongly supposed to have characterized all mediaeval thought. Apparently the cry of "Dogmatist!" is not a new invention. Of those who followed Aristotle regarding theory of motion, Olivi writes: "It must be understood from the outset that Aristotle's theory is unsound, although, enslaving their minds as though he were some god of theirs, they think this or any other argument of his the best, however sophistical, just because it has been set down and 'revealed' by their god."

86. Once again issue must be taken with Miss Maier's formulation: $V:V' = (F-R):(F'-R')$. It will be noticed that this interpretation is the same as that which we have given to Theory I. Not only does the meaning of "sequi proportionem" appear to have been misread in the same way as before, but an examination of the text of Bradwardine's first refutation of this theory clearly shows that the refutation does not follow (and is, in fact, meaningless) on the basis of Miss Maier's formula.

87. It should be noted that this second objection is also inapplicable, on the basis of Miss Maier's formulation of the theory, since, according to her, there would be no question of resistance being made proportionate to only the remainder of motive force.

88. Cf. Borchert, "Die Lehre von der Bewegung bei Nicolaus Oresme," and A. Maier's chapter, "Die Wesensbestimmung der Bewegung" in her Vorläufer Galileis.

89. This statement seems, perhaps, no more than a reiteration of Theory III. The crucial difference between that theory and Bradwardine's lies in the meaning which is to be attached to the phrase, "follows the proportion." That meaning emerges clearly in the theorems which follow.

90. It is, perhaps, somewhat anachronistic to attribute a logarithmic formula to a fourteenth-century writer, but the alternate form $\left(n^V = \frac{F}{R}\right)$ does appear to express accurately the sense of the text. The essence of Bradwardine's theory is that to double a velocity is to square the proportion of motive force to resistance associated with it, to treble the velocity is to cube the proportion, etc. In order for the equation, $n^V = \frac{F}{R}$, to fulfill this requirement universally, it is necessary to posit that n (normally the log base) is a constant equal to $\frac{F}{R}$ when $V = 1$; unless this condition is met, the formula does not fulfill Bradwardine's requirements in the most general sense. Actually, since whatever the relation between V and $\frac{F}{R}$ is established to be will be uniform for any given units of measurement in which

$V = 1$ when $\frac{F}{R} = c$, the formula is workable, with the proviso that, when $V = 1$ and $\frac{F}{R} = c$, $n = c$.

91. Theorem VI possesses a special interest in connection with Bradwardine's previous argument that if one man can scarcely move a weight, two can move it more than twice as fast. Such a man would not have an F which is twice as great as the R which he moves, and, consequently, when aided by a second man of equal strength, the two together will move the resistance at more than twice the velocity. If the man in question could move the resistance easily, then the addition of a second man would not double the velocity of the motion.

Not only are these alternative cases confirmed by the sort of rough and ready physical observation that entered into the formation of mediaeval physical theory, but they follow most appropriately from the nature of the formula, $n^V = \frac{F}{R}$. As may be seen in the contrast between Theorems IV and V, and Theorems VI and VII, the case in which $\frac{F}{R} = \frac{2}{1}$ is not only a special case; it is also a critical case. As F is successively doubled from 1 to 2, V behaves quite differently than it does when F is successively doubled from 2 to n.

92. It is interesting that, by this tour de force, Bradwardine is able to demonstrate as a theorem what Aristotle had treated as an axiom; the impossibility that any motion should arise from an equilibrium of forces is demonstrable from the basic formula, $n^V = \frac{F}{R}$, on purely mathematical grounds.

93. It is worth noting that this proof makes it clear that Theorem VIII, Chapter I, does not refer simply to terms in continuous proportion but to terms in discontinuous proportion also.

94. Physics, IV, viii, 215a 25-28.

95. For the sake of brevity, the proofs of the above conclusions are omitted.

96. See Gustav Eneström, "Sur l'auteur d'un traite 'De motu' auquel Bradwardin a fait allusion en 1328," Archeion: Archivio di storia della scienza, II, 133-36.

97. While Duhem describes Gerard's work as having to do with the concept of angular velocity, Professor Marshall Clagett has suggested to the author that curvilinear and curviplanar velocities are what are actually involved. The need of further study of the relation between Bradwardine and Gerard regarding this point seems to be clear.

98. In this connection it is interesting to note the similarity of Bradwardine's theory of the distribution of the elements to Kepler's theory of the spacing of the planets in accordance with the series of five regular solids of Euclid. Bradwardine

was not alone in finding the geometry and mathematics of
Euclid a fertile source of suggestions for the mathematical
analysis of physical structure and process.

99. Abu-l-Hasan Thabit ibn Qurra ibn Marwan al-Harrani (born
826-27 or 835-36 and died 901), referred to in the De proportionibus as Thebit filius Chorae, was born in Mesapotamia
and spent his productive years at Bagdad. Besides having been
a physician, mathematician and astronomer, he was one of
the greatest of the translators from Greek and Syriac into
Arabic. Apollonius, Archimedes, Euclid, Theodosius, Ptolemy,
Galen, and Eutocius were translated by him or under his direction. His Preamble to Ptolemy's Almagest, to which Bradwardine alludes, was presumably translated into Latin by
Gherardo Cremonese. See Sarton, op. cit., I, 599-600. Abu-l-
Abbas Ahmad ibn Muhammad ibn Kathir al-Farghani (fl. ca.
861), referred to in the De proportionibus as Alphagranus or
Alpharganus, and born in Transoxiana, was one of the greatest
of the astronomers employed by Al-Ma'mun and his successors. His Elements of Astronomy (or Differentiae scientiae
astrorum) to which Bradwardine here refers, was translated
into Latin by Gherardo Cremonese and John Hispanensis in
the twelfth century and exerted a great influence on astronomy
before the time of Regiomontanus. This work has recently
been edited by F. J. Carmody (Berkeley, Calif., 1943). See
Sarton, op. cit., I, 567.

100. References to Dumbleton are based upon a translation, from
MSS. Merton Coll. 306 and Cod. Vat. Lat. 954, (portions of
his Summa logicae et philosophiae naturalis) kindly provided
by Professor Ernest A. Moody.

101. This and the following allusions to Dumbleton's theory of "intension" and "remission" are taken from Part II, chapters
16-23, of his Summa.

102. Buridan, Joannis Buridani Quaestiones super libros Physicorum, Book VIII, Qu. xii.

103. Duhem, Études sur Leonard de Vinci, III, 302.

104. Duhem, op. cit., III, 429.

105. Anneliese Maier, Die Vorläufer Galileis, p. 111.

106. Anneliese Maier, An der Grenze von Scholastik und Naturwissenschaft, p. 181.

107. Ibid., p. 156.

108. Maier, Die Vorläufer Galileis, p. 122.

PROLEGOMENA

1. A transcript of the text of this edition was made available
through the kindness of Professor Ernest A. Moody.

2. Another such is the MS. B.N. Latin 625.

TEXT

PROEMIUM

7 Boethius: "Constat igitur quisquis haec praetermiserit, omnem
philosophiae perdidisse doctrinam." — <u>Patrologia Latina</u>, (Ed. J.
P. Migne, Paris 1844-80, Vol. LXIV, Col. 1081 D.)

CAPITULUM PRIMUM

140, 143 Boethius: <u>Arithmetica</u>, II, <u>Musica</u>, II

155 Euclid: <u>Euclidis Megarensis Opera a Campano tralata</u> (<u>sic</u>),
Venice 1509; <u>Elementa</u>, V, Def. iv; f. 32v

196-97 Ametus filius Josephi (Ahmad ibn Jusuf): <u>Epistola de pro-</u>
<u>portione et proportionalitate</u>, (Bodleian Library, Ashmole MS.
357, f. 78, Cf. Note: Part I, p. 26 of this study.

212 Euclid: <u>Elementa</u>, V, Def. vii.

255 Euclid: <u>Elementa</u>, V, f. 36v: "Permutatim proportionalia," Def.
xii; "Econtrario proportionalia," Def. xii; "Disiuncta proportionalia," Def. xiv; "Coniuncta proportionalitas," Def. xiii;
"Eversa proportionalitas," Def. xv; "Aequa proportionalitas,"
Def. xvi

272 <u>De proportionibus</u>: Quamquam a manuscriptis (Vaticanus Latinus 1108) Euclidi attributum, ex eo quod suppositionum numeri
dati cum illis Euclidis <u>Elementorum</u> minime conveniunt, opus
illud arbitramur ab aliquo alio auctore compositum esse.

Ad eandem quaestionem confer istius tomi partem primam,
p. 28.

291 Euclid: <u>Elementa</u>, V: "Suppositio iv," Propositio vii, f 40r;
"Supp. v," Prop. viii, f. 40r; "Supp vi," Prop. ix, f. 40v; "Supp.
vii," Prop. xvi, f. 42r; "Supp. viii," Prop. xxv, f. 44r.

426 Euclid: <u>Elementa</u>, V, Def. x, f. 35

CAPITULUM SECUNDUM

2 Aristotle: <u>De caelo et mundo</u>, I, vi, 274a 7-9

9 Averroes: <u>Commentaria Magna De Physica Auditu</u>, Venice
1560, Vol. IV, f. 132 v, F.

11 Averroes: <u>Ibid.</u>, f. 266v, E.

13 Averroes: <u>Ibid.</u>, f. 268v, D.

24 Aristotle: <u>Physica</u>, VII, v, 250a 4-6

28 Aristotle: <u>Ibid.</u>, 250a 7-9

43 Aristotle: <u>Physica</u>, VII, v, 250a 25-28

55 Aristotle: <u>Physica</u>, VII, v, passim.

59 Averroes: <u>De phys. aud.</u>, Vol. IV, f. 132r

59 Averroes: <u>Ibid.</u>, Vol. V, f. 47v

64 Aristotle: <u>Physica</u>, VII, v, 250a 5-9

72 Averroes: <u>De phys. aud.</u>, Vol. IV, f. 267r (<u>Phys</u>. VII, Comm. 36)

79-80 Aristotle: <u>Physica</u>, VII, v, 250a 25-28
88 Averroes: <u>De phys. aud.</u>, Vol. IV, f. 268r (<u>Phys</u>. VII, Comm. 38)
110 Aristotle: <u>Physica</u>, IV, viii, 2 15b 1 - 2 16a 8
163 Averroes: <u>Comm. magna</u>, Vol. IV, f. 267r (<u>Phys</u>. VII, Comm. 36)
188 Aristotle: <u>Physica</u>, IV, viii, 2 15b 6-8
201 Aristotle: <u>De caelo</u>, I, vii, 275a 32-275b 2
205 Aristotle: <u>Physica</u>, VII, v, 250a 1-2
211 Aristotle: <u>Physica</u>, IV, viii, 2 16a 14-17
216-17 Aristotle: <u>Physica</u>, VII, v; Averroes: <u>Comm. magna</u>, Vol.
      IV, f. 268v (Comm. 39, Para. (D)).
220 Aristotle: <u>Physica</u>, VIII, x, 266b 10-11 and 16-18.
227 Aristotle: <u>De caelo</u>, I, vi, 273b 31-274a 1.
232 Aristotle: <u>Op.cit.</u>, III, ii, 301b 11.
236 Jordanus Nemorarius: <u>Jordani Nemorarii . . . De Ponderibus</u>
      <u>Propositiones XIII . . . editus . . . Petro Apiano</u>, Nuremburg
      1533, Prop. I. Cf. Appendix.
402-3 Averroes: <u>Comm. magna</u>, Vol. IV, f. 342v (<u>Phys</u>. VIII, Comm.
      79 (D)).
424-25 Aristotle: <u>Physica</u>, VII, iv, <u>passim</u>.
432-33 Aristotle: <u>Physica</u>, IV, viii, 2 15b 14-16
440 Aristotle: <u>Rhetorica</u>, I, vii, 1363b 7-9
452 Boethius: <u>Omnia Opera</u>, "Musica"
453-54 Averroes: <u>Comm. magna</u>, Vol. IV, f. 267r, f. 268r (<u>Phys</u>.
      VII, Comm. 36 (C), 38 (A-B)).
456-57 Averroes: <u>Ibid.</u>, Vol. V, ff. 49v-50v (<u>De caelo</u>, I, Comm. 65
      (F-D)).
463-64 Euclid: <u>Elementa</u>, V, f. 36v ("Permutatim proportionalia,"
      Def. xii)

CAPITULUM TERTIUM

6 Averroes: <u>Comm. magna</u>, Vol. IV, f. 132r (<u>Phys</u>. IV, Comm.
   71 (A)).
14 Averroes: <u>Ibid.</u>, f. 132v (Comm. 71 (F)).
17 Averroes: <u>Comm. magna</u>, Vol. V, f. 125v (<u>De caelo</u> II, Comm.
   36 (F)).
22 Averroes: <u>Op.cit.</u>, Vol. IV, f. 266v (<u>Phys</u>. VII, Comm. 35 (E)).
27 Averroes: <u>Ibid.</u>, f. 268v (Comm. 39 (D)).
176 Aristotle: <u>De caelo</u>, I, vii, 275a 1-24
181 Averroes: <u>Comm. magna</u>, Vol. V f. 47v (<u>De caelo</u> I, Comm.
    63 (E-F)).
255 Averroes: <u>Comm. magna</u>, Vol. IV, f. 252v (<u>Phys</u>. VII, Comm.
    10 (D)).

CAPITULUM QUARTUM

10 Euclid: <u>Elementa</u>, I, f. 4r (ex definitionibus generalibus initii
   libri, et non literaliter).

13 Euclid: Op. cit., VI, f. 46r (literaliter).

15-16 Euclid: Op. cit., I, f. 4r (non literaliter).

19 Euclid: Elementa, I, f. 4v, "Petitio iii."

23 Euclid: Op. cit., VI f. 49v, "Propositio xviii."

26 Euclid: Op. cit., XII, f. 114v, "Propositio ii."

28 Archimedes: De curvis superficiebus, Prop. iii (Ed. M. Clagett in Osiris, 11, p. 307). Note Bradwardine cites this as Prop. v. but in the original text it is Prop. iii. Actually this treatise is not simply a fragment of the De sphaera et cylindro of Archimedes but rather as a commentary by one Johannes de Tinemue.

32 Euclid: Elementa, XII, f. 121v, "Propositio xv."

35 Archimedes: De curvis superficiebus, Prop. vi. (Ed. cit., p. 315). Note that Bradwardine cites this as Prop. viii.

95 Gerard of Brussels: De proportionalitate motuum et magnitudinum, Axiom iv, (Cf. Pierre Duhem, Études sur Leonard de Vinci, III, pp. 292-293.)

135 Theodosius: Theodosii Tripolitae Sphaericorum Libri Tres, Berlin 1852, (Ed. Ernest Nizze), p. 86; Cap. I, Propositio 6A.

203 Averroes: Comm. magna, Vol. V, f. 121r (De caelo II, Text. 32)

205 Averroes: Op. cit., Vol. V, f. 216r (De caelo III, Text. 47)

214 Alphraganus (i.e., Alpharganus, al-Farghani): Differentie scientie astrorum, Berkeley-California 1943, (Ed. F. J. Carmody), p. 38; Differentia 21, par. vi.

219 Ptolemy: Ptolemy, Mathematical Composition (Almagest), (Classics of the St. John's Program), Annapolis-Maryland 1939, (Ed. Catesby Taliaferro), pp. 250 ff.; V, xvi ("Concerning the magnitudes of the Sun, Moon and Earth").

BIBLIOGRAPHY

Ahmad ibn Jusuf (Ametus filius Josephi). De arcubus similibus, in Mitteilungen des Copernikus Vereins, ed. Max. Curtze. 1887.

Al-Farghani. Differentie scientie astrorum, ed. F. J. Carmody. Berkeley, California, 1943.

Archimedes. Archimedis opera. Apollonii Pergaei conicorum libri IIII, etc., ed. Is. Barrow. London, 1675.

Averroes. Aristotelis Stagiritae opera omnia . . . cum commentariis Averrois Cordubensis. Venice, 1560. 10 vols.

Barnes, Joshua. A History of Edward III. Cambridge, 1688.

Beschreibendes Verzeichniss der Amplonianischen Handschriften-Sammlung zu Erfurt, ed. W. Schum. Berlin, 1887.

Birchington, Stephen. Vitae Archiepiscoporum Cantuariensium a prima sedis fundatione ad annum 1369, in Anglia Sacra, ed. Henry Wharton. London, 1691. I, 42-43.

Boethius, Anicius Manlius. Omnia opera. (Patrologia Latina, ed. J. P. Migne, Paris 1844-80, Vol. LXIV.)

Borchert, Ernst. "Die Lehre von der Bewegung bei Nicolaus Oresme," Beiträge zur Geschichte der Philosophie und Theologie des Mittelalters, Vol. XXXI, Heft 3. Münster, 1934.

Bradwardine, Thomas. De cause Dei contra Pelagium et de virtute causarum, ad suos Mertonenses, ed. Henry Savile. London, 1618.

Broderick, George C. Memorials of Merton College. Oxford, 1885.

Buridan, John. Joannis Buridani quaestiones super libros physicorum. Paris, 1509.

Campanus de Novara. See Euclid.

Canonici Lichfeldensis indiculus de successione archiepiscoporum Cantuariensium, in Anglia Sacra, ed. Henry Wharton. London, 1691. I, 119.

Cantor, Moritz. Vorlesungen über die Geschichte der Mathematik, 2nd ed. Leipzig, 1900.

Chambre, William de. Continuatio historiae Dunelmensis, in Anglia Sacra, ed. Henry Wharton, London, 1691. I, 765-84.

Clagett, Marshall. Giovanni Marliani and Late Mediaeval Physics. New York, 1941.

Curtze, Maximilian. "Tractatus de continuo von Thomas Bradwardine," Zeitschrift für Mathematik und Physik, 1868 Suppl. to Vol. XIII.

Dene, William de. Historia Roffensis, in Anglia Sacra, ed. Henry Wharton. London, 1691. I, 375.

Denifle, H., and Chatelain, A. Chartularium Universitatis Parisiensis. Paris, 1891. Vol. II.

Duhem, Pierre. Études sur Leonard de Vinci. Paris, 1913. 3 vols.

Eneström, Gustav. "Sur l'auteur d'un traité 'De motu' auquel Bradwardin a fait allusion en 1328," Archeion: Archivio di storia della scienza, II, 133-36. Rome, 1921.

Euclid. Euclidis Megarensis . . . Opera a Campano interprete fidissima tralata [sic] . . . Lucas Paciolus . . . detersit: emendavit . . . Scipio Vegius . . . diligentiam: et censuram suam praestitit. Venice, 1509.

Fabricius, Johan A. Bibliotheca Latina mediae et infimae aetatis. Florence, 1858. Vol. I.

Gesner, Konrad. Bibliotheca Universalis. Zurich, 1549. Vol. I.

Graesse, Johann G. Trésor di livres rares et précieux. Dresden, 1859. Vol. I.

Hahn, Sebastian. "Thomas Bradwardine und seine Lehre von der menschlichen Willensfreiheit," Beiträge zur Geschichte der Philosophie des Mittelalters, Vol. V. Munich, 1905.

"Historical Papers and Letters from the Northern Registers," ed. J. Raine. (Rerum Britannicarum Medii Aevi Scriptores. No. 61.) London, 1873.

Hook, Walter F. Lives of the Archbishops of Canterbury. London, 1860-84.

Jordanus Nemorarius. Jordani Nemorarii . . . de ponderibus propositiones XIII . . . editus . . . Petro Apiano. Nuremberg, 1533.

Knighton, Henry. Chronicon, ed. J. R. Lumby. London, 1889-95. Vol. II.

Laun, J. F. "Thomas von Bradwardine, der Schüler Augustins und Lehrer Wiclifs," Zeitschrift für Kirchengeschichte, XLVII (1928), 333-56.

Maier, Anneliese. An der Grenze von Scholastik und Naturwissenschaft. Essen, 1943 (2nd Edit., Rome, 1952).

——. "Der Funktionsbegriff in der Physik des 14. Jahrhunderts," Divus Thomas. Freiburg, 1946.

——. Die Vorläufer Galileis im 14. Jahrhundert. Rome, 1949.

Moody, Ernest A. "Galileo and Avempace," Journal of the History of Ideas, XII, No. 2 (Apr., 1951), 163-93; XII, No. 3 (June, 1951), 375-422.

Murimuth, Adam of. Continuatio chronicarum, ed. E. M. Thompson. (Rerum Britannicarum Medii Aevi Scriptores, No. 93.) London, 1889.

Munimenta academica, Part I, "Libri cancellarii et procuratorum," ed. H. Anstey. (Rerum Britannicarum Medii Aevi Scriptores, No. 50.) London, 1868.

Olivi, Pierre Jean. Quaestiones in secundum librum sententiarum, ed. B. Jansen. Quaracchi, 1922-26. 3 vols.

Pits, John. De illustribus Angliae scriptoribus. Paris, 1623.

Ptolemy. Ptolemy, Mathematical Composition (Almagest), in Classics of the St. John's Program, ed. Catesby Taliaferro. Annapolis, Maryland, 1939.

Rashdall, Hastings. The Universities of Europe in the Middle Ages,
eds. F. M. Powicke and A. B. Emden. Oxford, 1936. 3 vols.

Rymer, Thomas. Foedera, conventiones, literae . . . . London,
1727. 20 vols.

Sarton, George. Introduction to the History of Science. Washington,
D.C., 1927——. 3 vols.

Smith, David E. History of Mathematics. Boston, 1923-24. Vol. II.

Stamm, E. "Tractatus de continuo von Thomas Bradwardine," Isis,
XXVI (1936-37), 13-32.

Tanner, Thomas. Bibliotheca Britannico-Hibernica. London, 1748.

Theodosius. Theodosii Tripolitae sphaericorum libri tres, ed.
Ernest Nizze. Berlin, 1852.

Thorndike, Lynn, and Kibre, Pearl. Catalogue of Incipits of Mediaeval Scientific Writings in Latin. Cambridge, Mass., 1937.

Überweg, F. Grundriss der Geschichte der Philosophie, ed. Bernhard Geyer. Berlin, 1928.

INDEX

INDEX

Note: This index is primarily to proper names and major concepts. No attempt has been made to index casual place names or the authors of secondary works, except in a few special instances. But since the notes are collected in one place, the reader will readily find citations to secondary authors.

2005

p 76 Comporta

space 128 — City B
130